Feilden Clegg Bradley

the environmental handbook

The creation of a building is a collaborative process; the creation of this book even more so. While the authorship of each project is given in the schedule at the end of the book, over the years the practice has been moulded by many more people who have contributed to the body of knowledge that the book represents. Specialist expertise resides with the key individuals who have helped write the Primer section, and they are credited accordingly. We are also indebted to the many consultants with whom we have worked and who have helped to educate us in the issues that constitute the environmental agenda of our work. We have been fortunate in working with many of the best environmental engineers – eminent practices such as Max Fordham, Buro Happold, Atelier Ten, Fulcrum, Arup and Battle McCarthy, as well as specific experts in key areas such as ESD (energy systems), Grant Associates (landscape design) and Ben Hamilton-Baillie (transportation planning).

We have found that the production of a book is as complex as that of a building, and we are indebted to Stephanie Laslett at FCBa for co-ordinating and managing this process so creatively. Steph has been supported by many people, in particular Jo Laurence who has been responsible for collating most of the words, and Fliss Mills for the images and credits. We are also indebted to Rob Gregory and Herrick Ho who helped with the intial research and writing and to David Littlefield who worked on the graphics of the cover and section breaks. Finally our thanks go to Ian Latham and Mark Swenarton who have struggled with us creatively throughout the long process of gestation.

In a fast moving world with ever increasing environ-mental problems as well as potential solutions, the infor-mation in this book is constantly being superseded. The Primer will be regularly updated on our website, and we welcome any comments. We can only solve problems by sharing solutions.

Peter Clegg

Edited and designed by
Ian Latham and Mark Swenarton

First published by Right Angle Publishing,
161 Rosebery Avenue, London EC1R 4QX

British Library Cataloguing in Publication Data
A catalogue record for this book is available from the British Library

ISBN 0 9532848 5 9
ISBN-13: 978-0-9532848-5-6

Feilden Clegg Bradley
the environmental handbook

written by Peter Clegg with Keith Bradley, Richard Feilden and Bill Gething, plus Max Fordham, Randall Thomas, Gavin Thompson, Harry Montresor, Patrick Bellew, Andrew Grant, Peter Rickaby and Ben Hamilton-Baillie

edited by Ian Latham and Mark Swenarton

Richard Feilden
29th March 1950 – 3rd January 2005

This book began life around 35 years ago when Richard and I were studying at Cambridge under Alex Pike and Dean Hawkes. It was well under way by the time of Richard's tragic death in 2005. So much of the work embodied in it results from his definition of architecture as a social and environmental art.

Richard was a great collaborator. He was the first to give credit to colleagues, clients, contractors and consultants. All of them have helped contribute to the body of knowledge within this handbook, but none more so than the under-appreciated environmental engineers who have helped develop our knowledge of low-energy systems. Responsibility for the authorship and design of buildings is never very clear, particularly in the case of the buildings that emerge from our practice, but Richard's name will continue to be associated with the body of work illustrated in this book, and his influence through the practice will live on. It is with great affection that we dedicate this book to him.

Peter Clegg

Foreword

As a friend and admirer of Richard Feilden I am both honoured and sad to be writing the foreword to this book in his absence. However, from my many conversations with him about these issues, I feel confident that he will sympathise with these brief thoughts. He was only too aware of the alarming scale of the environmental challenge we face. For most of us, this is a recent awakening. But Feilden Clegg Bradley Architects are different. They can fairly boast that the environment has been at the heart of their work for the last 25 years – when for much of the time the environment was far from a fashionable issue.

This book is not the usual self-regarding architectural monograph. It focuses on the way in which a concern for the environment has driven the work of the practice. And, even more usefully, it shares with generosity the knowledge built over the years. In addition to widely publicised examples of its work – the Greenpeace headquarters, the Earth Centre or, more recently, the new headquarters for the National Trust in Swindon – Feilden Clegg Bradley has achieved an impressive body of completed projects which are characterised by a high quality of contemporary design and innovation in their environmental approach.

The stories behind these projects are organised into chapters around specific building types and they will assuredly provide an invaluable source of wisdom and knowledge for others embarking on similar schemes. While most books of this type tend to focus on the 'good' news, it is typical of this practice that the partners both acknowledge and explain those projects which did not quite work out as intended.

As a practice, Feilden Clegg Bradley has always been involved in education and research. It is not surprising therefore that this book not only summarises the partners' preoccupation with sustainability but also provides a 'primer' on environmental design – a wealth of information built up over many years of research and development. I am sure that it will be an invaluable reference for both students and practitioners.

Both Richard Feilden and Peter Clegg were extraordinarily helpful to me as I struggled to organise my own ideas for the first RIBA Annual Lecture which I had the privilege to deliver in 2002. I am therefore especially delighted to give this book my warmest recommendation.

Jonathan Dimbleby – Hon FRIBA

The Architecture Shop in Canton Place, Bath. The practice was set up in 1978 by Richard Feilden and Peter Clegg as a pioneering attempt to demystify architecture and bring it literally into the community. Architectural advice was available at £2.30 per hour.

Designing with climate: the principles of sustainable architecture

Dean Hawkes

One of the wisest books ever written about the environmental function of architecture is Victor Olgyay's Design with Climate.[1] Published in 1963, this appeared, probably not coincidentally, at precisely the moment when mechanical plant began to be the dominant instrument of environmental control in many buildings throughout the world – the time when Le Corbusier's proposition of, 'only one house for all countries, the house of exact breathing' had become commonplace. In opposition to the implication in Le Corbusier's bâtiments hermétiques of the dissolution of the historical and complex relationship between architecture and climate, Olgyay issued a reminder that it was possible, even necessary, to fashion buildings for the modern age that engaged with, rather than mitigated against, the climate in which they were set. A decade before the so-called energy crisis of the 1970s, this book laid the foundations for the emergence of the school of environmentally responsible – now dubbed sustainable – architecture that today constitutes such a significant strand of both theory and practice.

Inspiring and informative as Olgyay's book was, and remains, inevitably it constituted a mere beginning for a philosophy of design. While the clarity of the analysis was impeccable, the worked examples of designs were limited in scope and relevance when compared to the wider stage upon which practice must perform. The necessity for practice to elaborate theory, to test its propositions, was all too apparent. But now, four decades later, much of that has been achieved and the collected works of Feilden Clegg Bradley represent one of the most consistent and comprehensive records of exploratory practice in the field of designing with climate, with all of its local and global environmental consequences.

How do we characterise this approach? What are the elements of a sustainable architecture? How do we translate principle into form? These are crucial and, in some respects, difficult questions. But the corpus of work from the offices of FCBa may be examined as a body of data that offers more than individual answers to specific problems. It is now possible to draw out general themes and principles.

If we begin with the Solar Courtyard houses at Milton Keynes, the fundamentals can be clearly established. This is an architecture of orientation, cross section and envelope. The principal rooms face southwards. The cross section presents a high south facade to the sun and a low one to the north. The envelope is generally highly insulated and, to the south, is elaborated by high-performance glazing and internal and external shading devices. This might appear to be analytical and reductive, a formula for literal representation of the devices of environmental management but, right at the outset, the design reveals an understanding of the primacy of inhabitation in making architecture. These are first and foremost places in which to live.

The design for the Greenpeace headquarters building in London brought the same principles of technical understanding and human regard to bear in transforming an existing urban building into an exemplar of energy-conscious design. Here, in the city, the orientation was given, an inevitable consequence of the urban grain. But once again the principles of orientation, cross section and envelope lie at the heart of the solution. The treatment of fenestration on the north and south facades denotes their different conditions and the newly inserted stairwell rises to a south-facing rooflight. The cross section, again, is fine-tuned to both context and programme. In a manner similar to that of the Solar Courtyard houses, the envelope to the south is redefined as a layered zone in which solar shades/lightshelves are poised inside and outside the original glazing line, bringing environmental benefits and manipulating the scale of the tall industrial spaces within. Within, canvas sails, suspended artificial light fittings and mechanical ducts express the new purpose and operation of the building. The outcome of these interventions is an environment that is in tune with Greenpeace's mission, but that is also a testbed for a view of the office environment that challenges the assumption of the ubiquitous, mechanically-controlled, sealed box.

In contrast to houses and offices, which in many respects have similar environmental characteristics, theatre buildings are highly specialised. The suspension of disbelief inherent in theatre implies an impermeable boundary between the auditorium and the external environment. Since the nineteenth century, theatres have almost always been mechanically ventilated, sealed boxes. The Olivier Theatre at Bedales school however offered FCBa the opportunity to reconsider the nature of the auditorium and this led to a design that occupies an important position in its output. The quiet rural setting of the school allowed the use of natural ventilation for the auditorium and the physical processes of this have a direct influence on the cross section and external appearance of the building. The square plan auditorium sits at the centre of an overall rectangular pavilion and its pyramidal roof rises high to a louvred ventilation lantern. Beneath the floor a void provides passive cooling to incoming air. A ring of roof glazing admits daylight for occasions when blackout is unnecessary; it is simply closed off with blackout blinds when darkness is required. The cross section is, as with other building types, the key. As such it is strongly expressed in the silhouette of the building. The envelope is constructed of sustainable, home-grown timber.

The commission to design the Environmental Office Building at the Building Research Establishment was, prima facie, an ideal project for FCBa. Intended by the BRE to serve as an exemplar for future office design, the project permitted a degree of experiment and demonstration that more conventional commissions rarely allow. The design exhibits, as usual, the principles of orientation, cross section and envelope, but adds a new level of process and detail. At first sight the most radical development is the group of five solar chimneys that dominate and organise the composition of the south front. These stand as symbols of the building's environmental credentials. This reading is reinforced by the arrays of solar shades that span the spaces between the chimneys and the adoption of photovoltaic panels as cladding to the lecture theatre block, to the west of the main entrance. In its detail the building continues the explorations into the nature of office space first seen at Greenpeace. Here the improvisations of canvas sails are replaced by a sinusoidal concrete slab forms that simultaneously provides thermal mass, cross-ventilation and uniform distribution of artificial lighting.

Since the completion of the Environmental Office Building, FCBa has built a number of other buildings that further explore similar ideas. The Berrill building at the Open University is, at first sight, a simple five-storey office building. The 14 metre deep plan allows good natural lighting and simple cross-ventilation; again the cross section is the key. Upon this simple figure the treatment of the east and west facades is subtly inflected to acknowledge the different environmental conditions in each case. To the east, where a degree of solar gain is welcome at most times of the year,

a system of fixed perforated aluminium panels stands in front of the glazing. On the west face, where solar gain can be problematic in the warmth of the afternoon, photocell-controlled roller blinds provide protection. The whole is an unassuming but effective solution that is modestly expressed in the architecture – a striking contrast to the BRE building but perhaps a more relevant exemplar for general application.

The Rare headquarters at Twycross consists of a central building, housing shared facilities, which is connected by covered walkways to a series of 'workstation barns'. The barns adapt a generic pitched-roof form to the conditions of both programme and context. They have a simple section surmounted by a continuous lantern, with remotely operated vents. The envelope incorporates an array of simple environmental devices; opening lights, light shelves and screening shutters. The extension to the Martial Rose library at King Alfred's College, Winchester, is a further essay in the development of the environmentally ordered facade. The issue here is solar protection for the principal, south-facing facade, where continuous, horizontal louvres provide shade from the high summer sun. The short east-facing facade, behind which are small group-work rooms, employs perforated metal shades that are similar to those at the Berrill building. In these buildings apparent simplicity rests upon a sophisticated, and now mature, understanding of environmental principles that is adapted to the particular conditions of the site and the needs of the users.

Housing is the key to the creation of a sustainable built environment. It is the largest single building type and it is essential to find better solutions than those of the conventional developer. From the beginning, designs for housing have featured in the work of FCBa. Just as in the other projects, these apply general principles to diverse programmes and sites. The multiplication of repetitive units in usually relatively low-cost developments establishes different constraints from those that apply to public, cultural or commercial buildings. Not least are the obligation to social sustainability and questions of density, landscape, the relation of public to private realm and the accommodation of the private car.

Many, but not all, of FCBa's housing projects have been in the educational sector. Their designs for student housing – at Panns Bank in Sunderland, the West Downs student village at Winchester,

Lakeside residences at Aston and the student village at Queen Mary University of London – share a common technical strategy, in which high standards of thermal insulation operate in concert with high efficiency mechanical systems. The site layouts promote social interaction. In the more general field of housing design, Century Court at Cheltenham incorporates a wide social mix of houses, flats and penthouses on an environmentally and historically sensitive site. Again a high standard of thermal insulation provides the first level of environmental response. The extensive Accordia project in Cambridge follows a similar technical approach and, with its combination of public and private open spaces, is an exemplar for social sustainability. The Vallecas social housing project in Madrid moves the thinking of the practice into an engagement with a very different culture and climate from that of cool, temperate Britain. In terms of details, deep shading of windows and visible ventilation stacks bring new expressive elements to the repertoire.

The designs discussed so far are, in their essential features, transformations of the familiar elements of architecture; orientation, cross section and envelope, in the realization of new levels of sustainable performance. This strategy is directed towards the reduction of demand for conventional energy sources and these buildings clearly show its success. But, however frugal they may be, these buildings, by their nature, remain consumers of energy. At the BRE Environmental Office Building the array of photovoltaic panels on the south facade hints at the prospect of future buildings becoming, in some measure, producers rather than consumers of energy. In two important projects FCBa have further explored this prospect.

The Earth Centre is built on reclaimed colliery land in Yorkshire and is devoted to demonstrating the potential for environmentally responsible development. The client set demanding sustainability criteria, ranging across energy conservation, environmental impact and the use of sustainable materials. FCBa's contribution to the project consists of the arrivals building (containing the information centre plus a cafe and meeting room) and the Planet Earth gallery, which presents a narrative exhibition on themes in global sustainability. These contrasted structures demonstrate respectively the sustainable use of timber and glass and earth-sheltered masonry.

Soon after their completion, the space between them was

covered by the Solar Canopy. This spectacular structure, with its timber space frame, supports a vast array of photovoltaic cells, which generates something like one third of the electrical energy requirement of the two buildings. The relationship of solar canopy to inhabited space is also demonstrated at the Oxstalls campus at the University of Gloucester. Here the entire north-light roof of the sports hall supports a photovoltaic array in a configuration that balances the direct benefit of natural light in illuminating the space below with its indirect conversion into electricity to support other energy needs within the campus. In these two designs we see the emergence of new typologies of sustainable architecture. These propose further evolutionary steps in the relationship of design with climate in FCBa's work.

The early projects, from the Solar Courtyard houses to the BRE Environmental Office Building, were explicit demonstrations of the mechanisms of what was then commonly dubbed 'passive solar' or 'energy-conscious' design. The differentiation between north and south aspects, the layering of south-facing facades and the overt expression of passive 'plant', as in the solar chimneys at BRE, are all explicitly displayed as badges of environmental awareness. The buildings are, in a positive sense of the term, didactic. Recently, however, these elements, though still present, have been reinterpreted in a less demonstrative language. The two visitor centres at Painshill Park in Surrey and the Yorkshire Sculpture Park at Bretton are instances of this.

Both designs are about the interpretation of the cross section in relation to orientation. They also, as we would expect, explore the nature of the envelope. In this they are absolutely consistent to the practice's approach. But now their environmental credentials are worn lightly. At Painshill a shady – and shading – south-facing loggia serves as the entrance porch to an informal arrangement of amenities that are grouped to the north. At Bretton the building is again approached end-on through its revealed cross section but this time the route bisects the plan, until it emerges amongst sheltering trees at the south-west corner. Both buildings sit in a lineage that is recognisably modern. But the language is subtly calibrated to both the physical context of the English climate and the specific – and in each case – beautiful English landscape setting and the architectural tradition that this evokes. It is perhaps an indication of maturity that sustainable design need no longer demonstrate its credentials through exaggerated forms and devices.

The design for the new central offices of the National Trust at Swindon is in many respects a summation of FCBa's work to date. It gives a new twist to the explorations into the nature of the sustainable office building by fusing the strategies of their previous designs with their interest in the potential of the roof plane, or canopy, as an element of environmental management. It also demonstrates a new degree of response to historical context, namely the former Great Western Railway works. The building adopts a deep plan form that owes something to industrial architecture. The plan is trapezoidal, with double-height and two-storey spaces and open courtyards disposed beneath an array of pitched roof structures that run diagonally across the plan. In this configuration the roof plane becomes a major environmental element, a variant of the solar canopy. The building is designed to achieve a high standard of daylighting and is entirely naturally ventilated. Arrays of rooflights bring natural light into the deep spaces and rooftop 'snouts' work in tandem with automatically opening windows to provide ventilation and summer-time night cooling. The roof also supports energy producing solar water heaters and photovoltaic cells.

The sequence of building designs by FCBa can be represented as a process by which technical knowledge is transferred into practical application. In addition, it provides a test-bed for theory, validating and refining the science of the built environment. If we are to build responsibly, sustainable design must be founded on the objective certainties of building science and technology. But, by their nature, scientific and technological concepts are abstract. It is in their application in the practical world that they are given concrete form and, in the field of architecture, acquire cultural relevance and the semblance of a language.

There are some who hold the view that a sustainable architecture will, in its very fundamentals, be different from other ways of building. For example, Brenda and Robert Vale have proposed a formula for a 'green aesthetic', an 'architecture that would… determine beauty through performance'.[2] There is a powerful strand in British architectural culture that supports this point of view. This is probably most strongly expressed in works such as

JM Richards' The Functional Tradition, where he wrote that these buildings 'have a clarity of form and a subtle modelling of solids and voids that many works of a more sophisticated origin might envy. Then there is their expressive use of materials and their trimness of detail. In fact they display, unobscured by the irrelevances of ornament, the essential attributes of architecture'.[3]

The work of FCBa seems to enjoy a constructive relationship with this tradition. Each design exhibits the 'discipline' that comes from the application of environmental principle, given expression through clarity of form and directness of detail. But that is only part of the story. The oeuvre to date now contains a sufficient number of projects for it to be seen no longer as a number of discrete cases but rather as an interconnected whole. As such it may be considered a research or an exploration into wider themes, including the question of the relationship between principle, form and language. It is this that gives it its maturity and, hence, its wider relevance.

The biologist and philosopher of science PB Medawar observed that 'as a science advances, particular facts are comprehended within… general statements of steadily increasing power and compass – whereupon the facts need no longer be known explicitly… In all sciences we are being progressively relieved of the burden of singular instances, the tyranny of the particular. We need no longer record the fall of every apple.'[4] With FCBa's work of the past quarter century we have been freed from the tyranny of the particular.

Notes
1 Victor Olgyay, Design with climate: a bioclimatic approach to architectural regionalism (Princeton 1963).
2 Brenda and Robert Vale, The New Autonomous House (London 2000).
3 JM Richards with photographs by Eric de Maré, The Functional Tradition in Early Industrial Buildings (London 1958).
4 'Two conceptions of science', in PB Medawar, The Art of the Soluble (London 1967).

Dean Hawkes is emeritus professor of architectural design at Cardiff University and emeritus fellow of Darwin College at Cambridge University.

The environmental agenda

Peter Clegg

A century ago a revolution began to take place in the way that we see the world. The influence of cubism in the arts, futurism in literature and the extraordinary innovations of the Bauhaus gave us what has come to be known as the Modern Movement. In architecture this led to the most significant change in built form since the Renaissance, an aesthetic shift that recognised that technological developments and social change could give birth to a radically new built environment.

Although the impact of changes in building technology were evident in the first half of the century, social change did not really begin to take effect until the second half. Anticipated changes in class and family structure only began to emerge in the 1950s and 1960s, providing opportunities for a new architectural language envisaged 50 years earlier to become more mainstream – and bringing with it unforeseen problems. This in turn led to a re-evaluation of social aspects of architecture in the late 1960s at a time when environmental concerns were also emerging. When we founded our practice in 1978, it was rooted in what was then termed 'community architecture', with an office in an empty shop in Bath. We made our houses in converted farm buildings just outside the city where, with inevitable naivety born of enthusiasm, we set about trying to produce all our own food and some of our own energy needs – taking charge of our lives. From a somewhat self-indulgent rural lifestyle, and a community based local practice, we have over the years become more interested in issues of urbanism and in the development of larger scale community buildings, though the fundamental principles of a social and environmental focus to our work have remained consistent.

This book aims to record what we have learned from experimenting with an environmental approach to architecture over the last twenty-five years. It documents our involvement with passive solar design in housing in the 1980s through to more complex energy equations in the institutional and commercial buildings with which we have subsequently been involved. While it deals primarily with the impact of environmental thinking on our approach to design, it also makes reference to the social principles that are of equal or greater importance at the conceptual stage of any project. And inevitably it illustrates our aesthetic preoccupations over a quarter of a century of design development.

But the book is primarily concerned with the environmental agenda and we should start by giving our definition of what that is. Contemporary environmental thinking emerged in the 1960s with a series of discrete but inter-linked concerns. Rachel Carson drew the world's attention to pollution through the use of persistent pesticides such as DDT.[1] Paul Erlich popularised concerns over the twentieth century population explosion.[2] In 1972 'The Limits to Growth' explained that if pollution or population did not result in the downfall of the planet then exhaustion of the earth's resources and fossil fuels would.[3] The oil crisis in the 1970s when the Arab nations began to restrict their exports brought the fossil fuel issue into sharp focus. This gave new impetus to what had previously been minority interests in the design of buildings to capture and utilise solar energy.

But it was not until the twin spectres of global warming and ozone depletion were recognised in the 1980s that we began to see that the abuse of the planet and its resources by an expanding population with an extravagant lifestyle was not sustainable. The emphasis on the environmental agenda changed. We needed to reduce energy consumption, not because fossil fuels were running out, but because we were burning them and releasing greenhouse gases into the atmosphere at a rate which was causing a more rapid rise in global temperatures than had ever before been recorded. The evidence of the extent of man's interference with every aspect of nature was becoming clearer and clearer. By the 1980s we had destroyed two thirds of the rainforest that existed in the 1950s, and we were beginning to impact on fragile ecosystems such as Antarctica.[3] But climate change breached the last natural boundary. We had begun to realise that the way we led our lives on earth affected our entire atmosphere and therefore the complex energy balances of the planet.

The Bruntland Report of 1987 gave a clear definition of 'sustainable' development – that it should 'meet the needs of the current generations without compromising the ability of future generations to meet their own needs'.[4] This has always been quite a mouthful and subject to a variety of interpretations. It has, however been usefully disaggregated by The Natural Step, an international organisation dedicated to developing the use of a common framework to guide society towards a just and sustainable future.[5] The framework

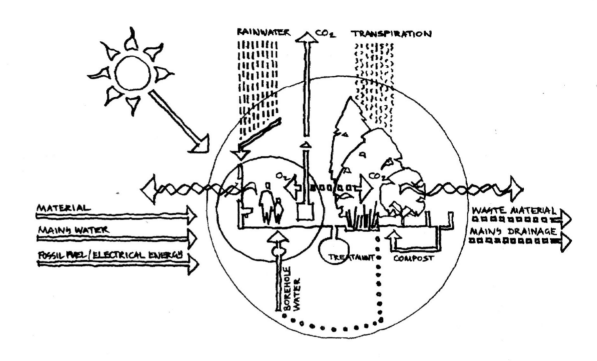

is based on systems theory and organisational learning and defines four 'system conditions' which are useful for the application of sustainability to architecture. Paraphrased, these are:

• substances extracted from the earth's crust must not systematically increase in nature;
• substances produced by society must not systematically increase in nature;
• the physical basis for the productivity and diversity of nature must not be systematically diminished;
• we should be fair and equitable in meeting basic human needs.

The first condition has been breached over the last 150 years by increasing our use of fossil fuel reserves. Operational carbon dioxide emissions from buildings in the UK result in more than 50 per cent of the contribution of greenhouse gases to the upper atmosphere. The embodied energy in the construction industry accounts for a further 10 per cent. Until we manage to develop renewable energy sources and alternatives to fossil fuels, global warming is set to continue. Predictions suggest global average temperatures will increase by 1.4-5.8 degrees C over the next century and allied to this there will be a projected sea rise of between 0.09 and 0.88 metres.[6] But there are other significant concerns resulting from our delving into the earth's crust. For example, the rate of depletion of mineral resources is difficult to predict. Twenty years ago it was thought that our entire reserves of copper would be consumed before the end of the century. Technological changes and, to a certain extent, improved recycling pathways have allayed those fears but if mineral extraction continues unchecked it could become a major environmental concern. We must now regard metals as a technological resource, continually cycled from one manufacturing process to another.

The second condition makes reference to persistent and toxic chemicals that accumulate in nature. Whereas the principle culprit over the last few decades has been chemical agriculture, there are issues that are pertinent to the building industry. In order to create sophisticated low-energy architecture we rely on some highly processed materials and components, but we need to be sure that their manufacture, installation and eventual reuse or recycling have a clean bill of health. By international agreement, ozone depleting chemicals, CFCs and halons have now virtually been eliminated from the construction industry, but volatile organic compounds, mainly in the form of solvents, are still part of our building technology, and the organic chemical industry that has given us a wide range of 'artificial' materials still needs to be treated with circumspection. To amass the wealth of data around the manufacture, use, disposal and recyclability of a material can be a daunting task, and can paralyse the decision-making process. If we rely on instinct then 'natural' and 'local' generally mean 'safe' and 'good'.

The third system condition aims to preserve the productivity and diversity of nature, and the built environment can of course be destructive not only locally but globally. We need to seek to find ways of increasing biodiversity alongside built development as well as providing the vital psychological link between internal environments and a natural world. But we also need to be aware of the destruction that we are causing elsewhere. In the last 25 years we have seen wholesale elimination of vast areas of tropical rainforest and both the removal of the CO_2-absorbing vegetation and the burning of the brush have caused a massive additional load in terms of global greenhouse emissions. Fortunately we are now able to see the results of regulatory frameworks such as the Forest Stewardship Council providing certification of good management systems which have resulted in both adding value to the forest ecosystem and providing us with sustainable low-CO_2 building materials.

The fourth system condition deals with social and environmental equality. Ecological footprints provide a useful measurement of environmental equality. The ecological footprint of any sector of human population is the land and water area that is required to support indefinitely its lifestyle given a prevailing technology. Taking global population and the total available area of bio-productive land and sea gives an 'earth share' of 1.9 global hectares per capita. The UK ecological footprint is almost three times as much as this (the US is almost double again at more than 10 gha, whereas Mozambique is rated at about 0.5 gha).[7] This inequity in the use of global resources needs to be addressed and once again our work is concerned with both the local as well as global level. Promotion of social equality and the fostering of a sense of community is essential to the development of urban spaces as well as the organisation of buildings. Issues of hierarchy, accessibility and human scale have to be at the core of design and decision making. And as with all social and environmental issues, the process of design and our internal practice organisation management helps us to define the issues that are important in the architecture that we produce. The development of the practice as an organisation as well as the body of work we produce is part of a continuous process of social and environmental enquiry.

The four system conditions of The Natural Step translate nearly into the four principle concerns of our 'environmental agenda'. First and foremost is the energy use and carbon dioxide production resulting from the way we deal with heat, light and air in our buildings. Second is the holistic environmental impact of the materials we use. Third is the intimate relationship between buildings and their natural environment, and the flows of air, water and materials that bind the two together. And fourth is the all important component of social sustainability. These core principles, along with formal contextual preoccupations, shape our architecture; the moral burdens have become liberating.

So what are the aims of this book?

First, we wanted to record what we had learned over the last twenty five years and go through the exercise of recapitulation and re-evaluation that is part of a healthy design process.

Second, we felt it would be useful to look at the issue of energy use in buildings from a typological perspective. From our experience in education, both in schools of architecture and in passing on knowledge to younger people who have joined the practice, we find there is a general misunderstanding over the key energy issues related to different building types. If reducing CO2 emissions is a basic goal, then daylighting and ventilation become much more significant in schools and offices whereas energy for heating is still more significant in housing. In student housing hot water usage becomes paramount. Benchmarks for different building types can be confusing and reliable data on building performance, even on our own buildings, is hard to come by and then often out of date. If we are serious about reducing operational CO2 emissions in our buildings, we need to pay attention to both calculated and monitored annual consumption ratings much as we consider the fuel consumption of a car. What we have attempted to do therefore is to quantify CO2 data from various sources, look at the performance of our buildings where it has been possible to obtain

data, and at least contribute to the difficult debate on measuring building performance.

Third, through illustrating our work across a range of building types, we wanted to consolidate the data that we use throughout the design process. In many areas of energy and environmental design we tend to rely on the expertise of our engineering partners, but we do feel that we have acquired a breadth of knowledge from past experience, and this makes up the final section of the book – the Primer. It has taken the production of the book to stimulate us to assemble this knowledge in one place, and we hope that it will prove useful for other architects and particularly students in setting down basic principles of bioclimatic design.

Finally we wanted to celebrate the contribution to our schemes of our consultants, specifically environmental engineers. We have therefore asked some of our key collaborators to comment on their own design work, and their part in the process. The development of form, aspect and orientation, the definition of fabric, transparency and permeability, are all issues which environmental engineers and architects need to develop together, and we are fortunate in the UK in having a small but growing number of consultants who understand architectural language, and work with us on the development of environmental systems that are integrated into architectural thinking. We hope this book will be a celebration of that collaboration.

We started thinking about this book five years ago, before climate change began to hit the headlines; before Katrina and the 'inconvenient truth' hit the USA, and before the Stern Report appeared in the UK. As a practice and as a profession we now have much greater awareness not only of the environmental impact of climate change but also its economic impact. Shortly the European Environmental Performance Directive will force us to label the energy performance of our buildings as we do our refrigerators and our cars. Sustainability is not just about counting carbon in our buildings; it is also about creating greater awareness of the environment through architecture and urban design. A century ago the modern movement provided a radical shift in our social and technological approach to architecture: it will require no less a radical shift in our environmental approach if we are to meet the threat of climate change.

Notes
1 Rachel Carson, Silent Spring (New York 1962).
2 Paul Erlich, The Population Bomb (New York 1968).
3 DH Meadows, J Randers, WW Behrens, The Limits to Growth (New York 1972).
4 G Bruntland (ed), Our Common Future: The World Commission on Environment and Development (Oxford University Press 1987)
5 See www.naturalstep.org
6 IPCC Climate Change Synthesis Report 2001: Working Group Summary for Policymakers.
7 Living Planet Report 2002, WWF International.

The place called home has huge social and psychological signifi-cance. It is our place in the world from which we come and go, a place of physical reference and security. It is more than just shelter from the elements or a piece of real estate investment; to most people a home has a value and meaning that gives us status in our communities, as well as the opportunity for individual expression. To be without a home – to be homeless – is one of the great human indignities of our time. The making of personal space – the truly private realm – and how it relates to the public world of streets and external spaces has fascinated us since the practice was first formed.

Probably more than any other building type, the house express-es both the social values of a particular generation and its response to the external environment. There cannot be many finer exam-ples than that of our home city of Bath. Planned principally in the second half of the eighteenth century, Bath was built in response to a lifestyle captured and implemented by the patron Ralph Allen, with his architect John Wood. The grand streets, parades and squares for public life were formed by houses that, internally, had a social hierarchy that gave the architecture both meaning and dignity. Built of Bath stone, with a refined sense of proportion and a profound understanding of the material, they created partic-ular forms in relationship to the hillside topography within the eighteenth-century landscape tradition.

Much of the early work of the practice was undertaken in the city of Bath, working from a community shop 'office' in one of the run-down areas of the city. The publication of The Sack of Bath in the early 1970s had already alerted us to the risks of losing some of the 'ordinary', but equally important, parts of the city. Substantial areas had either been demolished, or were under threat, as the old was swept away for the new. The practice's early work of the late-1970s and early-1980s involved us in getting to know the fabric of our city, with small conversion projects for private individuals or for communities, often working with the assistance of grants. This involved reusing the existing historic fabric, adapting and adding to it not only to achieve modern-day living standards, but to signifi-cantly improve its environmental performance. Maximising the reuse of elements of the building, upgrading its thermal perfor-mance and adding passive and active solar elements were our first

steps into sustainable architecture. Early projects added solar spaces to existing dwellings while competition schemes like the 'solar skin' project for a European passive solar housing competi-tion extended our thinking about the environmental responses of domestic architecture.

Urban infill projects on difficult sites that had remained un-developed were our first forays into what is now called brownfield development. These first experiments with new-build dwellings at Cleveland Reach and Hedgemead Park featured sections that were generated in response to the steeply sloping sites and explored the use of daylight and passive solar gain. These new dwellings, stitched into existing communities, incorporated high levels of insulation as well as new (at the time) Scandinavian high-perfor-mance triple-glazing systems. At Cleveland Reach we even experi-mented with trombe wall technology, although, like many other over-ambitious projects from that era, we now suspect that the solar gain would have been more than offset by night-time heat losses through the glazed skin!

Our own houses, whether adaptations of historic buildings or new-build on small infill sites, continue these explorations of a section that responds to site, light and solar orientation. Many of these early works were undertaken with the practice acting as developer in partnership with a contractor, using self-build labour on extremely low budgets – making the most of limited resources and collaborations to make new homes and communities.

After these early projects where we were building within a historic urban framework, it was something of a contrast to under-take a number of projects in the new town of Milton Keynes. The Milton Keynes Development Corporation was setting new stan-dards in the environmental design of new dwellings and even had its own energy performance targets as part of this programme. Two projects there were designed to push the boundaries of low-energy house design. The first, which became known as the super-insulated house, was designed for a mainstream development of low-density (primarily semi-detached) houses constructed by a private developer. It was built using highly insulated timber wall and floor systems, fabricated off-site. Constructed in 1985, the window wall provided U-values in excess of the 2002 revision to the Building Regulations; heat losses were reduced to the extent that a

Cleveland Reach

Hedgemead Park

Solar Courtyards, Milton Keynes

conventional central heating system was not required and was replaced by a 1.5kW heater battery within a whole-house ventilation system. One of four of the houses monitored had a space heating bill of 1500 kW/hr per year, equivalent to a gas bill of £6 a year. The miniature heat source in the ventilation systems consisted of a gas water heater feeding a very highly insulated hot-water cylinder. A similar system was used on a much larger district heating scheme in Bristol, where a centralised gas-fired boiler provided piped hot water to a courtyard of elderly-persons' flats.

The second Milton Keynes scheme, in contrast, looked at maximising direct solar gain. It consisted of a less traditional single-storey courtyard form, allowing large areas of south-facing glazing while maintaining privacy. The solar 'aperture' comprises 27 square metres of quadruple-insulated south-facing glazing, with a U-value of less than 1.0, incorporated various shading devices, including interstitial blinds, to reduce summertime solar gain while maximising winter sunlight.

Interestingly the performance of these houses was far less successful than the earlier superinsulated development. It reinforced our opinion that it is much easier to reduce energy use by increasing insulation than by harnessing solar energy. Other schemes looked at maximising passive solar gain through roof spaces or attached greenhouses; but the monitored performance of the buildings demonstrated that while we might obtain, say, 25 per cent of the annual space-heating load from solar energy, the more we insulated, the shorter the season in which heating was required. In the UK climate there may be a useful solar contribution in spring and autumn but in a really well insulated house the heating season is reduced to November to February, when potential solar gain is minimal.

The late 1980s was generally a bleak time for housing design in the UK. Even the housing associations had rejected their often more experimental approach for the predictable formula of the volume housebuilder. During this period we undertook a number of specialist housing projects that allowed a more specific design and environmental agenda. This work was to generate a series of what we regarded as 'big houses' for residential schools or communities for handicapped young adults, with children at one end of the age spectrum and elderly people at the other. These 'houses'

for the Sheiling and Camphill Communities in Gloucestershire, Hampshire and Milton Keynes were designed to accommodate anything between six and 20 people, living as an extended family, with private rooms around the communal facilities of bathrooms, kitchen and dining/living spaces. The identity of these places as 'homes' within what is inevitably an institutional environment was a major driver of the design. The buildings were set in matured landscaped grounds which were 'farmed' to provide as self-sufficient and sustainable an environment as possible, creating a strong relationship between the inside and outside, both functionally and emotionally. Simple 'vernacular' buildings relating to 'agricultural' typologies such as farmhouses, barns and outhouses were given a sense of identity by an organic response to the site geometries, in both plan and section, with references to early twentieth-century European expressionism (many of the clients were followers of Rudolf Steiner's philosophy) and the English arts and crafts movement. Environmental objectives included the use of natural and, where possible, local materials; natural light and ventilation; and appropriate orientation, combined with a highly insulated fabric. Our work with the Steiner communities also introduced us to the possibilities – and the problems – of on-site sewerage treatment using reed bed technologies. We learned that they required dedicated maintenance and odour tolerance!

Back in Bath around 1990, we designed a new residential home for the elderly on a steeply sloping and compact riverside site close to the city centre. The brief from Bridgecare, a newly formed charitable trust, was to provide a dignified non-institutional home for 32 elderly residents of varying degrees of dependence. Creating this 'home from home' with all the required access and medical provisions was to be the real challenge. The institutional feel was broken down by making smaller groups of rooms around shared living spaces, that then linked to the main central dining hall. A hierarchy of spaces extended from the more public areas of the 'community home' to the more private areas of the individual's room – a 'progressive privacy' that allowed individuals choice over their degree of interaction within the big house. There was no attempt to recreate the domestic scale of the actual homes in which the residents had previously lived; we saw this new building type more as a grand residential hotel or country house, a palazzo

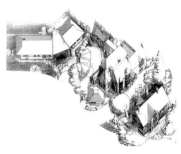

Cherry Orchards

Laurels Farm

Woodbridge Farm

on the river. Two wings of accommodation, one parallel to the river, the other to the street, open the plan up to the south and create in between a double-height space for the central hall (with roof garden over) which opens out onto the riverside gardens via a wintergarden. Plan and section respond to the sloping site and solar orientation, with the wintergarden acting as a passive solar collector.

Bengough's House was a follow-on project from Bridgecare – a residential home for 40 people on the outskirts of Bristol. Its 'sub-urban' site, positioned adjacent to two heavily trafficked roads, led to a scheme that created a hard and heavily protective street side, with an open lightweight and accessible garden side formed by two interlocking low-rise open courtyards. These courtyards open to the south and create a protected external microclimate which encourage the residents to use their individual external terraces and balconies. Bengough's draws on an almshouse model of communal living around accessible landscaped courts.

During the mid 1990s we were becoming increasingly involved with the design of student housing, which allowed us to develop ideas on high-density, affordable and car-free living environments. This work involved the creation of new residential communities around pedestrian-dominated spaces on previously developed sites. It coincided with the beginnings of what has been referred to as the 'urban renaissance', probably starting with Richard Roger's Reith Lectures in 1995. The Urban Task Force followed, headed by Rogers, with a comprehensive report published in 1999, an urban white paper and legislation in the form of PPG3 later in 1999. This set the scene for bringing living back into the city, with higher densities and mixed-use communities, using brownfield land to reduce urban sprawl and dependence on the motor car. The government issued target figures to address the need for an additional four million new homes by 2004, with the goal of locating 60-75 per cent of these on brownfield sites.

This was the context for our first major new-build high-density brownfield scheme for a volume housebuilder. Century Court, in the centre of Cheltenham, is a 96-dwelling development of apartments and terraced houses on a one hectare site previously occupied by a 1960s office block, with a density of approximately 400 habitable rooms per hectare. The design creates a hierarchy of

buildings in relation to their position on the site related to the historic domestic forms of the city. A five-storey 'grand' terrace forms the principal street frontage, with lower terraces and villa buildings enclosing a landscaped garden court that provides the main pedestrian and vehicular access, with below-ground parking. The environmental story here addresses the wider issues of density, urban location and site re-use, but we also discovered for the first time the benefits of using an external insulation and render system that simplifies all the cold-bridging problems associated with conventional construction.

Our second major urban housing project, The Point, is located on the south side of Bristol City Harbourside, where a one hectare site, previously used as a railway siding for the docks, was developed for 114 mixed-type dwellings. This involved making public frontages and integrating a new community at a density of more than 450 habitable rooms per hectare. Lillie Road for the Peabody Trust was an exercise in high-density, mixed social housing, fabricated off-site. Recent work includes an environmental housing project in Madrid, which looks at modifying the traditional urban house typology to enhance summertime comfort without instant recourse to air conditioning, while Accordia in Cambridge was an exercise in planning at a major urban scale to create a new residential quarter for the city. The medium-density landscaped scheme took a new look at public/private land use, with houses and apartment buildings designed around a square of public gardens. All of these projects are examined in more detail in the case studies that follow.

Over the last 25 years we have seen changes in the nature of the energy and environmental agenda in relation to the design of housing. When we began in practice, our interests focused on reducing space heating bills, which were then responsible for up to 75 per cent of energy used in the home. By 1995 half of the energy use of a typical new-build house might go in space heating, and a quarter each in hot water and electrical usage. Currently, with the very high standards of insulation now enforced, the proportions have changed to more like one-third each for space heating, hot water and electrical consumption; but, given the additional carbon dioxide burden attributable to electrical usage, it is likely that more than half of the carbon dioxide burden would result from electrical

Bridgemead

Bengough's House

usage in new homes. This means that the bulk of resultant carbon dioxide emissions are generally beyond the control of the architect; we can specify low-energy light fittings but will they be used? Designing for good daylighting is less significant in houses which our current lifestyles dictate are often unoccupied for most of the daylight hours. We incorporate glazing for delight rather than daylight and we recognise concern about the extent of glazing, solar heat gain and the inexorable desire for air conditioning.

The increased share of the energy burden attributable to domestic water heating and electrical use has led to a growing interest in solar domestic water heating and photovoltaics. So far we have not had a chance to incorporate these into house design, although we hope to use both in new schemes for C&J Clarks in Street and the Brighton 'One Planet Living' Community. In these projects we have begun to look at overall energy consumption resulting from transportation and embodied energy as well as operational energy consumption. In addition we have again looked at the use of district heating and larger-scale combined heat and power plants, serving communities with a mixture of uses and therefore a daily balance of energy demand. There are also interesting possibilities with two new PPS7 'country houses', a sector in which there is a growing expectation that buildings should be energy autonomous. Housing design presents us with a unique problem, but an even greater challenge is to integrate spaces for living, working and recreation, thus producing truly holistic sustainable communities.

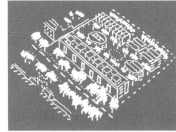

Century Court, Cheltenham

EMV Housing, Madrid

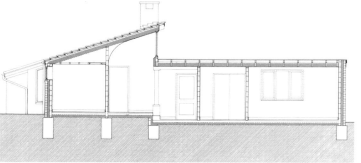

Solar courtyard housing
Milton Keynes

1985

with John Willoughby

The solar housing built in Milton Keynes was an attempt to maximise passive solar gain in a suburban house type, without the problems of lack of privacy, overheating and glare associated with large areas of glazing. A design concept was developed, in collaboration with engineer John Willoughby, for sites which faced east onto the street frontage, based around a single-storey plan that produces 55 square metres of south-facing glazing in a house with an overall plan area of 120 square metres. The glazing was specified to the highest performance then available, with three layers of glass, two low-E coatings and argon filling, providing a U-value of $1.2W/m^2K$ and a total solar transmission of 55 per cent. All the living areas had clerestory lighting, with an external venetian blind set behind a fourth (outer) pane of glass.

The houses were monitored extensively and the total annual solar contribution to the space heating load was calculated to be 27 per cent. However, the actual heat loss was much greater than anticipated, particularly the ventilation component, which resulted from poor quality of workmanship at the junctions between external materials in the building. There was also a heat reclaim ventilation system which exhausts air from bathrooms, utility rooms and kitchens (with a boost extractor over the cooker hood) and passes it through a cross-plate heat exchanger and also delivers fresh air to bedrooms and living rooms. Although this type of ventilation system had been used successfully in two previous housing schemes, it did not operate well here due to the length and the depth of ductwork involved and the poor airtightness performance of the building.

The houses sold well and the privacy of the courtyard gardens and the

quality of the internal daylighting was particularly appreciated. The design team's concerns over potential problems from overheating did not materialise, with inter-pane joins proving very effective and the combination of external pergolas and an internal slatted light-shelf helping to reduce glare.

A post-occupancy evaluation was carried out after ten years, measuring the annual consumption of gas and electricity for three of the houses. This showed that they performed at around 50kg of carbon dioxide per square metre. An occupant questionnaire revealed that, while most people appreciated the houses, their main concerns were the difficulty of cleaning the inter-pane blinds and the performance and servicing of the heat reclaim ventilation system. Some occupants complained of the noise; many did not understand how it worked. A further conclusion drawn from this project is that the combination of large areas of glazing with considerable thermal mass (construction was conventional, with high-density blockwork for the internal leaves of cavity walls and partitions) did not result in overheating. In other words, increased solar gain with increased thermal mass can bring increased architectural delight.

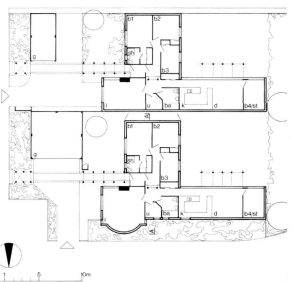

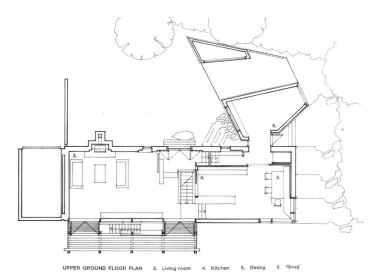

MEZZANINE LEVEL PLAN   1. Study / Studio   2. Void over living

UPPER GROUND FLOOR PLAN   3. Living room   4. Kitchen   5. Dining   6. 'Snug'

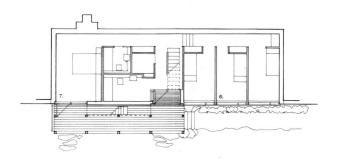

LOWER GROUND FLOOR PLAN   7. Bedroom (Parents)   8. Bedrooms (Children)

Upper Lawn
Bath

1998

with Whitby & Bird

This house sits at the edge of Bath, with the city lying below to the west and protected countryside rising up behind to the east. The low building form is long (17 metres), a single room wide (4.85 metres) and cut into the slope of the ground. The raised street elevation is formed by a massive Bath stone-faced cantilevered wall aligned with the adjoining terrace at the height of the projecting garden walls – an unassuming outbuilding-like frontage behind which the rooms are organised.

The plane of the Welsh slate roof follows the slope of the ground and is lifted above the coping of the eastern wall to form a clerestory which captures the rising sun as it appears over the hillside. This environmental response to orientation, taking in the morning sun at high level to warm the house for the day and with controlled evening sun for the night, is the simple passive solar concept that drives the form. The massive rear masonry wall acts as a heat sink to absorb and gradually distribute the heat in the winter and spring while providing some 'coolth' for the summer. A woodburning stove on this wall is lit on cold winter nights to warm the single living space and the masonry mass, allowing the background gas-fired heating to be turned off. High levels of wall insulation and high performance glazing help to ensure the house is well wrapped against the elements.

The softer 'interior' elevation is treated as 'furniture' to the garden. Douglas fir structural frames at 2.25 metre centres are in-filled with high levels of insulation and joinery-finished cedar boarding; glazed screens open up the house to the garden, views and the setting sun to the west. The loggia balcony acts as a framework for climbing plants and creates a mediating in-between zone, filtering the sunlight to reduce overheating, framing the view and bringing the garden up to the higher level living space.

The accommodation is organised around a central staircase which takes up the difference in external ground level across the plan. The main entrance – a 'hole in the wall' – leads onto a raised threshold platform overlooking the open living spaces with city views beyond. The living space is a single volume at one end and a split-level kitchen with study mezzanine above at the other. An 'outrigger' snug room projects from the main body of the house at the south end, enclosing the entrance courtyard. The staircase continues down to the more private and intimate realm of the bedrooms – cool night time spaces that face onto the garden with children at one end and parents at the other.

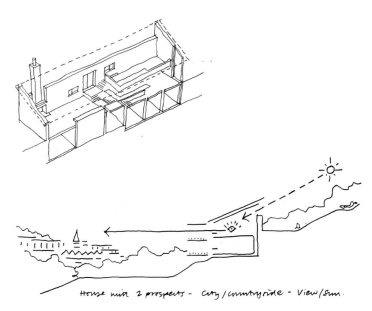

House with 2 prospects – city / countryside – View / Sun.

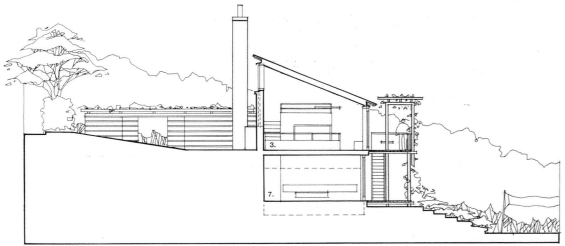

Market Lane
Shepherd's Bush

2001
with Atelier Ten

For an estimated 500 people in Britain, half of them in London, home is the city streets. Many prefer to be outdoors, living with drug or alcohol problems, disillusioned with society. Market Lane in London's Shepherd's Bush provides a centre for the homeless which offers a place where they can wash, eat, drink and meet each other, and where they can also take steps back into a more conventional society, if they wish. The project comprises a day centre, a 15-bed hostel and 12 one-bed flats providing short-term 'move-on' accommodation. The three buildings are clustered around a small courtyard and form a welcome oasis behind Goldhawk Road, near Shepherd's Bush market.

The project attempts to address issues of 'social' sustainability head-on, by providing a refuge and a route back into society for those who, for any number of reasons, have opted out. Part-funded by the West London Rough Sleepers Initiative and the Peabody Trust, the scheme was developed in consultation with agencies who care for this challenging client group. The design process included presentations to planning officers, local residents and typical clients to ensure that a potentially controversial development met the needs and aspirations of its users, while minimising disruption to its neighbours.

The key move in a very simple organisational framework was to create a dynamic roof form that announces the entrance to the day centre and links the ground and first floors with the south-facing enclosed courtyard space. The copper-sheathed roof curves up to a double-height gallery, where the medical rooms, laundry, shower and 'healthy living' spaces are located. On the ground floor are the reception, a cafe and a small living room. These look out onto a sunlit courtyard with planting and sheltered areas where those who feel unhappy about entering the building or who want to stay outside (often with dogs that form important companions) can wait.

The S-shaped curve of the roof provides shade from the south sun and also helps achieve good quality natural ventilation, which can be necessary in a building that from time to time houses people whose attention to hygiene is unconventional! But the double-height space itself is intended to provide somewhere that is both welcoming and uplifting. Galleries and windows help to signify transparency but also allow informal supervision. It is one of two or three instances in the otherwise modest and logical rectilinear plan where curvilinear gestures soften the architectural form.

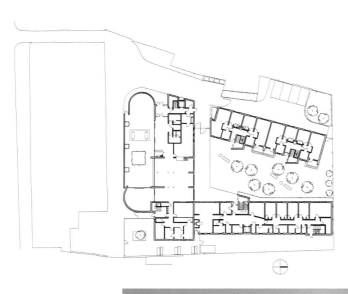

The Point
Wapping Wharf
Bristol

2001
with BME Partnership

The Point is a private speculative development comprising 105 apartments and nine town houses. The strong contemporary design brings new life and optimism to this hitherto neglected area of Bristol. As an essay in high-density brownfield development it creates 114 dwellings (about 400 habitable rooms) per hectare, which is equivalent to or higher than some of the denser Georgian and Victorian terrace areas of Bristol. This density is combined with our generation's desire for natural light, views and privacy within for the occupants.

The one hectare site is on the south side of Bristol's 'floating' harbour, between the Bristol Industrial Museum

and the Brunel's SS Great Britain. It was previously used as a railway sidings and freight storage area as part of Bristol's once thriving docks. Memories of this remain with retained disused tracks, which run along the whole of the site's 250 metre harbourside frontage. The site geometry is a long thin triangle with its long side facing north onto the floating harbour, with views across to the harbour regeneration area. The southern side backs on to existing, mainly early-nineteenth century terraces and villas sitting some three to four metres up from the site. To the east, the site thins down to almost a point end and looks out along the harbourside towards the Industrial Museum.

The shorter western boundary, perpendicular to the harbourside, abuts an existing car park/public square, which forms the main arrival space for visitors to the SS Great Britain. From here there are views across the SS Great Britain towards the distant built slopes of Clifton Wood and the landscaped hills of Ashton Court.

The site forms part of the Bristol Harbourside Regeneration Planning Brief (1995, revised 1998), which designated it for residential use as part of a plan to generate more homes in the city centre docklands. A high-density development was to be welcomed, within the sensitive planning constraints of the site, consideration being given to

the amenity of neighbouring residents and the retention of long distant views across and along the harbourside.

In 1998 the developers Beaufort Homes (now Crosby Special Projects) submitted a detailed planning application prepared by a Bristol-based firm of architects. While the scheme complied with planning guidelines and was recommended for approval, after vicious opposition it was refused at committee. We were appointed in January 1999 to start afresh with a new design, maintaining the density of the previous application and planning guidelines.

With such strong public opinion, as is often the case with the urban brownfield sites, we decided to devise a more

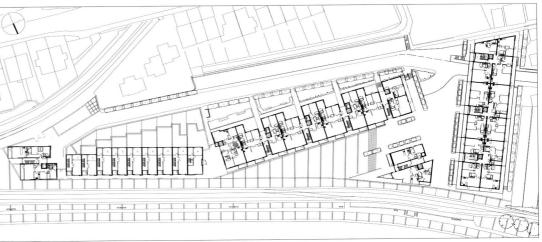

collaborative route towards a planning application. Advised by our planning consultants Chapman Warren and with the assistance of Jeff Bishop, a consultation procedure was devised with the local residents and interest groups. These groups were numerous, from residents' associations through general amenity interest groups to specific parties, such as local businesses and the SS Great Britain and Industrial Museum.

A series of workshops was set up to start an 'open book' design process, to be managed and recorded towards a planning application. The first meetings, without drawings, established a scoping exercise to define concerns and aspirations, and further sessions defined design explorations. This was not design by committee, and was strongly led by our team – essentially we were sharing the design interactions that usually go on behind architects' closed doors. All this was done within a strict commercial framework. A consensus emerged (which inevitably did not suit everyone) and the design went to committee, where it was approved unanimously.

The main aim was to try and make public external spaces while providing the privacy required for those who live within. Our towns and cities are full of good traditional examples of this, whether Georgian, Victorian or Edwardian. Much post-war housing has adopted different models, designed around the requirements of the car and frequently failing to make good streets and public spaces.

Our aim also was to create a group of buildings, with each one playing a different role as they each respond to their particular position on the site. These buildings change in scale from 'domestic' at the east end of the site to larger industrial scale at the west. Construction is typically in situ concrete frame and slab, with loadbearing cross walls for the town houses and external insulation to the fabric. High levels of insulation, combined with thermally broken low-energy glazing systems, provide thermally efficient structures within the constraints of producing large areas of north-facing glazing for harbourside views.

An Environmental Assessment: Peter Rickaby – Rickaby Thompson Associates

Wapping Wharf was designed with the issues raised by the Urban Task Force in mind, particularly that low-density suburban 'sprawl' might be less 'sustainable' than higher-density urban developments; urban residents might travel more on foot, by bicycle and public transport, and less by car, than their suburban counterparts.

To test this, we assessed the project in comparison with a theoretical suburban development of 114 houses typically offered by a national house-builder. The study considered the energy efficiency of the dwellings, the residents' likely patterns of travel, and the effect on fuel use and carbon dioxide emissions. Two variants of the comparative development were considered: one designed to minimum Building Regulations standards and the other with a higher standard of energy efficiency, comparable to Wapping Wharf. Although both schemes contained 114 dwellings, the units at Wapping Wharf were larger, and accommodate fewer people (279 as against 368) in less floor space (11,277 as against 11,782 square metres).

Wapping Wharf is well insulated, reasonably airtight and efficiently heated. However, it also provides more floor space per person than typical developments and this has the effect of offsetting the overall reduction in fuel use (per unit of floor space) which arises from the higher energy efficiency.

Wapping Wharf contains mostly apartments, which inherently have a smaller heat loss area than that of a house, but windows and external doors make up a much greater proportion of the total. From an energy efficiency viewpoint it would be logical to reduce window size; however, large windows provide good daylighting and exploit views, which the architects believed were essential in a development designed to attract middle-income homeowners back to the city. So if high standards of energy efficiency are required in high-density developments, particular attention should be paid to insulation and the thermal performance of windows and doors.

Overall, estimated domestic fuel use at Wapping Wharf is approximately 20 per cent less than for a suburban development with similar floor space and overall energy efficiency, with corresponding carbon dioxide emissions about 10 per cent less. However, because Wapping Wharf provides more floor space per person, domestic fuel use per person is 6 per cent higher, and the associated carbon dioxide emissions per person are 13 per cent higher. However, transport emissions from Wapping Wharf are only 56 per cent of those from the suburban development, because jobs, schools, shops and public transport are closer. As a result, when both sectors are combined, the total carbon dioxide emissions from Wapping Wharf are 21 per cent lower than those from the energy efficient suburban development, but the carbon dioxide emissions per person at Wapping Wharf are only very slightly lower.

Overall the study suggests that relatively high density urban housing is no less 'sustainable' than lower density suburban housing built to a similar standard. But it also shows that achieving sustainability is just as difficult in urban areas as elsewhere. Residents' expectations of floor space (given that they may not have gardens) and personal mobility can complicate the picture. High-density urban housing appears just as capable of delivering sustainability as other types of housing, and it brings other benefits as envisaged by the Urban Task Force.

Sources
• Dwelling emissions and fuel use assessed using Building Research Establishment Domestic Energy Model (BREDEM).
• Travel patterns, fuel use and emissions assessed using the Transport Statistics Great Britain and Vehicle Certification Agency.

Comparative carbon dioxide emissions	tonnes/yr	kg/m²/yr	t/person/yr
Wapping Wharf, Bristol			
Dwellings	381.3		1.37
Travel (to work, school and shops)	68.95		0.25
Total emissions	450.25	33.8	1.53
Bradley Stoke (energy efficient version)			
Dwellings	445.9		1.21
Travel (to work, school and shops)	123.88		0.34
Total emissions	569.78	37.8	1.55
Bradley Stoke (Building Regulations version)			
Dwellings	499.9		1.36
Travel (to work, school and shops)	123.88		0.34
Total emissions	623.78	42.4	1.70

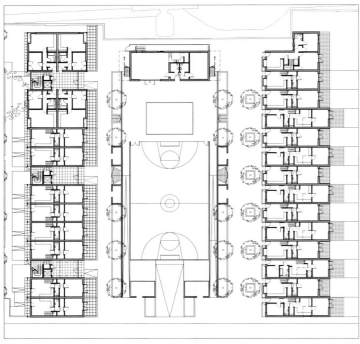

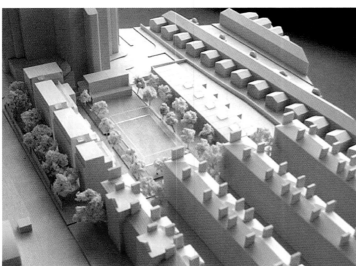

Beaufort Court
Lillie Road
Fulham

2003

with Max Fordham

As a model of modern affordable housing, this project epitomises the UK government's current agenda for housing: high density with accommodation split between shared ownership, key worker and rented provision, including four disabled units. The scheme aims to unite a new and an existing community around a new external recreation space. Commissioned by the Peabody Trust, it is located on a central London site previously occupied by a large Victorian school, close to Earl's Court and adjacent to a Peabody estate that dates from the early years of the twentieth century.

The brief called for a high-density scheme utilising innovative methods of construction and prefabrication techniques. The project was to provide 65 units comprising a mix of one- and two-bedroom flats, three- and four-bedroom maisonettes and houses, and one-bedroom Rough Sleeper Initiative bed-sits, supporting this disadvantaged sector of the community to live independently. The site area is 0.53 hectares and the scheme provides 365 habitable rooms per hectare.

Three blocks form the edges to a raised landscaped courtyard which forms the internal focus for the site and conceals semi-basement car parking. The three blocks are treated individually according to their location and the type of accommodation they contain. The central landscaped space, which is protected from the busy road to the north, is designed to unify the two estates and provide a general amenity space for all the residents. The project features a range of public and private spaces, with the thresholds between them defined by materials, landscaping and changes in level. While the flats have private balconies, the houses have gardens accessed from principal rooms which

are oriented to receive maximum amount of sunlight.

The project uses a prefabricated steel loadbearing construction system incorporating large-scale cold rolled panels and three dimensional modular construction. The light-gauge steel panel approach provides flexibility in design and minimises transportation costs and difficulties of site access to inner city sites such as this. Minimising the structural weight also reduces the extent of foundations. Cold-rolled panels are incorporated into the structural system providing additional design flexibility, permitting large window openings and extensive balconies, infilled with a prefabricated rainscreen system. For bathrooms and lift shafts, fully fitted, three-dimensional modular loadbearing construction is employed. To reduce off-site transport, modular construction is limited to these highly finished and serviced areas, providing high-quality finishes with limited waste and future defects.

A low-energy building services strategy is adopted not only for environmental reasons but also to reduce running costs for residents, many of whom are on low income or benefits. The building fabric has high thermal performance and a well sealed exterior shell which achieves thermal and acoustic performance far in excess of the current Building Regulation requirements. The stair atria that serve the primary block have large south-facing glazed walls which act as large multi-levelled winter gardens, providing passive gains to the adjoining residential units.

Accordia
Brooklands Avenue
Cambridge

2006
with Roberts & Partners

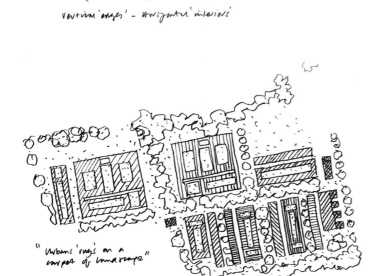

urban blocks in the landscape.

vertical 'edges' - horizontal 'interiors'

"urban 'rings' on a carpet of landscape"

'Living in a garden' but with a high density was our seemingly contradictory brief for Brooklands Avenue, a landscape-generated masterplan with homes organised around defined external spaces, to allow increased privacy and solar aspect. The scheme comprises 213 houses and 169 apartments (70 per cent private sale and 30 per cent affordable for rent) located on a 9.6 hectare site next to the Botanic Garden on the south side of Cambridge. This is a strategically important new residential quarter, occupying the largest allocated brownfield site between the city centre and the open landscape to the south.

FCBa was the masterplanner and designer of approximately two-thirds of the dwellings. To increase the variety across the development, we appointed MacCreanor Lavington Architects and Alison Brooks Architects to undertake the design of the remaining third.

Like many of the historic urban residential areas of Cambridge, the site is on the edge of the city centre. These principally late Georgian and Victorian developments are characterised by domestic-scaled (two-to four-storey) terraced and villa dwellings, creating a series of rectilinear streets and courtyards arranged around larger areas of open landscape space (greens or 'pieces'). The masterplan structure of the Brooklands Avenue scheme is similarly organised, with a full hierarchy of dense urban built form set within a strong landscape framework.

The scheme also includes a number of larger (five- to eight-storey) buildings, which are located adjacent to the key major public open spaces in the centre site and along a principal landscaped edge which includes Hobsons Brook. These buildings, which have more of an 'object' quality, have a relationship with the landscape similar to that of some of the larger college buildings within the city. The change of scale is expressed in the design of these structures, helping to create the hierarchy and visual orientation necessary in a large development.

The site has a strong existing landscape structure, with mature trees and designated landscape space along Hobsons Brook. The principal master-planning concept was to develop tight, high-density urban blocks within a framework of generous public and semi-public garden spaces. The idea of

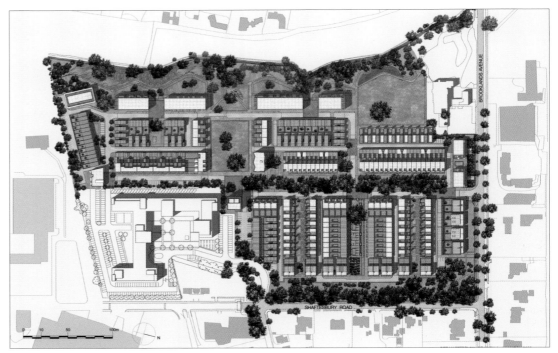

a 'big garden' comprising a series of interlinked areas with individual identities (such as play spaces and productive or ecological gardens) derives from the Cambridge landscape tradition. Each dwelling has views and access to these spaces, which account for over one-third of the site area. Due to the generosity of these garden spaces, the overall density of the scheme, which includes a number of large family houses, is about 40 dwellings per hectare.

Running north-south is a central tree-lined street, off which mews streets and courts are accessed. These are tightly planned spaces with shared surfaces designed to reduce the emphasis on the car in favour of the pedestrian and

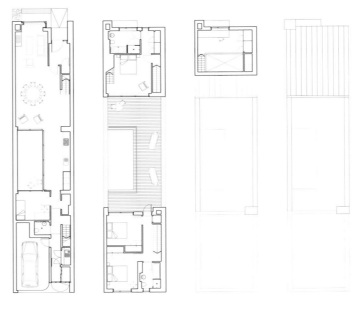

2-storey 'Long house'.

3-storey courtyard house.

cyclist. In contrast to the larger open landscape spaces and principal streets, they are small scale and intimate in character.

The principal architectural frontage, accessed by pedestrians only, looks onto the shared landscape gardens. Private terraces, courts and balconies open out onto these, forming green spaces which act as 'home zones' or 'living streets – residents can move freely from their homes to the street gardens without the disturbance of vehicular movement. Due to the generous provision of landscape spaces in the public and semi-public realm, the private external spaces of the dwellings are more intimate, allowing open views and contact with a number of rooms on different levels and maintaining a high degree of privacy.

The building forms are designed and orientated to maximise solar orientation and minimise overshadowing. Therefore the higher buildings are organised on a north-south axis (with east-west orientation) and the lower buildings on an east-west access (north-south orientation). All principal rooms receive sunlight at some point during the day, with landscaped roof spaces available for solar water heating panels or the future installation of photovoltaic panels.

Off-site fabrication methods were investigated to reduce construction waste, increase airtightness, reduce nuisance on site and improve health and safety. Prefabricated insulated panels are faced with either brick or rainscreen copper cladding, and provide higher levels of thermal insulation. Roofs are landscaped with sedum to reduce run-off and increase site biodiversity. External hard surfaces, where possible, are permeable to reduce storm water run-off and to irrigate the landscaped areas.

4-storey townhouse

3-storey courtyard house

45

Vallecas social housing
Madrid

2006
with Max Fordham

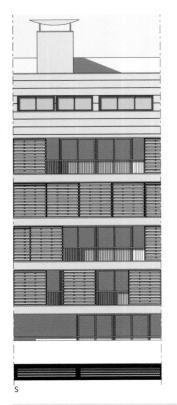
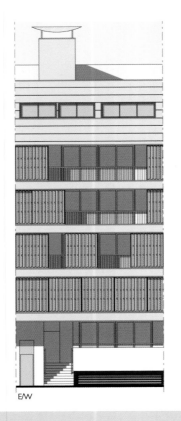
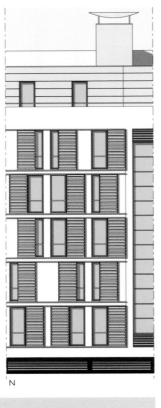

S

E/W

N

This project forms the first block in a new suburb on the outskirts of Madrid. The brief called for a bioclimatic approach that would establish energy targets for the remainder of the development and we worked closely with Max Fordham LLP to devise a solution.

Madrid has hot, dry summers but surprisingly cold winters. In June the average daytime temperature is 27 degrees C, falling to 13 degrees C at night, and relative humidity is quite low. This provides a climate where night-time cooling can be used to contribute to comfort conditions and air conditioning is not necessarily required. The mean temperature in December is lower than that of London, and although the winter season is shorter, household heating costs are still relatively high because of low standards of insulation.

The urban block that constitutes the site is exactly one hectare in area. The requirement was for 140 apartments with two to four bedrooms, averaging approximately 70 square metres in floor area, plus one parking space per apartment. The urban design brief contained very strict regulations on provision of a street frontage up to five storeys high, with cut-off corners at intersections resulting in an octagonal block form.

In terms of establishing priorities, the strategy adopted was firstly to look at dramatically increasing insulation standards; secondly to look at protecting the internal environment from excessive solar gain in summer; thirdly to look at the possibilities of using night-time structural cooling to produce thermal comfort in summer; and finally to look at solar collection to offset both electrical and hot water demand.

Thermal insulation was upgraded essentially by transferring technology from northern Europe and utilising 100mm of external insulation and render on an exterior block wall – more than double the conventional local standard. Similarly windows were given low-E glazing units, which is also unusual in Spain.

Solar gain was reduced by introducing an outer skin of sliding shutters over all the external windows. Bedroom windows have inward opening tilt-and-turn frames with an external sliding shutter face. Kitchens and living rooms face south (or east and west into the courtyard) and have large areas of sliding glazing with external sliding timber shutters, a development at a larger scale of the traditional external layering that characterises vernacular housing in Spain. The texture and grain of the shutters changes with the orientation. Those facing south cut off the high-level summer sun but allow a view downwards into the street or courtyard, while those facing east and west have vertical boarding which cuts out low-level sun but allows views to the north.

Natural cooling was facilitated by creating individual ventilation chimneys from each house through to the roof. Courtyards in deep-plan urban Spanish housing work very well in terms of creating an updraft ventilation but they provide no advantage in terms of day-lighting and, with windows from several apartments into one vertical courtyard, acoustic transmission can be a problem. A series of vertical shafts was created, one to each flat, which discharge above roof level beneath a horizontal canopy that provides rain protection.

Flat-plate solar collectors on the southern block supply domestic hot water to the whole scheme via a gas-fired community heating system that is individually metered at each apartment. Photovoltaic cells on the chimney canopies supply electricity for the communal lighting to each stairwell.

Typical 1-4 Floor Flat, 3 Bedroom Flat
North Block

Key

1 Bedroom 2
2 Bedroom 3
3 Master Bedroom
4 Hall
5 Showeroom

6 Bathroom
7 Kitchen
8 Living / Dining Area
9 Balcony
10 Central Ventilation Ducts

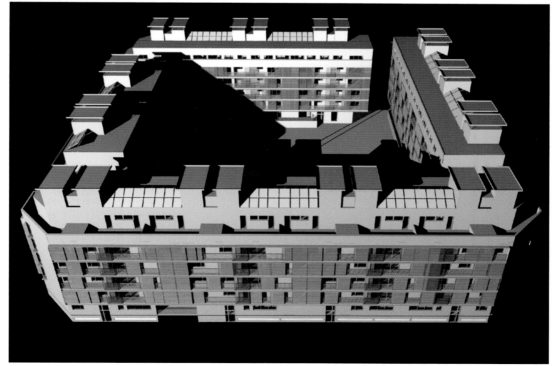

47

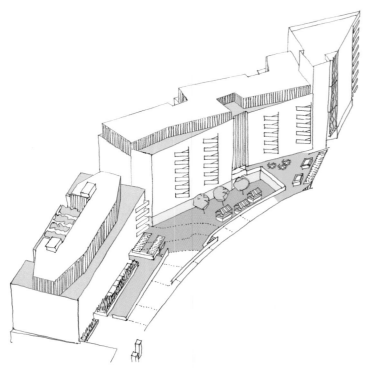

The Brighton 'One Planet Living' community

2005-

with Fulcrum Consulting

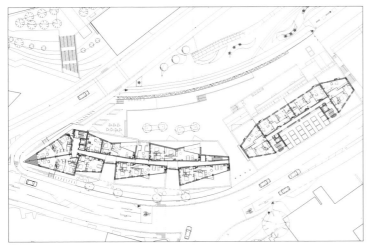

BioRegional is a charitable organisation that promotes more sustainable lifestyles for all. Together with the Peabody Trust it developed the ground-breaking BedZED community in south London, designed by Bill Dunster architects. Its philosophy is based on the concept of One Planet Living, ten principles for sustainable development promoted by BioRegional in collaboration with the World Wildlife Fund. One Planet Living refers to the fact that if everyone consumed resources as we currently do in the UK, we would need the equivalent of three planets.

The Brighton One Planet Living Community is part of the New England Quarter, which is adjacent to the main train station. The £16m development, due for completion in 2008, is a joint venture with Crest Nicholson and BioRegional Quintain, which has been established to realise a new generation of sustainable communities.

The Brighton development is part of a network of One Planet Living communities planned and in progress around the world. It will accommodate a high-density mixed-use scheme of 172 residential units above community and business uses. These units share facilities of an on-site car clubs, community centre, creche and a cafe, together with a small amount of purpose-built office accommodation. Residents will be encouraged to grow their own food in sky-gardens which are incorporated at various levels throughout the building. The building will also have its own green lifestyles officer who will facilitate services and community events.

One Planet Living schemes seek to address sustainability beyond just architectural and technical solutions. They acknowledge that some of the most significant and cost-effective carbon reductions are to be made in community-based services, such as car clubs and on-site food growing. The ten principles addressed at Brighton are as follows:

Zero Carbon In addition to exceptionally high U-values the development will utilise low-energy appliances throughout. On-site renewable energy is provided by a biomass boiler for hot water and space heating, the latter being provided via whole house ventilation systems in each flat, which incorporate highly efficient purpose-built heat exchangers. Roof-mounted wind turbines provide 15 per cent of the electricity requirement; the remainder comes from green electricity supplied by an energy services company. A small photovoltaic array is used to power the car club's electric car.

Waste Recycling and composting is made easy through the provision of on-site segregation and bokashi composting facilities which can rapidly compost all organic matter safely including meat. The 'smart waste' auditing process will be used during the construction phase.

Sustainable transport The development has excellent access to local services and public transport and this will be complemented by the provision of a car club and facilities for cyclists.

Local and sustainable materials Materials will be carefully selected for impact in sourcing, manufacture and transportation. Timber products will be FSC certified and UK sourced. Low toxicity materials will be used throughout with the use of ultra-low VOC paints and a ban on PVC. Concrete will use a minimum of 20 per cent recycle aggregates and use cement replacement materials.

Local and sustainable food The design provides residents with opportunities for on-site food production within sky-gardens and terraces incorporating mini-allotment planters for individual residents. There will be an organic cafe selling seasonal foods, and a food co-operative providing fair trade products.

Sustainable water Water consumption will be reduced by the use of low-flow fittings and appliances and dual-flush toilets. Rainwater harvested from roofs will be stored at each level and used for automatic irrigation within the sky-gardens. Any overflow will be used for wcs in the community facilities.

Natural habitats and wildlife A small amount of exterior space will contain a selection of native planting at ground floor level, but extensive vertical planting facades are envisaged to provide visual amenity and space for insects and birds.

Culture and heritage A community trust will be set up with all flats having access to a community intranet. A green lifestyles officer will be employed to support the ongoing sustainable management of the development and education of the residents.

Equity and fair trade The development will create a mixed-use community offering both private and affordable homes including a proportion of 31 square metre 'eco studios' to address the challenge providing low-cost houses in the local market. The aim will be to provide a diverse and inclusive community as well as a mix of uses within the building.

Health and wellbeing High levels of indoor air quality will be achieved using natural clay plasters on Ziegel clay blocks to provide breathable and moisture-absorptive construction. Residents will have access to outdoor spaces at many levels of the building, with balconies positioned to direct views up and down rather than across adjacent streets. Exercise will be available through an on-site bouldering wall!

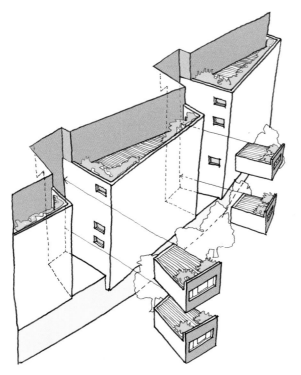

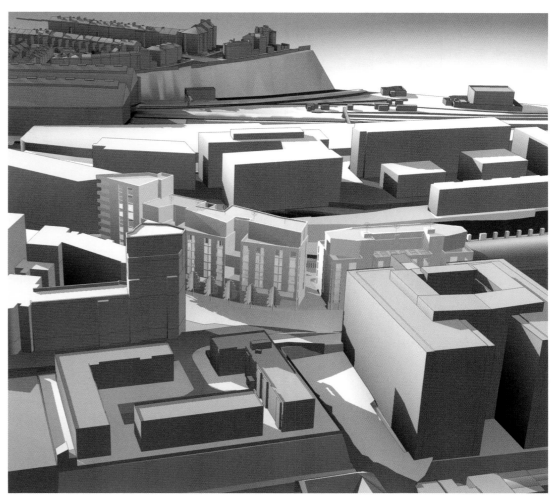

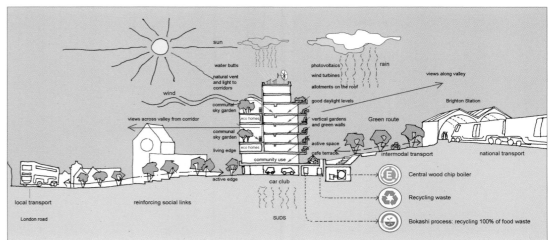

Student housing

During term time, nearly one per cent of the population of Britain lives in purpose-designed student housing at institutions of higher education. This number has been growing steadily as participation in higher education increases and, notwithstanding moves towards studying in local institutions and living at home, the trend is likely to continue. Yet the design of student housing has attracted little attention in spite of the fact that it accounts for over 400,000 bed-spaces representing an investment value of £8 billion or more. This housing is also a significant user of energy and thus an important area for attention when considering environmental issues.

At its worst this form of housing can degenerate into barrack blocks built down to a price and sadly this accounts for a significant proportion of current output. We believe that this is a wasted opportunity since it can also provide a lively environment which enriches students' experience. Quality student housing will also enhance the attractiveness of the host institution and facilitate third-party income from conferencing.

Most institutions offer accommodation for all first-year students, to get them off to a good start in a new life away from home. At this stage many are vulnerable and a significant number do not survive their courses into their second term. Good student housing can help to overcome these problems, by encouraging interaction and helping students feel part of their university community.

Early student housing tended to follow one of two models, either the Oxbridge courtyard and staircase pattern or the catered 'hall' which was typical in the 1960s. Perhaps the best known example of the Oxbridge model is Powell & Moya's Cripps Building at St John's College, Cambridge, which elegantly linked a more modern approach with the traditional form.

The 'hall' residences were sometimes built on campus; at Bath they were part of a megastructure that gave a compact character to the hilltop site of the institution. At other times these halls could be built a few miles away where land was cheaper and low build-costs could make for financially viable schemes. Many of these remote halls have proved unpopular and are being disposed of as institutions rationalise their estates – our schemes at both Aston University in Birmingham and Queen Mary, University of London, result from such rationalisations.

The vast majority of new student housing provides self-catering accommodation. Groups of between five and nine students share a kitchen/dining area that becomes the heart of the unit. Creating financially viable schemes has always been problematic for institutions and, when interest rates are high, construction tends to come to a halt. In recent years however there has been something of a boom, and standards have been rising. There is now a convention that student rooms should not be less than 10 square metres, with an en suite shower room in addition. The en suite adds construction costs but is easily justified in terms of lettability and out-of-term conference trade, for which en suite is becoming almost a prerequisite. There is a downside to this in environmental terms as we will see below.

In design terms student housing presents both problems and opportunities. The problems tend to focus around financial viability and the largely repetitive character of the accommodation, which can lead to uninspired buildings. Our scheme at Sunderland shows a marked contrast to this pattern, with great variety both in building forms and in individual rooms, but this was made possible by generous external funding. This scheme has proved extremely popular and one of the reasons is the variety that has been achieved – very few rooms are the same.

Architectural opportunities arise from the relatively large scale of some of the developments and the potential that this creates for making communities that can operate at a number of different levels – in flats, stairs, courtyards or streets. Good student housing makes a variety of places and a rich public realm.

In environmental terms, by far the most significant issue is water heating and this has become far more significant with the provision of en suite accommodation. Services issues are aggravated by conference use, which creates surges of demand as delegates all want to shower at the same time in the morning, but research at one institution has suggested that the average time a student spends in the shower is around seventeen minutes. When they are not alone in the shower, apparently this time increases…

In most projects, hot water is provided by gas boilers, but there are many different patterns that are encountered. At Sunderland University we provided four medium-sized plant rooms, each delivering space heating and hot water to around 75 rooms. At King Alfred's College (now the University of Winchester), a domestic

St John's College, Cambridge, Powell & Moya, 1967

Panns Bank

West Downs Student Village

type arrangement was adopted with individual boilers provided for each flat/house. Only about a third of this scheme was en suite and this may account for relatively good energy consumption figures, but this arrangement has caused operational difficulties and it is not one we would repeat.

The student housing at Aston University has the most sophisticated environmental strategy of any of our built schemes, with two central plant rooms, one serving nearly 500 units. Unfortunately the performance figures are less good that some other schemes, with showers and the ventilation that is needed to maintain conditions within rooms consuming far more energy than had been hoped. Reducing flow from shower heads would in retrospect have provided lower consumption figures but it is hard to see how the 'shower culture' can be checked.

Space heating in rooms is a limited consumer of energy, although heat will be sucked out by the ventilation systems that are an essential aspect of the en suite arrangement. Given good fabric insulation, it is possible to have very small radiators in rooms and these do not have to be located below windows. The high thermal mass that is inherent in the majority of schemes will help to provide temperature stability. Most of our schemes use gas rather than electric heating to provide space heating but in purely economic terms this is clearly not justifiable, given appropriate controls.

Higher education has been a significant installer of combined heat and power plants (CHP) and including the residential accommodation will help to provide a balanced energy load. For the scheme for 180 student bedrooms at the Oxstalls Campus at the University of Gloucestershire we asked Paul Ruyssevelt of ESD to evaluate the option of using CHP. Significantly this becomes more attractive if space heating is provided by well controlled electrical resistance heaters. The idea was that they should provide heat to a background level of 15°C, with a manual boost control to provide heating to 20°C with a one-hour run-on timer. This provides a more continuous electrical load (17kW) which can be balanced with approximately 80 per cent of the annual water heating load (30kW). Despite the capital cost saving of a radiator system however the overall cost of adding a CHP plant could not be justified in what was a low-budget scheme, but we are certain that CHP does have a future as part of a university energy policy.

Control systems are undoubtedly the key to energy economy. The performance of our scheme at Sunderland for instance was significantly enhanced when thermostatic radiator valves were installed – they had been initially omitted as a (false) economy. We believe too that radiators should be as small as possible so that students who leave their windows open actually get cold. It is not easy to persuade students to be responsible with energy usage and although installing check meters on flats may appear attractive, the management issues that this creates seem to defeat best intentions.

Low-energy lighting makes sense but the design should help minimise the use of artificial light. In student rooms the placing and sizing of windows is important, but it is also possible to design circulation areas so that natural light is achieved, although this is rarely the case. One of the attractions of the maisonettte type used at Sunderland and King Alfred's College was the ability to get natural light into stairs and circulation above and below.

Ventilation has become increasingly important with better sealed buildings. Both capital and running costs are significant and there is also a risk of buildings becoming cluttered with extracts, in addition to maintenance issues. We have sought to include heat recovery systems in a number of schemes but only at Aston was it justified because of the proximity of a very major and noisy road. The system installed allows ventilation without opening windows and the extracted air heats incoming air that is introduced into corridors. Control of ventilation is also an issue. The traditional overrun on bathroom ventilation is obviously one possibility, but a better option for shower rooms is to use humidity control.

Our most recent student housing project is for a scheme for nearly 1,000 units for Queen Mary, University of London. The main environmental problem here was to do with acoustical isolation from the main line railway running along the north of the site. A 12-storey linear block significantly improves the acoustic environment for a series of lower courtyard developments to the south. In keeping with its size, the scheme contains social facilities such as cafe and bar, laundry and multi-purpose room, as well as reception facilities for the site as a whole. As student housing schemes become larger, the challenge is to create a sustainable urban community with communal facilities and a shared public realm, to complement a potentially vibrant social culture.

Oxstalls Campus

University of Bath

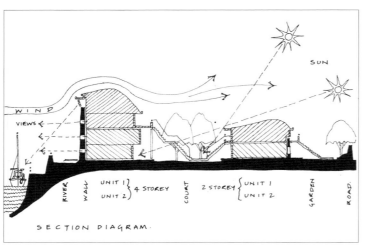

SECTION DIAGRAM.

Panns Bank residences
University of Sunderland

1994
with Ove Arup & Partners

Higher education is seen as playing a significant role in the regeneration of the north east of England and one of the most visible manifestations of this is along the banks of the River Wear for the University of Sunderland. Following a limited competition, Feilden Clegg Bradley was selected to design the first student housing on the south bank, facing the new St Peter's campus across the river. The design quality of the project has been achieved through a diversity of rooms and a degree of complexity that is normally unaffordable, aspects that have proved to be particularly valued by the students.

The competition-winning scheme was based on two courtyards that provided 271 beds and largely filled the two areas of land available, while maintaining access to a slipway that was approximately in the middle of the site. Each courtyard provides a secure and sociable student environment and also a microclimate protected from north-east winds. The curving riverside blocks form an 'inhabited wall', echoing the scale of the cliffs behind and returning in the centre of the site to create a secure arrival area.

The majority of the student rooms are in the riverside blocks. These are arranged as maisonettes, with access to the upper units via partly external stairs. The maisonette form was adopted both because it was seen as domestic rather than institutional and it offered the opportunity of getting natural light into the circulation spaces through the internal stair.

The brief called for no more than six student rooms in the majority of units with generous requirements for shared space. Living areas run through the blocks, with river views on one side and typically (at lower level) opening on to the courtyard or (at upper level) having balconies looking onto the courtyard.

In environmental terms the scheme seeks to make the most of natural lighting in both rooms and circulation. To some extent the natural lighting is compromised by the orientation, since many of the rooms face north with river views, and on the top floor the rooms have south-facing clerestories to offset this.

The scheme is very well insulated and achieves 'good' energy consumption, although initial savings on capital costs proved unwise. In operation it was found that south-facing rooms could overheat while north-facing rooms remained cool until thermostatic radiator valves were installed.

The scheme has proved to be the most popular with the students, in spite of a setting that initially appeared inhospitable. Fears about security have proved unfounded and the scheme has triggered a number of other developments along the river bank, contributing significantly to urban regeneration.

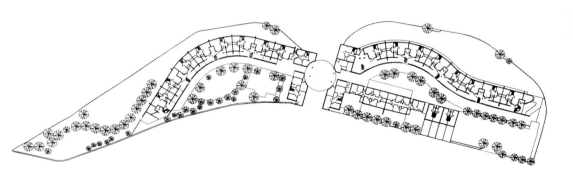

West Downs Student Village
University of Winchester

1996
with Halcrow Gilbert Associates

This student housing project, for an eventual total of 865 units, was built to address a substantial shortfall in appropriate accommodation in an expensive part of the city. To be viable for a relatively small institution, the scheme had to be designed and built within very demanding cost and time constraints.

Architecturally the scheme seeks to create an urbanity based on a simple pallete of brickwork, precast lintels, wooden windows, shallow-pitched metal roofs and external metalwork. The scheme also has rich landscaping which complements the surroundings and greatly adds to the quality of the completed project.

There are three main elements of the scheme. The first is the central pedestrian street, with four-storey blocks on either side. The street is made up of simpler versions of the maisonette form used at Sunderland; the kitchen/dining rooms are reduced in size, so that they can be stacked over student rooms, with projecting bays. The ground floors are set about a metre below the street, protected by a landscape strip for privacy. Upper maisonettes are reached by external stairs which enter the building one storey above street level and provide much of the character of the street. At 17 metres wide the street is relatively narrow but it has proved a very successful space which promotes a sense of community throughout the village.

The second element is a series of two-storey terraces, each containing a number of eight-bedroom houses. All student rooms face south. On the north side are kitchen/dining rooms that look out onto secondary pedestrian routes leading through a series of arches onto the street. The limited scale of the houses was a response to the proximity of adjacent properties.

The third element comprises a number of flats at the northern end of the site with double-loaded corridors. Staircases serving a single flat per floor allow light into the ends of corridors and avoid an institutional feel. Inflection of the main block creates a sinuous form that encloses the public open space, linking the scheme both to the original school building and to the adjacent development.

High levels of insulation are provided by filled wall cavities, double-glazed timber windows and well insulated roofs. A domestic approach was adopted for heating and hot water, with an individual gas boiler for each flat, and a check meter for gas and electricity to identify those with excessive consumption. In practice this strategy did not prove particularly successful; hot water demand proved greater than capacity and the installation of boilers within the flats left them vulnerable to tampering by students. Nonetheless the performance has proved to be significantly better than 'good practice' standards, showing lower operational carbon dioxide production figures than some (apparently) more sophisticated schemes. Gas consumption figures are fairly typical for an efficient scheme but electricity figures are considerably less, helped by low levels of installed plant and good natural lighting throughout.

The scheme has proved very popular with students and its Housing Design Award citation stated that the street would make 'a great location for a staging of West Side Story' – a challenge that the Centre for Performing Arts at the college has threatened to take up.

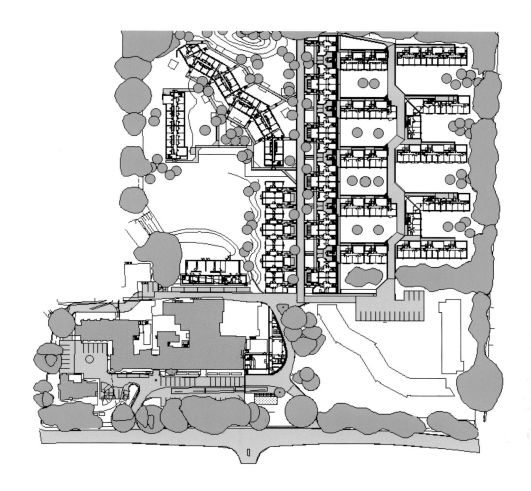

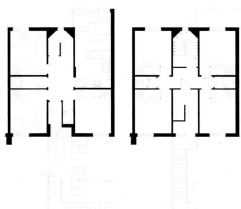

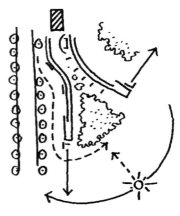

Lakeside Residences
Aston University
Birmingham

1999
with Buro Happold

Aston University was developed primarily in the 1950s and 60s as a technologically-oriented institution. Located at the edge of the heart of Birmingham, it was nonetheless separated from it by the inner city ring road. The main building at Aston is a megastructure that was designed in the 1930s but only built after the war, and much of the student housing is contained in twenty-storey tower blocks that had proved reasonably popular with the student body at the time we became involved in designing new housing.

When we were appointed to develop the new student housing scheme there was already an outline scheme in place that would have achieved between 650 and 700 units in a six- to nine-storey high 'doughnut' around the perimeter of a site of a little over a hectare. This represented a density of more than 700 habitable rooms per hectare and as such is among the densest of housing schemes in Britain. In student housing terms it represented a significant departure from the more common four-storey walk ups and it also represented a significant architectural challenge because of its highly visible site both at the entrance to the campus and on one of the main routes within Birmingham.

From the outset we felt that the perimeter development would not be satisfactory, and a design emerged that comprised two sinuous blocks with a north-south alignment that would give all rooms either an east or west orientation. The blocks created a secure courtyard which provided access to all rooms and which was opened to the south to bring light into the public space. The frontage facing James Watt Queensway (the inner city ring road) was built as an eight-storey block, rising to 16 stories plus basement at the southern end, and this required the installation of lifts

throughout which significantly added to the cost per bedspace. This block was intended to provide a buffer between the road and the university, as well as creating an urban frontage and helping to repair a townscape battered by road building. A significant issue was the future plans to change the character of this road into a 'boulevard' by removing multi-level interchanges, lowering traffic speeds and planting trees. This proposal was carried out in 2003 and has lead to a much improved setting for the building.

The scheme is known as Lakeside Residences because on the east side it provides the main frontage to the principle area of landscape on the campus and the largish pond, rather grandly titled the lake. Much of the block adjacent to this area is reduced in scale to four stories, configured as maisonettes to avoid the need for lifts, as well as producing more economical construction than the higher western block which utilised 'table-form' in situ concrete. At the southern end the scale is increased once more, this time to eight stories plus basement and the construction of this block is similar to the western block.

Student housing at this density presents significant design challenges and there are plenty of examples of schemes where the highly repetitive character of the brief has produced fairly dismal results. At Aston this is avoided partly by variety of scale and form, including the curved blocks, partly by using living rooms and staircases to break up the otherwise uniform fenestration arising from student rooms and partly by the treatment of external elevations. The materials used are a combination of carefully detailed red terracotta bricks and terracotta tiles on the larger blocks. The terracotta tiles were

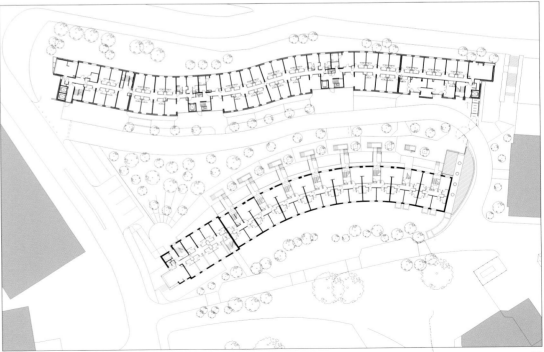

spaced off the cavity walls to create depth in the elevations, a relatively expensive detail but one that has added greatly to the end product.

The majority of accommodation in the scheme is organised as flats, typically with eight or nine students sharing a kitchen/dining room. The four-storey block is configured as maisonettes with an upper and lower unit, each containing seven bedrooms. The communal aspects of the scheme are relatively limited because the residences are very close to a range of other campus facilities. The only significant shared facility is a porters' lodge located at the entrance to the courtyard and this serves to provide both security and post distribution facilities.

Two main issues combined to make it dificult to adopt the simple low-tech servicing solutions that one finds in most student housing schemes. First, there was the scale and density of the development and second, the presence of the major road adjacent to the larger block, which created a need for permanent artificial ventilation to deal with acoustic issues. The solution adopted involved basement plantrooms at the southern end of both blocks, distributing hot water for showers and heating in corridor ceiling voids, and risers integrated with bathroom pods and vertical ventilation extraction in each riser. The ventilation extracts were connected at roof level, making use of additional headroom and fed into cross-plate heat exchangers which preheated incoming air that was fed into corridors and thence into bedrooms via undercut doors. This is essentially a 'hotel' system and it was hoped that it would lead to good levels of comfort and also economical running costs. Heating was provided by radiators in each room although with high levels of insulation and good airtightness it proved difficult to find radiators that were small enough for the very modest loads.

In practice the scheme has not proved to be outstandingly economical. While gas consumption figures are satisfactory and almost in line with best practice, electricity consumption is higher than 'typical' levels. The explanation of this is thought to be twofold; first the inclusion of lifts with their resulting power consumption, and second the relatively sophisticated air handling arrangements, also with significant power requirements.

However, the completed scheme, the result of a successful collaboration with engineer Buro Happold, has proved to be a significant addition to the university estate and a popular building with the people of Birmingham.

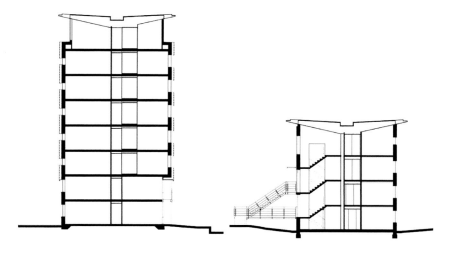

Westfield Student Village
Queen Mary
University of London

2004
with Max Fordham

This phased scheme for nearly 1000 rooms is one of the largest student housing schemes in Britain. It provides accommodation for students, visiting academics and conference use as well as a cafe/bar, multipurpose room and laundry plus shop and reception/office facilities for the student village.

The project was built on the last significant development area on the Mile End Road campus, which accommodates the majority of the college's facilities. The form of development is varied, to provide a range of room types in flats and maisonettes in groups of between four and nine people. The first phase comprises four-storey brick blocks which create open-ended courtyards of varying character, with most of the student rooms facing east or west. The second phase has two main elements, the first of which is a substantial eight-storey block running parallel to the elevated main line railway to the north. This block significantly improves the acoustic environment for the rest of the site. The rooms with a north-facing aspect are accommodated in cantilevered 'flippers' with far-reaching views and they are provided with acoustic insulation to provide a comfortable environment. The second element is a canalside block that contains

the 'premium' rooms and accommodation for visiting academics. These rooms
sit above the ancillary facilities which
are designed to make the most of the
waterfront location and provide a social
focus for the whole site.

The canalside block is finished in prepatinated copper and is intended to
provide a visual focus for the development from the opposite side of the
canal, where there is a newly created
park to which this block responds. On
the 'village' side this block, together
with the brick block it faces, creates a
street providing the main circulation,
animated by the cafe/bar and community room. All of the buildings were
constructed using a tunnel-form concrete superstructure and off-site fabricated composite bathroom pods which
allowed the scheme to be constructed
very swiftly.

In terms of the environmental agenda, the scheme is extremely highly insulated and well sealed. This has resulted
in a very high air tightness rating and
an extremely low demand for space
heating, which is met by electric heating as the capital cost of a gas-fired
radiator system could not be justified.
Gas hot water systems are however provided from local boilers in each block.
Extract ventilation is from individual en
suite units via risers to the roof level.

Phase three, which comprises 200
rooms, occupies a pivotal site connecting the student village with the academic buildings. Completed in summer
2006, it continues the theme of the
canalside building by placing a new
cafe and the student union offices at
ground level. This block is designed to
be more thermally and energy efficient
than phases one and two and incorporates heat reclaim ventilation.

Learning

For 20 per cent of our lives, schools are our daytime homes. They provide us with our first experience of a larger community beyond our family, and a complex of inter-related spaces beyond the scale of the home. In addition to this they provide the environmental backdrop to our educational development, intellectually and morally, socially and spiritually. After a long period of limited school-building activity, the UK government has now embarked on a hugely ambitious programme of construction. We believe it is essential that this programme produces buildings which are worthy of the role they play in the lives of our communities.

For many of us, the schools that we were brought up in were institutional buildings that sat uncomfortably between home and the larger community; but increasingly we are seeing schools taking on a wider role in their communities. School buildings need to function for more than the traditional eight hours of the school day, and their importance in a neighbourhood needs to be reflected in their architectural presence as well as the organisation of the building. In particular the assembly hall, arts and drama spaces, sports hall and also the libraries and conference spaces have more significance for the wider community, operating for more hours per day than the conventional school calendar. At John Cabot City Technology College in Bristol we made a distinction between these spaces, which formed a more formal frontage to the school, and the more flexible teaching accommodation arranged behind. Similarly at Haverstock School in Camden there was a desire to create a strong and unified street presence, which was achieved by wrapping the various public functions of the building in a semi-transparent copper skin, with the facade unifying the disparate functions. In our design for an Exemplar School of the Future, undertaken for the Department for Education & Skills [1], all the key community spaces are entered via a central covered courtyard space – a space that could give an identity not only to the school but also to the community it serves. Community use creates a series of security issues but we believe these can be handled by a combination of appropriate planning and 'smart' access systems.

In our initial thinking about any school design, we often use the urban metaphor, which helps develop understanding of a form that has some of the characteristics of a small town. The classroom can be seen as the home for the child, the corridor as a street and the hall or courtyard as a town square. Different pedagogical strategies begin to imply more complex layering of spaces. Thus within the Exemplar School, and later at the Paddington Academy, we defined clusters of four classroom spaces grouped around a shared space to form what was in effect a 'school within a school', a neighbourhood of spaces which provides an intermediate identity between the traditional class size of 30 and the larger community of 1,500 children in the school. Creating a balance between individual and group identities – based on the sense of the school as a community and in a community – is a key issue in achieving social sustainability within the organisation and the building. This concept defined the form of Northampton Academy in a radically different way, leading to a series of buildings linked by an upper floor corridor and ground floor cloister.

Benchmarks for energy performance in school buildings vary considerably. Performance figures published under the new BREEAM for Schools [2] (an extension of the DfES Building Bulletin 87 [3]) are generally acknowledged to be ambitious, but are based on an eight-hour school day and 120 days per year. The Movement for Innovation (M4i) benchmarks summarise existing school buildings and show how poorly they perform by comparison.[4] Both the schools that we completed during the early 1990s performed moderately well against these benchmarks. Both of them have been subject to post-occupancy evaluation and the learning process has been very valuable, but the key issue of hours of use must be acknowledged in any benchmarking exercise. It would be foolhardy for instance not to design for summertime occupation despite the fact that many schools are under-occupied during July and August. Equally, solar orientation strategies must take into account the benefit of the early morning pre-heating on an eastern elevation, as well as a necessity for solar shading on a western elevation, even though currently many schools are under-occupied after 4pm. We need to design for the longer hours of operation that come through flexi-time, which is just beginning to become popular in a number of schools.

Existing school buildings include a very wide age range. Most of them are poorly insulated, emitting an average of two kilograms of carbon dioxide for space heating for every one kilogram that derives from electrical consumption. But this ratio is likely to change as we

The school originated in the moment when a man who didn't know he was a teacher sat down beneath a tree to discuss his insights with other men who were unaware that they were pupils. The pupils learnt, and wanted to be like their master. They wanted to educate their children, too. For this purpose they created a suitable space, and the first school had appeared. This was an inevitability, since it was the consequence of human aspirations. The architect creates a space and gives it form after having understood how it ought to be in order to function properly.
Louis I Kahn

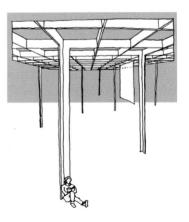

invest more in computer and projection technology, and produce buildings that are better insulated and use internal gains to provide the heating requirement. Our work on the exemplar schools project for instance showed that heating in an average classroom was required only when the external temperature fell below 6 degrees C, or for warming up the building at the beginning of the day before occupation. Given this situation, we find that the carbon contribution of the space heating is 30 per cent less than in a naturally ventilated school. The real challenge however is the provision of fresh air to provide oxygen and to remove both odour and humidity from 30 children confined in a relatively small space.

Schools have traditionally been naturally ventilated, but this has often meant in winter either poor ventilation (keeping the windows closed to avoid draughts) or discomfort for those who happen to be adjacent to the window. Recent research however shows that the accumulation of carbon dioxide in tightly built and poorly ventilated classrooms can easily rise above the maximum recommended health levels and so the lack of control provided by natural ventilation is being questioned.[5] At John Cabot CTC and in the deeper plan spaces of Haverstock School, we designed cross-ventilation systems to improve distribution and control and this is a fairly common approach. It does involve however shafts rising through the roof and these will be a major restriction on future adaptability, which is becoming an increasingly important issue. The Exemplar Schools project led us to investigate a low-cost mechanical ventilation system that can deliver air at a more controlled rate and with heating in winter, yet without the penalties of cost and fan power that are often associated with mechanical systems. A low-energy approach to mechanical ventilation would often support heat recovery, although this adds considerably to the cost, maintenance and fan power of the system. For the Exemplar School we devised a strategy that uses large 'builder's work' ducts beneath the ground floor of the building and delivers air to the perimeter of the classrooms at twice the rate required for ventilation, but also incorporates 50 per cent re-circulation from the atrium space that forms part of the return air path during winter. The absence of heat exchangers and filters means that the fan power can be extremely low (less than 1W/litre/second), ensuring that the net carbon dioxide cost of the system is similar to that of a naturally

ventilated building, but with a much higher degree of control. The underfloor labyrinth in this case also allows us to increase the thermal mass of the building and generate what in summer can become a 'coolth' store.

Excessive summertime temperatures are becoming more of a problem in school, as IT usage increases and both teachers and pupils demand higher comfort standards. Studies done for Haverstock school showed that the presence of an exposed concrete ceiling could reduce summertime peak temperatures by 2°C, so long as a simple system of night time ventilation was incorporated. During summer nights, the mechanical ventilation system of the Exemplar School could be run relatively cheaply in terms of energy, cooling down both the thermal mass within the classroom spaces and the more remote thermal capacity beneath the floor. This would also allow rooms which require acoustical isolation and would normally be air conditioned, eg music rooms, to achieve cooling from natural sources.

Carbon dioxide emissions from lighting represent about 15 per cent of total emissions in schools, although this is likely to increase as space heating becomes more efficient. We believe that daylighting is essential in schools, as much for its psychological benefits as for its contribution to carbon dioxide reduction. Studies in the USA have shown startling benefits to pupil performance relating to improved daylighting, and recent studies of 'green' versus 'non-green' schools by Brian Edwards have shown that the former score more highly on significant performance indicators such as behavioural problems, pupil performance and staff absenteeism.[6] The environmental agenda must take into account qualitative as well as quantitative performance analysis.

Our approach to daylighting at John Cabot CTC aimed to achieve even distribution of daylight throughout all the major spaces. This led to a strategy of maximising the glazed area and incorporating external solar control blinds, as well as using roof and clerestorey windows to provide light from more than one source. The blinds add life and colour to the elevations. A similar approach was used at Kingswood preparatory school, where adjustable louvres rather than roller blinds provide a finer degree of control. In both these schools the proportion of glass in the external walls is between 55 and 65 per cent – greater than the

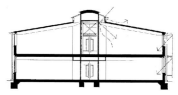

John Cabot School

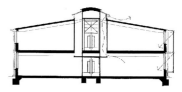

Haverstock School

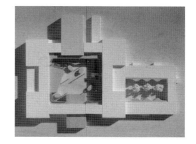

Exemplar School

conventional 40 per cent that many services engineers would recommend. But glare and solar heating do need to be managed carefully. We still suffer from the legacy of over-glazed school buildings from the 1960s and, with greater computer usage in schools, glare is becoming more of a problem. The rules we generated for the Exemplar School was that each room should have 50 per cent of the external wall glazed and 15 per cent opening, and that a substantial proportion of the glazing should be at very high level to get penetration of daylight deep into the space. The depth-to-height ratios for classrooms tend to follow those for office spaces, with a ratio of approximately 2.5:1 being appropriate for penetration of natural light as well as a sense of the outside from the back of the room. The DfES Building Bulletin 90 [7] provides rules of thumb dealing with window head height and room depth in order to achieve an average daylight factor of 2-3 per cent and an appropriate uniformity across the space.

Borrowed light from atria or day lit corridors rarely contributes significantly to measured light levels but can provide a welcome illusion of daylight and sense of transparency. With the Exemplar School all the 'corridors' are in fact balconies facing onto an atrium space; the calculated daylight factor in the central courtyard was 15 per cent, which we felt was enough to provide the impression of a daylit outdoor space that the classrooms could face onto. This space is primarily north-lit, although some direct sunlight is allowed in, to provide contrast and liveliness within the space.

School buildings can be 'didactic' and in themselves a part of the education of their pupils. Water conservation presents a further opportunity and although usage is less significant than in the domestic centre, conservation measures within the school need to be taken seriously in order to set appropriate standards for educational purposes. BRECSU has produced benchmarks for water consumption in schools varying from 3.65 to 5.44m³/pupil/yr.[8] The monitored consumption of John Cabot CTC was 5.3m³ and that was achieved without any particular effort to reduce consumption. The best rating equates to less than 19 litres/pupil/day, based on 190 days per year – only 10 per cent of domestic usage – and this could be achieved with standard technology such as PIR detectors on urinals and 7.5 litre wc systems. There is therefore scope for much greater savings with 6/3litre dual-flush wc's, percussion taps

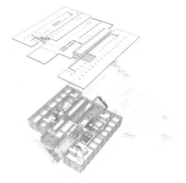

Paddington Academy

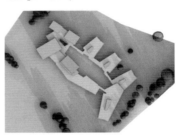

Northampton Academy

Northampton Academy rooflights

with automatic shut-off mechanisms and waterless urinals, all of which enhance water saving.

Recycling rainwater for wc flushing is likely to come relatively low down the list of financial priorities, although at the Exemplar School we did devise a strategy for draining the atrium roof into tanks located within the existing structure at roof level. This meant that there is no need for the additional provision of underground storage and the use of energy intensive pumping systems.

The landscape setting of the school is a key component of a holistic approach to sustainability. At John Cabot CTC we produced a relatively condensed plan in order to maximise the area of existing landscape for both playing fields and amenity use. The crescent shape of the building provided a backdrop for an amphitheatre formed in the hillside below. At Kingswood school we were presented with an existing Green Belt landscape, with mature trees and diverse planting. The large area of the walled garden formed a natural enclosure to the school but terracing the sloping side enabled us to create banks of vegetation which recalled the plan of the previous garden, together with tree planting which will provide additional climatic shelter for the building. Soft landscaping has a hard time surviving the rough and tumble of school play times, but it is essential the schools are designed with landscape that both has an educational value and complements the building.

By their nature, schools inevitably contribute to transportation problems and consequent energy use. The pressures of the 'school run' on the transport network and its energy use need to be addressed from a management and planning perspective, but we also need to encourage a return to cycling (prevalent 50 years ago) with the provision of covered, lockable, sheltered pupil lockers. The BREEAM for Schools system offers points for providing one cycle space for every ten pupils but this will only make a small dent in the problem. Well planned bus systems are likely to be more successful, but these require considerable provision in terms of space. In new school projects we try to give precedence to arrival by bus, foot and bicycle and, if anything, make it more difficult for those arriving by car. We also seek site layout strategies that make appropriate connections to their neighbourhoods and tie in with Safe Routes to Schools.[9] Our design for the exemplar school

was based on an all-age community school providing schooling from three to 18 for a relatively small catchment area. The reorganisation of the school system along these lines could reduce the time, cost and energy expenditure of travelling between home and school and provide a substantially more sustainable school system.

Schools need to be explicit in their approach to the sustainability agenda. Education in sustainability involves an understanding of the dynamic complexities of ecological systems. Intuitive understanding however precedes intellectual enquiry; it is at the primary school that we have the ability to work with a child's enquiring sense of wonder, in order to lay the foundation for a grasp of environmental principles that will shape later educational development. In the words of the educational philosopher AN Whitehead, 'when you understand all about the sun and all about the atmosphere and all about the rotation of the earth, you can still miss the radiance of the sunset'.[10]

1 www.teachernet.gov.uk
2 www.products.bre.co.uk
3 www.teachernet.gov.uk
4 M4i is now subsumed within Constructing Excellence, www.constructingexcellence.org.uk.
5 WJ Batty and AJ Shepherd, Air Quality in Primary School Classrooms, 2000, Applied Energy Group, Cranfield University.
6 Brian Edwards, Green Buildings Pay, 1998, Spon.
7 www.teachernet.gov.uk
8 BRECSU benchmarks, BSRIA, Rule of thumb (2003) pp40-43, Guidelines for building services, Kevin Pennycock, The Chameleon Press, BRECSU.
9 www.saferoutestoschools.org.uk
10 AN Whitehead, Science and the Modern World (1938) Penguin Books, www.usablebuildings.co.uk.

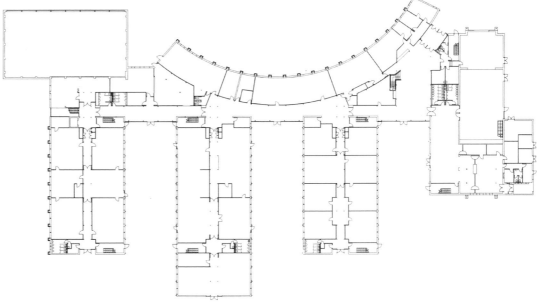

John Cabot
City Technology College
Bristol

1993
with Buro Happold

John Cabot CTC in Kingswood was the last of the 15 city technology colleges which were established as centrally funded, independently managed technology based secondary schools. It provides 900 spaces for children aged 11-18 within a total building area of 8,800 square metres.

The site, formerly occupied by an independent school, is set within an undulating landscaped parkland but the area to be built on was dramatically restricted by both topography and planning restrictions. The building therefore has a very condensed plan form, generally two storeys high but extending to three at the western end, with a clear linear organisational concept. The main

circulation route is an east-west central spine. This connects the main entrance at the 'head' of the school, providing access to the hall, reception area and a conference facility, to the secondary entrance at the west, which is associated with the sports facilities. The spine is a two-storey 'street' with views into south-facing courtyard areas alternating with wings of teaching accommodation. The upper-level circulation route follows the same pattern but is set back to give the street additional height, punctuated by bridges which lead to the teaching wings.

To the north of the street is a crescent of accommodation, the form of which derives from the topography of

the site, and which surrounds an amphitheatre within the adjacent landscape. The crescent houses the library, conference facilities, staff rooms and administration areas, while the more flexible accommodation is housed in the wings at the other side of the street. The clear and very condensed plan form contrasts with the variety in the sectional design of each element, which in turn is influenced by the functional requirements of the space and a desire to optimise natural light and ventilation.

The two-storey teaching wings consist of an 18 metre deep section with a 1.8 metre corridor zone down the centre. A 900mm zone to each side of the corridor contains sloping glazing at roof

level as well as vertical dampers. This zone performs different functions along the length of each wing. Sometimes it provides daylighting to a widened area of the corridor outside the classroom entrances. Sometimes it provides clerestorey lighting to an upstairs classroom. Sometimes it provides a duct to facilitate cross ventilation to a lower-floor classroom, or a space through which flues can be threaded to serve the technology spaces on the ground floor. The flexibility of the structure and the ability to naturally service the building have already been proven by subsequent alterations to the classroom layout, as well as the extension of the plan form on one of the wings.

The monopitch roof to the crescent generates a section which provides clerestorey lighting and cross ventilation to the upper-floor area, with the additional volume providing a mezzanine gallery in the library area. The sports hall also has a monopitch roof, with lighting from two sides. The larger area of north-facing glazing provides good-quality diffuse light, while adjacent deciduous trees provide additional solar protection. The smaller clerestorey window to the south is protected by a permanent vertical internal hanging blind which acts as a simple light diffuser.

At the 'head' of the building, a barrel vaulted structure incorporates the main hall, drama studio and music technology spaces. The spaces interconnect and retractable seating and removable screens allow for flexibility in their interconnection and use. While the central area of the barrel vault is opaque and timber-clad, the edges are glazed to illuminate the walls and provide balanced diffused natural lighting.

With glazing to all classroom spaces equivalent to approximately 65 per cent of the wall area, the dangers of overheating through conventional double-glazed units was quite high. To minimise unwanted solar gain the south and west elevations feature external roller blinds, operated locally by wall-mounted key switches in each room. A central override retracts the blinds at 5pm and disables them until the following morning. Classroom blinds are a dark blue colour which cuts out bright sunlight. Those on the south elevation of the glazed 'street' are yellow, which cuts out most of the solar gain without losing the sense of sunshine in the centre of the school.

The school was subjected to an exhaustive post-occupancy evaluation by a team funded by the DETR. The analysis showed that it performed well in relation to overall carbon dioxide when compared to Energy Efficiency Office guidelines, although electricity consumption ($53kgCO_2/m^3$) was higher than EEO benchmarks and gas consumption lower. The study concluded that the relatively high figure of $11.5kw/m^3$ for electrical consumption was attributable to almost 250 networked computers, together with sundry printers and photocopiers. It was suggested that by switching off the base units at night, electrical consumption could be reduced by more than 40 per cent. Consumption was also affected by two split DX air conditioning heat pump units serving the seminar room and network areas.

The additional heat from the electrical consumption obviously reduced gas consumption for space heating, although the study also uncovered problems with the overall airtightness of the building construction and the use of leaky dampers for ventilation purposes. Improved standards of airtightness and the use of sealed windows rather than dampers would result in considerable improvements. The study also noted that, while the blinds generally worked well, the daylighting savings did not appear to be realised because the only lighting control systems were manual switches. Photocell controls or intelligence in the fittings themselves – at that time a relatively expensive option but now much more cost effective – would guarantee improved benefits. The study concluded that the school was highly successful and well liked but energy consumption could be reduced by improving the use of centralised and local controls on heating, daylighting and ventilation.

Kingswood
Day Preparatory School
Bath

1995
with Buro Happold

This school provides general and specialist teaching space for 180 children in a new building set within a nineteenth-century walled garden. The garden stands in the grounds of a listed building, facing (and sloping) quite steeply to the south. Protected by mature trees to the west and north, it provides a quiet, sunlit and secure setting with mature natural surroundings.

One of the key principles that drove the form of the building was to retain the openness of the walled garden as much as possible, and to ensure that the new building reflected something of the character of the previous greenhouses which were arranged along the south-facing north wall. The wall itself

was demolished but its line was retained by the row of clerestorey windows which illuminate the upper-floor classrooms and circulation spaces. Immediately below this is a continuous band of rooflighting which illuminates the deep-plan areas of the lower floor. This continuous spine of daylight forms a constant feature in the centre of the sectional diagram, whereas the position of the outer walls varies to create an indented plan that provides alternating courtyards and 'bay' windows to each classroom. The architecture therefore emerges from the play between the continuous section, complexity in the depth of the plan and the width of the central circulation zone.

Classrooms are paired and share external courtyard spaces and internal entrance 'lobbies' which result from the widening of the corridor spine. Each classroom, 45 square metres in area and intended for up to 20 children, has a back door and a front door onto the lobby and the courtyard, a 'wet area' and two further alcoves off the main space, allowing a variety of activities to take place. The upper floor area at the east end of the building widens out to provide a hall for physical education. Kitchen and dining facilities, as well as nursery and reception classes, are provided in adjacent buildings.

The sectional design ensures that all classrooms have cross ventilation and

daylight from two sides. Glazed doors and windows provide further connections between each space – sometimes to help with supervision of groups of children who use the corridor areas as resource spaces, and sometimes to add a touch of playfulness, as with the circular windows connecting the upper-floor classrooms to a circular window in the end wall.

Environmental engineer Buro Happold studied energy consumption in the building and concluded that, with a normalised performance indicator of 180kwh/m³ for space heating, it fell into the M4i 'good practice' category for schools. Electrical consumption of 30kwh/m³ is also around average. These

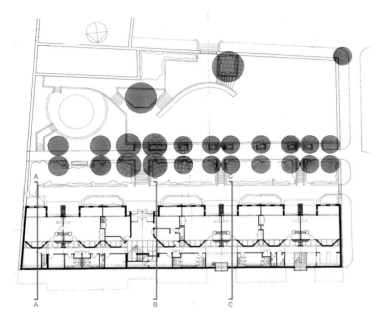

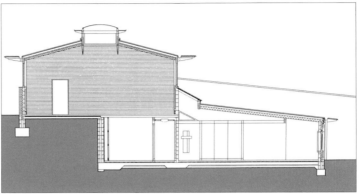

figures however yield a total rating of 51.5kgCO2/m³, which is just outside the top 25 per cent category produced by M4i. The Buro Happold study noted that levels of daylighting were excellent, although with manual control not all the potential savings were necessarily realised. Problems of overheating in summer were reported – teachers had not been told how to operate the solar control louvres and ventilation. The bursar, however, was very impressed with the low fuel bills compared with the rest of the school's building stock.

The south-facing glazing is protected from excessive sun by a variety of means, including extended overhangs on the shallow pitched roofs, and external canopies to the courtyard areas. The main zone of clerestorey lighting is protected by external perforated aluminium louvres which are electronically controlled by switches in each classroom. Sunlight is admitted through areas of rooflight, either into circulation areas or to strike the back walls of the classroom, where the light is diffused and heat is absorbed by the masonry structure of the building. Further shading will be provided by trees planted in front of the lower classrooms.

The landscape setting of the school was important both for environmental and historical reasons. The walled enclosure of the garden now provides shelter for children as well as plants, and has been terraced to provide a variety of external play spaces. These are broken up by both trees and low-level planting, with views out to evergreen banks to the north.

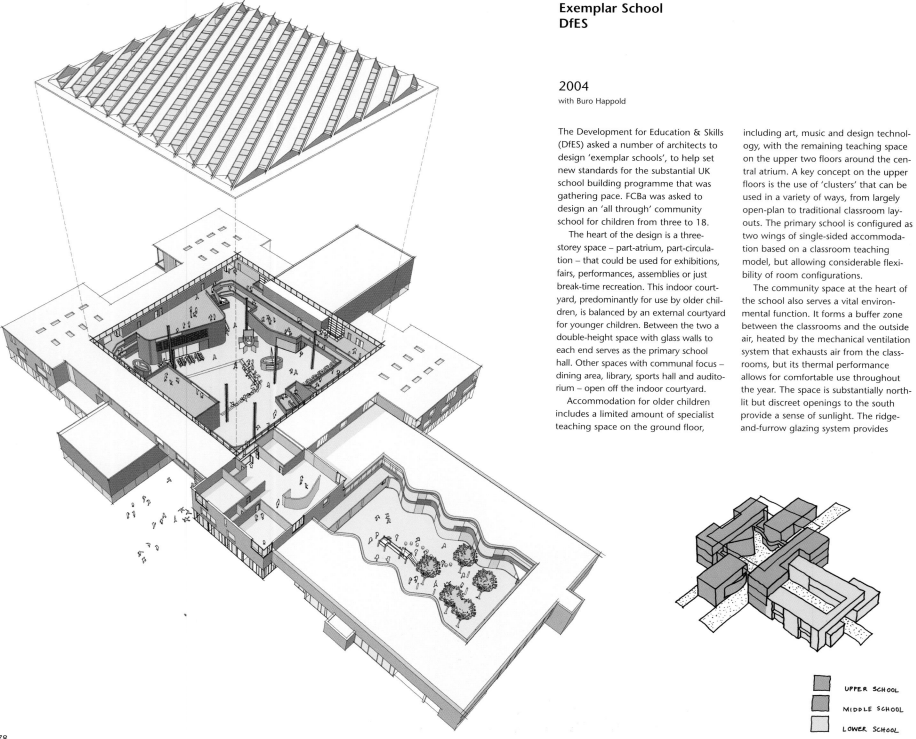

Exemplar School
DfES

2004

with Buro Happold

The Development for Education & Skills (DfES) asked a number of architects to design 'exemplar schools', to help set new standards for the substantial UK school building programme that was gathering pace. FCBa was asked to design an 'all through' community school for children from three to 18.

The heart of the design is a three-storey space – part-atrium, part-circulation – that could be used for exhibitions, fairs, performances, assemblies or just break-time recreation. This indoor court-yard, predominantly for use by older children, is balanced by an external courtyard for younger children. Between the two a double-height space with glass walls to each end serves as the primary school hall. Other spaces with communal focus – dining area, library, sports hall and auditorium – open off the indoor courtyard.

Accommodation for older children includes a limited amount of specialist teaching space on the ground floor,

including art, music and design technology, with the remaining teaching space on the upper two floors around the central atrium. A key concept on the upper floors is the use of 'clusters' that can be used in a variety of ways, from largely open-plan to traditional classroom layouts. The primary school is configured as two wings of single-sided accommodation based on a classroom teaching model, but allowing considerable flexibility of room configurations.

The community space at the heart of the school also serves a vital environmental function. It forms a buffer zone between the classrooms and the outside air, heated by the mechanical ventilation system that exhausts air from the classrooms, but its thermal performance allows for comfortable use throughout the year. The space is substantially north-lit but discreet openings to the south provide a sense of sunlight. The ridge-and-furrow glazing system provides

UPPER SCHOOL

MIDDLE SCHOOL

LOWER SCHOOL

south-facing roof slopes for photovoltaic cells that are capable of generating over half the electrical requirement of the building. The direction of the roof slopes can be varied to suit individual sites.

The scheme was designed to the new standards of sound attenuation brought in by the DfES Building Bulletin BB93. This requires much more stringent control over noise transfer between classrooms, as well as from outside to inside the building. Together with a concern about the difficulties of controlling the fresh air supply in winter with natural ventilation systems, this led to an investigation with Buro Happold of a variety of ventilation options. The preferred solution was a low-pressure mechanical ventilation system: supply air is delivered to each classroom via large ducts within an underfloor labyrinth, a one metre deep zone beneath the ground-floor slab which itself provides thermal mass for summertime cooling.

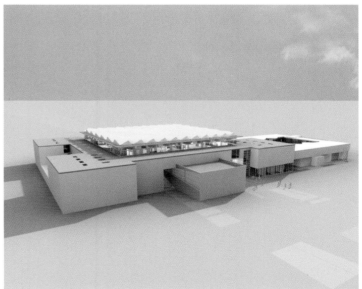

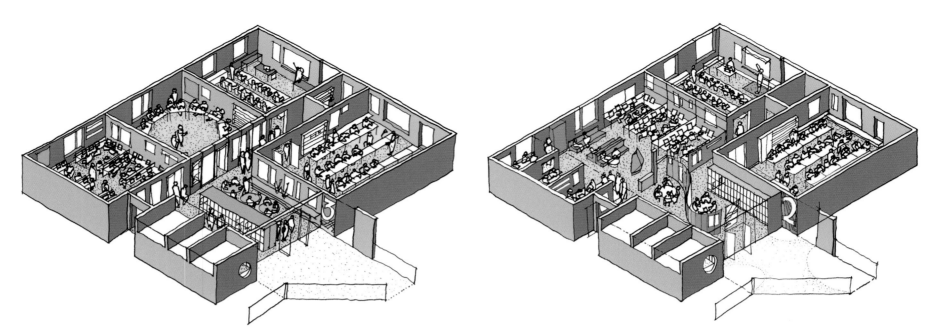

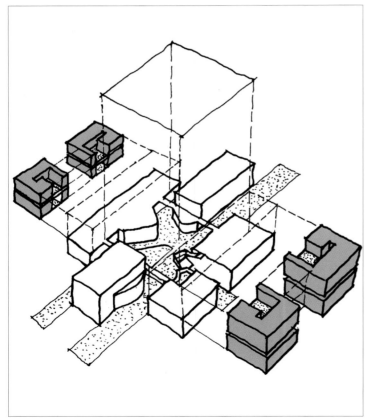

By increasing the size of the ducts and the volume of air delivered to each classroom, the winter-time fresh air supply can be delivered at 16 litres per second per person as a displacement ventilation system, with the supply adjacent to the window wall. The return air path is via attenuators which lead to corridor spaces and eventually back to the atrium where in winter there is 50 per cent re-circulation of the air, which in turn increases the supply air temperature to reduce draughts. In summer the air is exhausted at roof level in the atrium, and all of the supply air is drawn through the undercroft labyrinth, where it is pre-cooled before being delivered to the classrooms. With the internal gains from 30 children and potentially high equipment loads in many areas, through most of the year the building is self-heating, including the central atrium space. Heat would be required however at the beginning of each winter day and this is provided by direct gas-fired heating elements within the air stream in the undercroft. Calculations show that this form of mechanical ventilation system has a lower overall annual carbon dioxide emissions rating than heat recovery systems, which impede air flow and

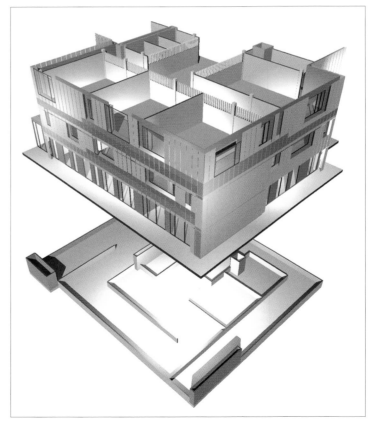

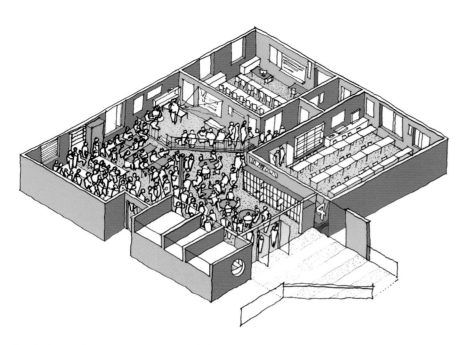

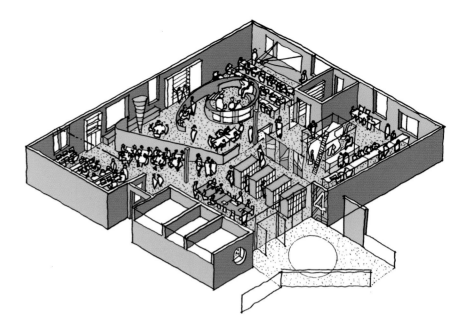

thereby increase fan power.

Opening windows are provided in each classroom to provide an additional, and psychologically important, source of ventilation, with one window per classroom equivalent to around 10 per cent of the floor area. By using a robustly designed mechanical ventilation system, however, high air quality can be provided both in summer and winter; pre-cooled air can be delivered in summer to reduce overheating; and acoustic isolation to each classroom can be achieved at relatively low cost. Separating the ventilation from window openings also means that conflicts between open windows and internal blinds for glare control or blackout can be avoided.

Natural light is provided to classrooms to ensure average daylight factors of over four per cent throughout rooms which are typically no more than 7.8 metres deep. Rather than provide the restrictive monotony of banded windows, the design is based on a variety of configurations that always provide 45-55 per cent of the external wall area as window and ensure that at least some of this is at ceiling level, to ensure good daylight penetration. Ceiling

heights are slightly higher than usual at 3.2 metres, in order to provide for better daylight penetration but also to suit the larger open spaces which can be achieved by removing internal partitions. All the main classrooms face outwards from the courtyard, but with an average daylight faction in the atrium of 15 per cent, smaller spaces that face 'internally' can also achieve adequate natural light.

The atrium roof provides for up to 1240 square metres of photovoltaic collectors facing due south at a 20 degree inclination. The roof structure allows the rooflight system over the atrium to be

independent of the orientation of the building, thus maintaining its performance. Photovoltaic energy could offset 30-50 per cent of the total carbon dioxide emissions from the building, depending on the efficiency of the cells.

The rainwater from this roof, together with the doughnut of flat roof covering the classrooms around it, discharges into two rooftop tanks located immediately above the toilet cores at each side of the building. Rainwater storage is thereby provided at high level within the fabric of the building, rather than locating it at ground level, where a separate chamber would have to be constructed and the

water pumped up to the toilets where it would be used. This system would provide more than 50 per cent of the water used in the toilets and urinals, at minimal additional cost.

The concept of a condensed plan form with a covered internal courtyard therefore pays for itself in many ways. The condensed plan also creates other benefits. There is a dramatic reduction in external wall area and in the overall thermal envelope, saving both capital and running costs. The central roof is an 'umbrella' that collects the rainwater, provides solar shading and also generates electricity. The central space

is an additional bonus to the spatial requirements of the brief, a vibrant multi-purpose space that is symbolic of the school as a community.

The internal architectural language is entirely of timber, floors, structural columns, beams and surrounding walls and balustrades. A non-orthogonal internal geometry contrasts with the plainer simplicity of the external walls, which could be clad in a variety of materials to suit different locations. The internal space epitomises the rich diversity of a school environment, the space that the school can give back to the public realm of the community that it serves.

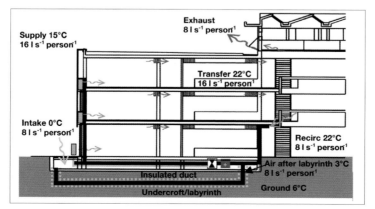

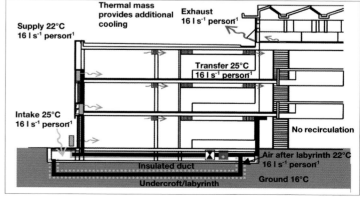

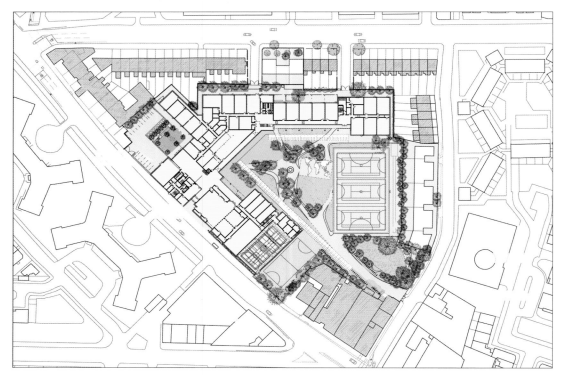

Haverstock School
Camden

2006
with Atelier Ten

Haverstock School is located in the heart of the London Borough of Camden on a site that has been occupied by schools for more than 120 years. The fourteen buildings on the site prior to the redevelopment provided a record of the ad hoc construction that has characterised so much investment in education in past decades.

The original school occupied a triangular site with three different frontages to the neighbouring roads. The council wanted to create a distinctive frontage to Haverstock Hill and it was decided to use the other two road frontages for housing. The intention was to help recreate a townscape that had been eroded by piecemeal development. The

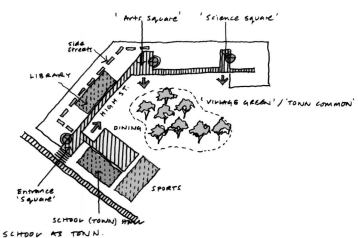

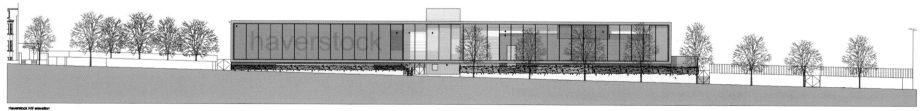

Haverstock Hill elevation

new building creates a bold frontage with a large perforated copper screen to Haverstock Hill. The body of the school hugs the site perimeter, enclosing a courtyard which can be used for informal play and which also provides more formal sports areas, including a floodlit all-weather surface.

The brief called for a departmental structure with significant community use of the site. The area available for the new building was very restricted and this was accentuated by the need to maintain operation of the existing school during the redevelopment. These factors resulted in a design that was largely on three storeys with significant areas of double-loaded corridors, a format that we normally avoid. Here however we provided mostly naturally-lit spaces with sufficient width to reduce any feeling of overcrowding. The ground floor provides the main circulation routes and here the corridors are single-sided, with the external landscaped courtyard acting as an alternative circulation route.

As far as possible the classrooms are both lit and ventilated naturally – a system of ventilation shafts at the back of classrooms helps achieve this. Thermal mass has been exposed since calculations demonstrated that this would deliver benefits in terms of reducing peak summer temperatures. Although these measures could conflict with those intended to achieve the new acoustic requirements, the acoustic lining of the natural ventilation terminals, together with wall and limited ceiling-mounted acoustic panels, has ensured performance levels are met. Another significant issue is reconciling good natural lighting with the avoidance of overheating and glare problems. At Haverstock this problem is dealt by external shading on south- and east-facing elevations but internal blinds are still provided in the majority of rooms.

This is the first time in its history that the school has been housed in a purpose-built structure. An essentially compact and efficient plan form is balanced by a larger external courtyard than existed previously and the Haverstock Hill frontage provides a distinctive public presence.

Northampton Academy

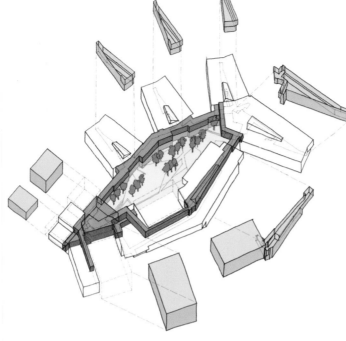

2005

with Buro Happold

Commissioned by sponsor the United Learning Trust as part of the DfES academy programme, this 1,420 pupil non-selective, non-feepaying independent secondary school offers specialism in sport with business enterprise. An extended school agenda provides both curricular and extra-curricular facilities for the pupils and wider community.

The design concept envisaged linked pavilions following a non-orthogonal geometry around a courtyard, with overlapping internal and external circulation. Each pavilion houses a separate faculty centred on a circulation hub, while the courtyard provides a focus for the whole school community. The enclosed circulation at first floor level is supported on a series of columns which in turn provide a cloistered enclosure at ground level. A series of level changes follows the slope of the site, which drops down to an adjacent watercourse.

An emphasis on a high level of natural lighting is expressed through large circular rooflights combined with solar-screened side lighting. This is further concentrated in the hub areas by large clerestorey rooflights opening up the roof plane and floating above each of the faculty circulation stairways.

While each faculty has its own distinct character, three of the four blocks have similar forms and plan arrangements, with perimeter rooms around double-height top-lit circulation areas, and they are designed to allow for flexibility in classroom use. The variety of functions (including administration and catering) clustered in the fourth segment of the building has led to more varied architectural forms, creating a public face to the academy. The entrance to the new building is framed by a double-height canopy that sits between the large volume of the sports hall and the glazed facade of the learning centre, providing

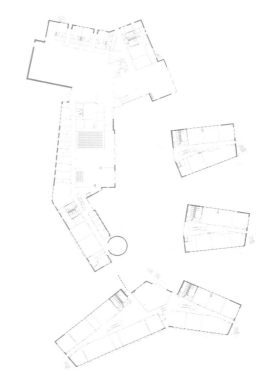

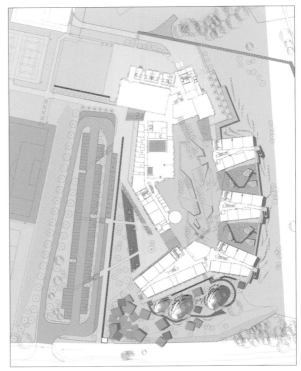

an explicit link between the school and the 'external' community.

The landscape design was given high importance due to the ecological significance of adjacent sites and the potential contribution to the learning process. Teaching gardens are located between each faculty and given direct access from ground-floor classrooms, with a dedicated science pond area adjacent to the science faculty. A key factor in the development of the site is the constraint imposed by the Environment Agency that surface water run-off should be restricted to an appropriate level. This is provided by the use of sustainable urban drainage systems, porous paving and water attenuation measures utilising the science ponds and a traditional 'swale' reservoir, all further enhancing the school setting.

The design team focused on specific academy building issues, with a view to reducing operational energy use and resource consumption, improving the local ecology through landscape design, and minimising adverse environmental impact through the choice of construction materials. We first addressed the issue of daylighting and thermal insulation in order to reduce energy consumption. The natural ventilation and thermal mass strategy was developed in detail in order to maintain good air quality while keeping energy use low.

The building design follows the recommendations of BB87 (Guidelines for Environmental Design in Schools) and has been assessed under the Schools Environmental Assessment Method (SEAM) as described in BB83. It also follows the guidance contained in BB90 (Lighting Design in Schools) with particular attention given to issues of natural daylighting. The design also addresses the issues of sustainability described in BB95 (Schools for the Future) and considers whole-life environmental impact and energy consumption in relation to the specification of the building fabric and services. The client will be encouraged to operate the building so as to reduce energy consumption over time, with the establishment of feedback and monitoring programmes to create a framework for effective decision making while the building is in use.

In addition to these passive design features a number of additional technologies were investigated which would reduce the operational environmental impact of the school while adding educational interaction. These included solar water heating, photovoltaics, wind turbine for electricity generation and rainwater harvesting for toilet flushing. Unfortunately these measures were subsequently omitted following cost reviews.

Paddington Academy

2006
with Buro Happold

This six-form entry secondary school for 1,175 students is sponsored by the United Learning Trust. The building is essentially a development of the concept and environmental strategy of FCBa's Exemplar Schools project, but designed for a very tight site with both footprint and height constraints.

Due to its independent status, the academy is not required to adhere to the current national curriculum, and its aim is to develop innovative and creative approaches to both teaching and learning. The school will benefit from embracing the cultural, intellectual and religious diversity of the local area. We encouraged community involvement in the early stages of the design process,

consulting closely with the local community and user groups.

The academy will offer specialism in media and performing arts, business and enterprise, and will provide excellent media and IT facilities. It is intended that the school will be fully accessible to the community and open for extended hours.

The concept of a dense scheme has developed in line with the requirement for well daylit spaces. The building is punctured by a series of top-lit atria each with different characteristics. Collectively, the atria also provide exciting, vibrant spaces for break-out, extracurricular and curricular activities, circulation and exhibition.

The accommodation is arranged in three distinct areas: to the sides of the building the flexible classroom floorplates form book-ends between which the more specific parts of the brief are agglomerated. The classroom floorplates knuckle at each end to create 'clusters' that can be fitted out in a variety of ways, supporting future flexibility.

The environmental strategy, developed with Buro Happold, is to:
• Minimise internal and solar gains by the design of glazing and shading, sensible lighting design with controls, careful selection of other heat-producing equipment with local extract as required; equipment is to be switched off when not in use and flat-screen

monitors are used throughout.
• Maximise thermal mass with exposed concrete slab soffits and masonry walls.
• Ensure effective ventilation throughout the year, coupled with a low-pressure mechanical ventilation system.

The small site and compact nature of the building has resulted in a high proportion of internal spaces which will rely on mechanical ventilation. With this demand, and the high site noise levels, a low-pressure mechanical ventilation system has been adopted in preference to natural ventilation for the general classroom areas. Mechanical ventilation has particular advantages:
• Noise attenuation between the classroom and outside as required on this

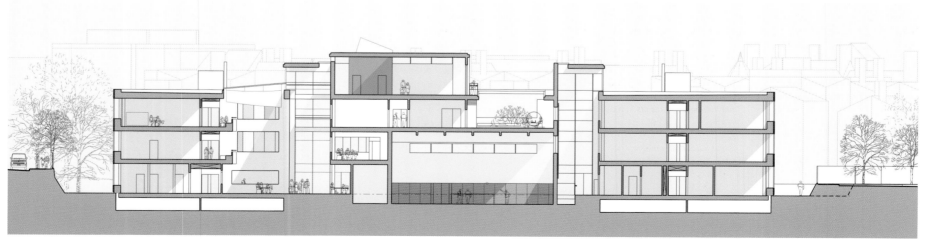

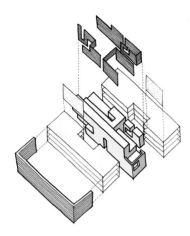

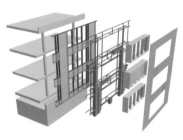

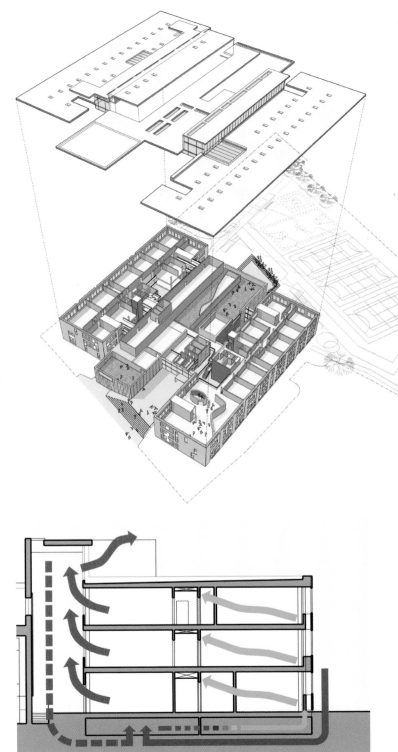

site under BB93 can be provided in a compact and cost effective manner.

• Noise break out from classrooms is greatly limited.

• Facades are simplified as large areas of opening elements are not required.

• It eliminates the need for natural ventilation chimneys which restrict the flexibility of the floorplate.

• Night-time cooling is controlled without the security risk of open windows. This will ensure classroom peak summertime temperatures are minimised with the use of heavy concrete soffits throughout.

• Local automatic controls (with manual overrides for the teachers) provide better control and hence improved air quality for the classroom occupants.

• Cold winter draughts are minimised.

The disadvantages often associated with mechanical ventilation are minimised by using simple modular equipment to reduce maintenance and simple local controls to ensure systems are easy to use.

The low-pressure ventilation system

is integrated with an undercroft, earth-coupled, air tempering system. The undercroft is pressurised by low-speed fans located in below-ground rooms at the perimeter of the classroom wings. Air enters the rooms via insulated ducts concealed within the cladding with wall grilles under the windows. Exhaust air then exits the classrooms via attenuators transferring via the corridors into the atrium. Recirculation air is provided via buried ducts routing between air handling units within the undercroft and the atrium. This allows higher ventilation rates in winter, with better distribution than is normally associated with opening windows for natural ventilation, and also results in reduced energy consumption. The heat gain through the undercroft combined with the re-circulation action of the undercroft ventilation system means that the school only requires heating in the morning during the winter months. Heat from the occupants will then warm the building through the rest of the day, or until the external air drops

below 5 degrees C. The all-air heating method for the general classrooms has the additional benefit of having a very fast response time.

The main benefit of the undercroft is that air is pre-warmed in winter and pre-cooled in summer, reducing the supply air volumes required to maintain comfortable conditions in summer and reducing heating loads in winter. In addition low-speed energy-efficient fans can be used, less noise attenuation is needed than in a conventional system and air handling and boiler sizes are reduced. With increasing summertime temperatures and four-term academic years the summertime pre-cooling effect of the undercroft will help to future proof the building.

Air passing to the atrium is heated by the classroom occupants, giving free heating to the circulation spaces. The atrium is naturally ventilated via roof-level vents and low-level vents adjacent to the dining room and above the main entrance. These are controlled via the BMS and double up as smoke vents.

As educational practices within the university have changed from lectures and tutorials to an increasingly shared and interactive process, so the architectural expression of the building type has developed. With boundaries between work, home and leisure becoming more blurred, the university is tending to become a city in miniature, providing not only specialised facilities such as laboratories and libraries but also dwellings, workplaces, assembly rooms, restaurants and shops.

Today, universities are increasingly acknowledged as one of the key drivers of the economy. Attracting the best staff and students to an area can directly affect the development of local industry and universities now develop specialisms and targets in the manner traditionally associated with business. Independent institutions compete directly to recruit the best staff and students and in this architecture has a big part to play. Image is all important – and, for most universities, sustainability is a key part of that image.

From initial work on departmental buildings at Gloucester, for example, where we worked within sensitive historic sites, through to city-scale work at Bath and Bristol, where we defined new campus strategies, we recognize that the design process needs to address a range of issues, many of which fall outside the traditional remit of the architect. No longer can we simply design a departmental building in isolation and drop it on a site. An intelligent approach to the incorporation of building management and control systems is essential, as it is to the flexible integration of emerging IT and communication systems. And, in terms of pursuing effective low-energy, sustainable building techniques, an intelligent approach to the life cycle of a building in terms of its design procurement, maintenance, and management is also essential.

The life of a university – its birth, growth and development into maturity – represents in many ways an accelerated version of the life of a city. A holistic approach to the design, procurement, construction, operation and even the demolition of its buildings is therefore needed. This applies particularly to the university campus, which demands the resolution of complex masterplanning issues at the urban scale as well as the detailed design of buildings and laboratories responding to emergent technologies.

At King Alfred's College (now the University of Winchester) for example, long-term strategic masterplanning provided an effective alternative to the traditional piecemeal procurement process, which often leads to fragmented and confused campuses. The original masterplan we produced in 1994 has led to ten commissions from the college. These principles are also illustrated in our work for the University of Gloucestershire, where we have produced a development framework for an entirely new campus on a large brownfield site, and in the design for Plymouth University's Portland Square which, as a large-scale urban intervention, seeks not only to provide extensive new teaching facilities but also to bring order and identity to an otherwise fragmented city-centre campus.

Perhaps more than any other category of client, we have found that universities are keen to establish their sustainability credentials. Both academics and students feel they want to belong to an institution that demonstrates respect for the environment. There are inherent conflicts however between these aspirations and the functional and operational requirements of a modern university that require significant design interrogation. As the university workplace assumes the characteristics of a commercial office space, there is a concern that clients may adopt less desirable commercial characteristics such as the pursuit of flexibility and spatial efficiency over and above their environmental agenda. As designers it is our responsibility to try to resolve these often conflicting demands.

Energy use in the higher education sector is not a very well understood topic. The Higher Education Funding Council of England (Hefce) has produced benchmarks for energy consumption in higher education buildings based on the different categories of building usage, ie catering, academic, residential, libraries, students' union, administration and recreation. These however are derived from the existing building stock and there is a huge variation in usage from catering ($249\text{-}352\text{kgCO2}/\text{m}^3$) at one end of the spectrum to naturally ventilated administrative offices ($39\text{-}80\text{kgCO2}/\text{m}^3$) at the other. One of the most significant issues in the published data is the difference between naturally ventilated and air conditioned buildings within each category; so for instance, for air-conditioned libraries the carbon dioxide ratings are $279\text{-}409\text{kgCO2}/\text{m}^3$ while for naturally ventilated libraries the figures are $60\text{-}97\text{kgCO2}/\text{m}^3$. Approximately the same differential exists between naturally ventilated and air conditioned administrative

University of Bath

Plymouth University

offices. While these figures need to be treated with caution, they illustrate that whilst there are specific energy uses associated with specific buildings, energy consumption can vary considerably.

Arguably university campuses change faster than any other building type, with departmental structures changing, academic areas coming and going and both institutions and subject areas increasing and decreasing in popularity. This means that flexibility is a key issue not only in terms of reducing the cost of reorganization, but also in terms of environmental impact, by being able to adapt buildings rather than demolish and re-build.

The university campus is now a 24/7, 365-day working community that is no longer constrained by the traditional three-term calendar. With unpredictable periods of operation, which not only fluctuate around seasonal term-time cycles but also change according to the programming of out-of-term conferences and summer school activities, any proposed environmental strategy must be responsive and controllable. But we no longer have a situation where heating or cooling systems are 'turned off' for days or weeks at a time. All the recent university buildings we have designed are heavyweight thermal structures designed for year-round use, with control systems that respond to daily changes in occupancy and external conditions but are never turned off.

High internal heat gains and continuous occupation suggest systems that can reclaim and recycle heat in winter and provide night cooling in summer. In three of the five buildings illustrated here, Termodeck systems have been used to provide a cost-effective low-energy solution to these requirements. By passing air through the holes traditionally formed in precast concrete planks to reduce their weight, thermal mass is exploited with access to the vastly increased exposed surface area. The concrete slabs act both as structural units and as passive thermal batteries for heat and 'coolth' which provide a stable and consistent source of ducted air.

The system operates in a number of modes. In summer, night purging cools the slabs which not only pre-chill incoming free air, but also absorb internal radiant heat gains; while in winter, by absorbing the surplus heat gains in the daytime, the structure offsets later losses, which in turn flattens out unwanted temperature fluctuations. While we have refined the system over the three installations we have worked on, in all three, once the control systems

have been set in place, it has delivered comfort conditions despite demanding internal gains.

Acoustics also needs to be taken into consideration, particularly given the diverse nature of student lifestyles. While noise generally needs to be abated and absorbed, with passive systems there is often a conflict between sound containment and naturally ventilated solutions that rely upon the free transfer of air. Furthermore, when exploiting thermal mass there is a conflict between the provision of dense and resilient thermal mass and the need to incorporate areas which offer sound absorption.

The key issue today nonetheless is that the working environment is increasingly dominated by VDU usage and therefore issues of glare, solar control, ventilation and the control of high internal heat gains predominate in our decisions. Herein lies a further contradiction in that, while VDU users cannot work with glare and want a thermally stable environment, they need to be able to rest their eyes on distant views and have a sense of the changing external environment. The window becomes the key design challenge.

A Termodeck solution requires a sealed building and normally suggests a 35 per cent glazing ratio. We feel that it is wrong to prevent occupants opening windows – although we have limited the area of opening lights for cost reasons as much as anything else, and we are sceptical about the quality of daylighting that can be obtained with less than a 50 per cent ratio. But we are also influenced by clients who say that interior openness and transparency are part of the philosophy of the university. Being able to see in is as significant as seeing out. Thus the fully glazed facades of the learning centres at Winchester, Gloucester and Plymouth are architecturally driven. They could not be justified in terms of energy saved by daylighting, and undoubtedly they add marginally to the heating energy costs, but the small increase in carbon dioxide emissions is offset by greater transparency and greater delight.

University of Bristol masterplan

Francis Close Hall Campus,
University of Gloucestershire

West Downs Centre, University of Winchester

Berrill Building
Open University
Milton Keynes

1997

with Buro Happold

The Open University was founded in the 1960s to provide distance learning and its campus in Milton Keynes mainly comprises administrative offices. The brief from the client was to take all the administrative functions on the campus and locate them in one substantial new entrance building, while a redundant studio in an adjacent building was converted to provide conference facilities.

The main office building is on a north-south axis, linked to the existing studio by a glazed concourse. On the ground floor a cafe opens onto an adjoining courtyard and, on the mezzanine above, a conference reception area connects into the main entrance at first-floor level. The administrative functions required wide open-plan floorplates, with only occasional cellular offices. The main floorplates have a floor-to-ceiling height of 3.2 metres (2.6 metres to the underside of beams) and a depth of 14 metres, which was regarded as the maximum that allowed natural lighting and ventilation and gave a sense of the outside from the centre of the plan. Cellular spaces have lower ceilings to allow ventilation paths to the main office to pass over them. On the top floor both daylight and ventilation are introduced through clerestories in the roof, allowing the floor depth to be increased to 18 metres and a row of cellular offices to run down each side, while still maintaining cross-ventilation through clerestory windows above. The aerofoil section of the roof maximises indirect light into internal spaces and gives a simple unifying character to the largest floor plate of the building.

To achieve all this within a very restricted budget of £750 per square metre, a basic curtain walling system with standard white spandrel panels was selected. Opening lights are 2.4 by 0.8 metre top-hung projecting vents. At

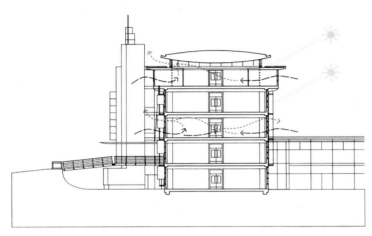

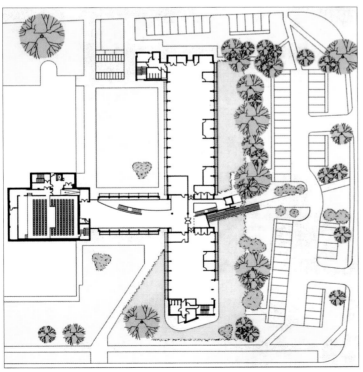

low level they are manually controlled while at high level they have automatic controls which can be overridden by the occupants. The curtain walling system is partially concealed and enriched by a layer of external solar shading. On the east elevation this consists of permanent vertical 'blinkers' made out of punched aluminium, suspended in the line of the columns at 3 metre centres along the facade. On the western elevation photocell-controlled external roller blinds are suspended on the outside face of the access walkway system. Although external blinds reduce solar gain, internal blinds were necessary to supplement the glare control on both elevations. The artificial lighting strategy is responsive to both occupants and natural light penetration. As daylight intensities increase, the fittings are automatically dimmed to a preset level (currently 10 per cent of full power). An upward lighting component illuminates the exposed concrete ceiling and enhances the apparent ceiling height.

The environmental systems proved to be very robust despite problems with the control of the external blinds on the west elevation. We also had problems with the size of the window vents, which were too large for a single actuator to operate. The incorporation of two actuators caused problems with synchronisation (lesson for the future: one window, one actuator).

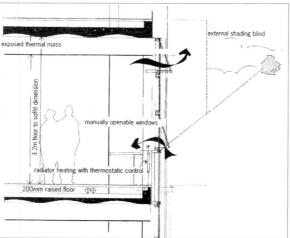

exposed thermal mass

external shading blind

3.2m floor to soffit dimension

manually openable windows

radiator heating with thermostatic control

200mm raised floor

Martial Rose Library
University of Winchester

2000
with Atelier Ten

Following the completion of the West Downs student village at King Alfred's College in 1996, attention focused on improving the main teaching campus by providing a new library which would be a landmark facility.

A 1,550 square metre three-storey extension was proposed which would shade the southerly facade of the existing building and provide a new face onto the principal external space of the campus. This would be linked to the old building by a new triple-height circulation hub and atrium and would provide a new integrated heating, ventilation, and daylighting strategy.

Early investigations demonstrated that cross ventilation would not meet the cooling loads imposed during the summer months nor harness the significant internal heat gains predicted from high student-occupancy and computer usage. Accordingly the environmental preoccupation focused on the building's winter condition, the principal challenge being how to achieve the target of four to five air changes per hour without throwing away valuable energy.

In response to these criteria the Termodeck balanced ventilation system was proposed. By providing passive heating and cooling, this exploits principles of thermal mass, heat reclamation and adiabatic evaporative cooling.

A number of conflicts was identified between, on the one hand, the desire to maximise daylighting levels and views through the large picture window and, on the other, the need to provide a robust and thermally stable envelope. Whilst in standard applications Termodeck recommend only 35 per cent glazing on any one facade, at Martial Rose the south facade was virtually 100 per cent glazed. Therefore to qualify for Termodeck's warranties, extensive work was carried out to integrate both supplementary external shading and additional perimeter heating, to offset troublesome downdraughts. This was ultimately reflected in the final cross-section, which comprised a ten metre slab with a return air bulkhead on the north side, exposed concrete slabs towards the south side, a supplementary heating trench along

the length of the window and an external layer of shading devices.

The adiabatic cooling system essentially provides an additional two degrees of cooling at virtually no extra running costs. Water is sprayed into the outgoing air path which is then evaporated and absorbs latent heat, transferring this 'coolth' to the incoming air stream via a heat exchanger.

We learned two major lessons from the Martial Rose project. The first was that the building management control system needs very careful design, commissioning and balancing throughout the first year. The second was that we had underestimated the value of the learning resources centre to the student body. Queues of ten to 12 students per workstation, to access their emails, were not uncommon at lunchtimes. The additional heating load, not to speak of the management problems, that this generated was unforeseen, but we did find that both the building and ventilation system were robust enough to cope with the success of the institution and its new facility.

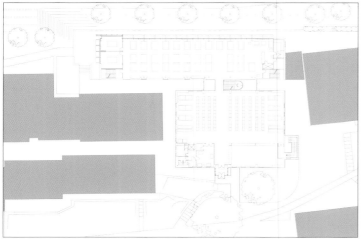

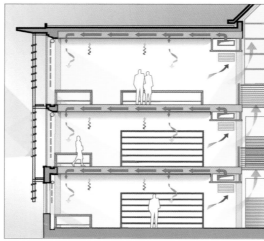

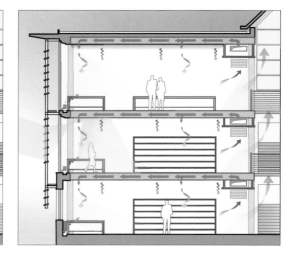

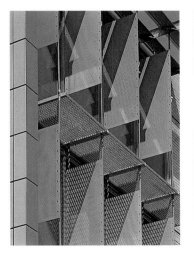

Oxstalls campus
University of Gloucestershire

2002
with WSP Buildings

This new sports science campus was intended to set new standards in sustainability for higher education buildings. Following research funded by EuBART and the DTI's ETSu programme, various innovations were introduced to enable the scheme to exceed current best practice. Located at the edge of Gloucester city centre on a six hectare site formerly occupied by a domestic science college, Oxstalls campus is the first stage in the 1998 FCBa masterplan aimed at providing a modern centre of excellence in sports science. Completed in 2002 ready for the attendance of 600 full-time and 1000 part-time students, the £14m first phase provides a high-tech learning centre and sports science building, as well as all-weather sports pitch and extensive landscaping.

In recognition of the parkland qualities of the site, which include the canalised Wotton Brook and a large number of mature trees, the disposition of the buildings form part of a landscaping strategy that seeks to create an appropriate setting for contemporary buildings (and cars) without adversely affecting the sensitive wildlife habitat. In response to the need to create a focus for the site and establish a primary circulation armature along which future phases can be placed, the two principal buildings are centered around a new landscaped pool fed by the adjacent brook. The two buildings, which both provide social and teaching spaces, are oriented to make maximum use of diffuse north light and manageable southerly passive solar gain. Together they create a new landscaped entrance space, which is defined on its opposite edge by a series of existing four-storey linked villas, providing new students' housing and a student common room.

The learning centre, which serves as the physical and operational nerve

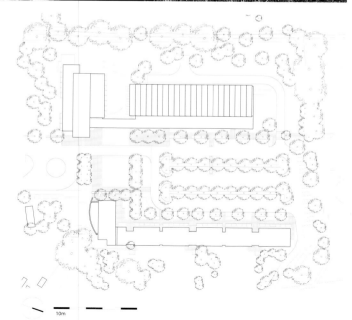

10m

centre for the new campus, provides space for 300 computer workstations plus a series of cellular teaching rooms and a lecture theatre for 200 people. Given the high internal heat gains associated with the high occupancy and IT capacity, the principal challenge was to reconcile environmental aspirations with the need to provide a mix of cellular and open-plan spaces that are welcoming and bright and take full advantage of the views over the landscape.

The building is organised along an east-west major axis and comprises three floors of accommodation. A central atrium and circulation zone, which is a key part of the lighting and ventilation strategy, unites the southerly cellular teaching spaces and the northerly open-plan teaching suites, both of which are conditioned by a Termodeck passive heating and cooling concrete slab system. Taking advantage of lessons learnt at the Martial Rose library at King Alfred's College, modifications were made to the air supply routes to improve the displacement ventilation strategy and reduce the perimeter heating required to combat downdraughts on the full-height glazing facing north over the landscaped pool.

In summer the atrium roof enclosure provides BMS-controlled natural ventilation paths via opening lights, while in winter the high-level plantroom reclaims exhaust air heat energy. The atrium also serves as an acoustic buffer between the more sociable shared teaching suites and the more traditional cellular classrooms and provides improved daylighting levels in the heart of the building's 25 metre cross-section. The reflecting pool improves the quality of light to the northerly teaching suites, while unwanted summer solar gains on the southerly facade are eliminated by external horizontal shades. Lighting

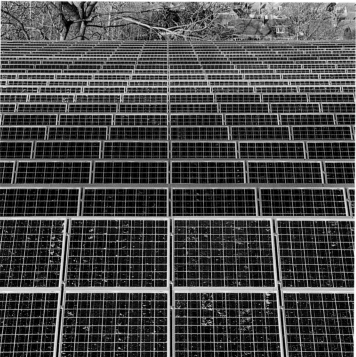

loads are reduced by occupancy and light-level sensors which control high frequency T5 fluorescent fittings.

The centre has an overall energy consumption target of 110kW hours per square metre per year, which represents approximately a third of the current best practice load.

The sports science building houses a series of relatively large spaces with 7.6 metre high ceilings, flanked by a double-tier single range of smaller cellular support spaces. The support spaces are formally distinct from the principal activity spaces, housed within a low-level concourse structure that physically and visually links the sports hall, poolside cafeteria and learning centre.

Over the major spaces the roof consists of a repeated northlight system spanning 18 metres. This provides glare-free daylighting and forms an ideal location for photovoltaic cells on the 30º pitch southerly-facing roofslopes. Grants from both the Department of Trade and Industry and the European Union contributed to the installation of the monocrystalline photovoltaic cells, which should provide approximately 65 per cent of the building's electrical load.

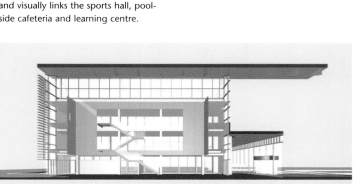

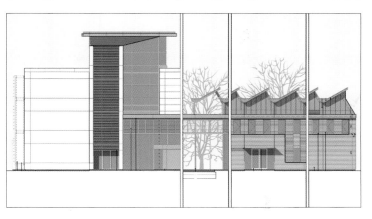

Portland Square
University of Plymouth

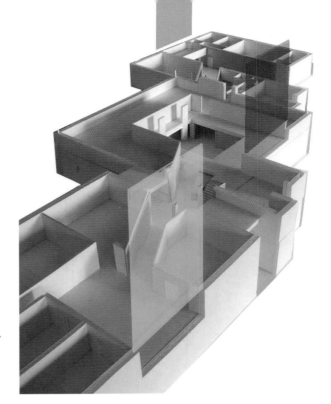

2003

with Buro Happold

Portland Square is a bold intervention into the existing urban landscape of the university and the city. It creates a new series of open spaces, each with its own identity, and dramatically improves the previous anti-social quality of the landscape. The brief was to create a building, within a very short timescale, that was inherently flexible and could provide traditional cellular academic offices, open-plan work spaces and administration support areas, as well as meeting rooms and teaching facilities. There was also a requirement for centrally timetabled teaching accommodation, including three lecture theatres and a number of seminar rooms. Our solution was to create a 'plinth' of teaching accommodation, surmounted by spaces for academics and research groups.

Because of the topography of the site, which drops by six metres from one side to the other, the plinth forms a one- or two-storey 'solid' base to the building, more introverted because of its use. The office work spaces above are configured as a series of three highly glazed cubes. These are staggered in plan to suit the constraints of the site and its surrounding buildings; linked to provide maximum flexibility; and organised around internal atria which not only help with natural lighting and ventilation to the work spaces but also give a communal identity to each building block. The strategy was based on the university's idea that sharing space will lead to a sharing of ideas.

The university also wanted a landmark building that would provide a new symbolic gateway to one of the main student entrances off Plymouth's North Hill. It was also important that the openness between departments should extend to an openness to the world outside the university. There was therefore a desire to achieve a degree of transparency in the building's structure and fabric, with use of atria spaces, nurturing the relationship between the inside of the university and those outside the building. The atria spaces are therefore enclosed by accommodation

on only three sides, with the fourth providing a view in as well as out. Two of the atria face inwards to the university campus but one faces outwards onto North Hill, marking the main entrance to the new complex.

The university also had a strong environmental brief. This led the design team to focus on minimising the requirements for air conditioning and mechanical ventilation, reducing space- and water-heating and maximising the potential for using natural rather than artificial light. Night-time cooling in summer is provided by using both natural buoyancy and wind-driven ventilation to cool the floor slabs at night, drawing air through the hollow cores of the planks from the outside wall through to the atrium and exhausting the air at roof level. Vents on the outside of the building and at the top of the atria, controlled electronically by a building management system (BMS), are all that is required to power the naturally driven night-time cooling system. Detailed thermal simulation has shown the strategy will provide significant additional cooling to the building in mid-summer conditions. This ventilation air path is completely independent of the natural ventilation to the habitable spaces on the perimeter of the building, where the curtain walling has been designed to provide both high- and low-level vents to single cellular spaces, with the high-level vents also being BMS-controlled to enhance the night-time cooling potential.

Although recognising that highly glazed buildings are seldom the most energy-efficient, the design team welcomed the client's desire for a highly transparent building. This paradox was exacerbated by the fact that the site itself was quite constrained and required a building form with an orientation that

was predominantly north-south, providing significant challenges on the east and west elevations where unwanted solar heat gain could be considerable.

The first design decision therefore was to adopt as standard a high-performance glazing system which would provide 67 per cent visible light transmission but only 35 per cent of the total solar heat admitted. The overall U-value of the frame and glazing is $1.5W/m^2K$, achieved by using a combination of low emissivity coatings and plastic spacer bars.

Fritted shading is then applied to the glass, in a number of variants in different locations. Where there are opaque insulated panels behind, the internal layer of glazing is fully fritted and the external layer has a 30 per cent striped frit, helping to give a sense of depth to the glazing and retain some of its reflectivity. Where the thermal modelling told us that we had excessive potential solar gain, a 50 per cent frit was applied to the outside layer of glass, above clerestory level, while on the west and south elevations an insulated fritted glazed panel was introduced over 20 per cent of the glazed area to reduce the potential solar gain.

The horizontality of the glazing is emphasised by the omission of external vertical bars and the placing of horizontal bars at irregular centres. This in turn contrasts with the verticality of the stone-clad lift and stair towers which project out from the rectilinear floorplates of the building. The stone is used in a more rustic coursed rubble form to clad the base of the building, where daylight is less essential, particularly in the lecture theatres and service spaces.

The three atria form an internal focus for the spaces contained within the lower two floors. These are linked by a diagonal 'street' that steps up through the site and connects with the routes through the building between each block. This helps to encourage permeability through the site from east to west, linking the series of new urban spaces that are defined in part by the staggered plan of the building and in part by the existing context.

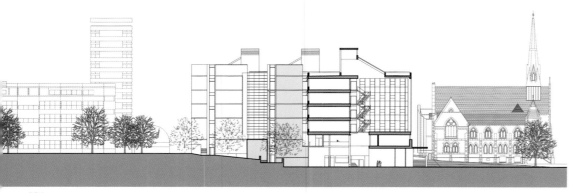

The three horseshoes: Gavin Thompson – Buro Happold

The desire for good daylight and the use of natural ventilation usually starts with the 'environmental ideal' of a narrow linear floor combined with open-plan working. It was clear, however, from some preliminary exploration, that a more compact modular building form would be required in order to deal with the required density and height constraints. By folding the linear floor plate into a horseshoe shape, it was possible to create a more compact form without compromising the environmental agenda. Glazing the open end also resulted in a greatly improved ratio of floor to external facade area. In this case, the relatively narrow floor plan in conjunction with the atrium yields good daylighting, with an average factor of six per cent.

With academic workspace there is often a conflict between the need for simple ventilation and summer temperature control and the desire for cellular space planning coupled with both transient and round-the-clock usage. The aspiration for high transparency led to the decision to employ a curtain wall facade but some form of solar control was needed in order to meet summertime target temperatures ('not to exceed a resultant temperature of 25/28 degrees C for more than five/one per cent of the occupied year respectively'). The cost of external shading, and its implications on facade access, proved prohibitive and so instead solar control was achieved by a combination of solar control glass, surface fritting and the introduction of a series of solid elements behind the curtain wall. In this way, transparent elements were restricted to roughly 50 per cent of the internal elevations. In most instances a continuous ribbon of window was maintained at high level to ensure good daylighting.

These measures alone however would not have provided sufficient control; exposed thermal mass was required to further modulate internal temperatures. Simple night-time window opening to remove the accumulated heat from the exposed concrete soffit was precluded due to the round-the-clock occupancy. Given the steel frame and precast hollowcore structural solution dictated by the programme, an alternative approach was adopted. Opaque curtain wall elements at each floor level open at night under automatic control and allow cool outside air to pass through the bores of the hollowcore precast units and into the atrium. The air flow is driven by a combination of natural buoyancy effects and, more significantly, by openings at the top of the atrium orientated to the leeward side of the prevailing wind. A rooftop weather station measures wind direction, which is strongly orientated along a south-west/north-east axis, and opens vents on the appropriate side of the atrium.

Fresh air ventilation was originally envisaged as natural cross ventilation from the building perimeter to the atrium, with floors open to the atrium itself. While this approach had been employed satisfactorily on previous projects, further cellularisation of the internal space seemed highly likely, which would impede natural cross-flows. Hence a simple mechanical ventilation system with heat recovery was provided, with underfloor displacement ventilation for those areas around the atrium perimeter. In practice, cellular space predominates and this provision has proved invaluable in providing the required space planning flexibility during fit-out.

After six months, and following some fine tuning of the window controls, environmental performance was slightly better than predicted.

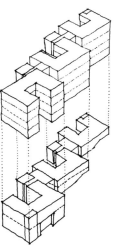

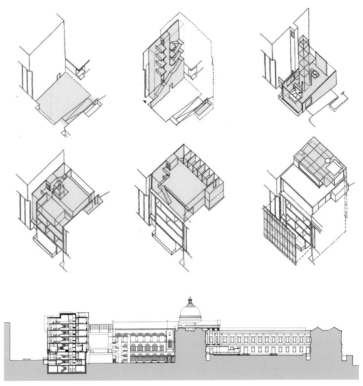

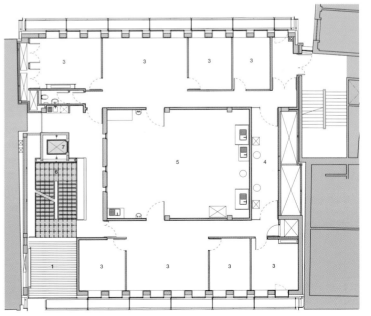

Third floor plan | Meeting area, 2 wc, 3 office, 4 service corridor, 5 lab, 6 main stair, 7 main lift.

London Centre for Nanotechnology Bloomsbury

2006
with Buro Happold

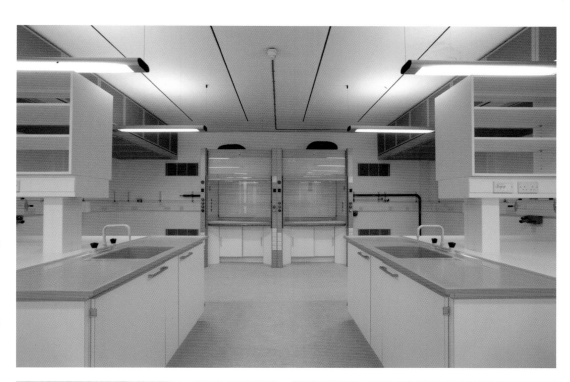

The London Centre for Nanotechnology was conceived by University College London and Imperial College as a world-class centre for encouraging interaction and the exchange of ideas within the sciences. The eight-storey building, which accommodates 120 scientists and research students, has an independent entrance off Gordon Street adjacent to UCL's Bloomsbury Theatre. The lift and staircase form a vertical circulation core alongside the party wall, creating social and spatial connections between the various functions and areas.

The structure, a concrete frame and in situ flat slab, offers internal flexibility and stability from the effects of vibration, and also provides internal thermal mass to reduce the demands of cooling from equipment loads. The building has two basement levels and uses sheet piling to provide an in situ concrete 'socket' while affording a high degree of vibration and thermal stability for some of the more sensitive equipment. The stair and lift structure is designed as a separate steel element, isolated from the main superstructure to prevent the transfer of vibrations which could dramatically affect the performance of the scientific equipment.

As many internal spaces need to be environmentally highly controlled, the efficiency of the building's energy usage is of prime importance. The principle energy source is from the UCL combined heat and power unit which serves the whole campus, with the building incorporating rooftop plant for mechanical ventilation, cooling and supply services for specialist equipment.

The office and study spaces are placed next to the external perimeter to maximise daylighting and act as a buffer zone protecting the inner laboratories from external sources of noise and vibration. The internal and below-ground laboratory spaces are ventilated mechanically using an active chilled beam system. The two clean room laboratories are serviced by full air conditioning to create highly stable environments for experimentation.

The front elevation comprises three parts, aligning with the base, middle and attic storeys of the adjacent classically composed street elevations. These vertical divisions also relate to the uses within: principal laboratories at a lower level, secondary laboratories and offices/study spaces above, and studio/office spaces at high level. The middle zone supports an outlying perforated stainless steel screen that visually contains the multitude of uses behind, provides solar screening and gives the building its identity. The front elevation also provides a visual representation of the research work carried out within the building. The relationship between the perforations of the exterior screen and the patterning on the stainless steel facade, designed with the artist Jacqui Poncelet, creates an intriguing moiré pattern as one passes by – a reference to an analysis method used in nanotechnology. The facade is designed to a 40 per cent optimum glazing daylight arrangement, with the perforate screen providing 50 per cent transparency and cut slots for views out. Combined with internal blinds, this arrangement is particularly effective at dealing with the low-angled sun falling on the principal east-facing facade.

In buildings with highly serviced spaces such as this, the opportunities to reduce energy consumption rest largely with the environmental engineers. The main architectural decisions, separating out the various climate zones, have resulted in a building with a climate-responsive zone surrounding a more artificially controlled, deeper plan environment.

Working

More than half of us spend our working lives sitting at a desk and the 'workplace' that accommodates all those desks is arguably the single most significant new building type of the twentieth century. The workstation has become more than a piece of furniture and now, thanks to the ubiquitous personal computer, caters not only for administrative tasks, but also for many roles in both service and manufacturing industries, replacing benches and drawing boards. The problem of how to locate people at desks within a collective working community has become a specialised architectural discipline. The workplace has become recognised as a social as well as commercial space, a machine for working in, and even an architectural statement. The development of the personal workspace, as well as collective office, informs us about the evolution of the wider built environment just as the analysis of urbanism can help us develop the microcosm of the social environment of an office.

Beyond the purely functional aspects of creating a workplace that are common to many building types, there are specific factors that need consideration when designing for a workspace-based community. The increased densities of people, the need for spatial adaptability, the increasing reliance on IT, extended and flexible working hours – all have implications on organisational layout and resource efficiency. Technology in particular has had a huge impact on working practices but the much predicted move towards tele-working – working from home and connecting electronically with colleagues – has not emerged. Instead it has become more evident that there is a need for people to come to work to meet other people and that, when this is enjoyable, the synergy leads to both increased productivity and a healthy work force in a healthy working environment.

The British Council for Offices suggests that the ratio between capital costs, running costs and staff costs for a typical office are in the ratio of 1:5:200.[1] So while energy consumption is an important issue for wider environmental reasons, we cannot afford to waste the potential of the primary resource of the work space – ie the people who occupy it. An imbalance in this synergy was highlighted when sick building syndrome (SBS) emerged in the 1970s. Following profligate use of energy in the post-war era, sealed buildings with vast air conditioning loads and spatially efficient yet alienating deep-plan interiors became problematic for users.

Lethargy, dry eyes and respiratory problems began to take their toll, at a huge cost to the economy in absenteeism and productivity loss – which even today in the UK is estimated to amount to £2 billion per year.[2] The highly controlled environments of these spaces had practical as well as social and psychological problems. As well as lack of the physical and biological factors of SBS – including toxic emissions from furnishings, static temperature, lack of air movement, unpleasant noise and light and the contamination of air by spores and fungi – large numbers of office workers found their work life to be an alienating experience, where they increasingly lost control of their environment. The management of the building knew best and everything was static, including the air and the spirit of the workforce.

As our technical ability to control the environment increased so we became more aware of the need for individual control. Environmental diversity is always more important than monoculture and while users need a degree of predictability in the background conditions of their environment (temperature, humidity, airflow, acoustics and light levels) they also need to be able to intervene to take control themselves. This is more than an issue of fine-tuning the system; it is a question of individual perception within a functional mechanised environment. Bill Bordass, who has analysed more workplace environments than almost anyone else, has said that 'a truly intelligent building is one that doesn't make its occupants look stupid'.[3] Amory Lovins has suggested we need to have a 'biologically and socially informed appreciation of what people are and what people want'.[4] The workplace exists as much for interaction as it does for isolated solitary work.

Throughout FCBa's existence we have developed our own workspaces, initially in our shop front office in Bath, which was extended four times in ten years, then in a converted brewery in Bath and finally in two London offices. These spaces have provided us with a useful testing ground for both practical and social experiments. We have probably been typical in experiencing major changes every five years or so and elements of refit or refurbishment on a more frequent basis.

In the City of London during the 1980s, 30 per cent of the building stock needed to be rebuilt to accommodate new computer technology. If anything, changes seem to be happening on a

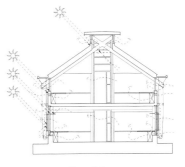

Rare headquarters, Manor Park

more frequent basis, and we seem to be further away from Alex Gordon's 1970s mantra of environmental design: 'long life: low energy: loose fit'. While there have been major advances in lowering energy consumption the same cannot be said for the energy and materials embodied in the furniture and finishes of a typical office fit out, if only because of the increased demands for new imagery and styling. Workstations go out of fashion as quickly as cars. This enormous waste of energy and resources helps explain why, in a major city such as London, 50 per cent of all materials sent to land fill comes from building work.

The problem is not necessarily those materials with a high embodied energy that go into the initial structure of the building. In an office building with a 60 year life, it is estimated that the finishes are replaced every five years, services every 15 and cladding every 20 years. The need for such regular refitting operations needs to be questioned as in these circumstances, the bulk of the energy burden swings towards finishes and fittings, where recyclability becomes a major issue.[5] Significantly this is also the area where formaldehyde in furnishing systems and volatile organic compounds (VOCs) in carpet treatments and paints provide an unhealthy working environment for the occupants – issues we researched in some depth when we designed the internal fit-out for Greenpeace in 1990 using natural carpets and naturally finished timber furnishings.

One of the determinants of flexibility in an office environment is the depth of the floor plate. While many speculative office developers opt for the supposed greater flexibility of deep-plan spaces, the requirements for view and a sense of the outside space, as well as for natural light and ventilation, suggest narrower plans. With the New Environmental Office for the BRE, we worked to a floor plate depth of 13.5 metres, then regarded as a little narrow. At the Open University entrance building this was stretched to 14 metres with a projecting top floor (where daylight and ventilation can be provided through the roof) of 18 metres. An even more extreme position was taken by the software company Rare, who demanded that each workstation should have its own window and so floor plates were reduced to 6.5 metres. Cellular accommodation on each side of a corridor, required for academic offices in the Portland Square project at Plymouth, suggested a depth of around 9 metres. At the other end of the scale, the new National Trust offices on a very introverted site in Swindon, show that deep-plan floor spaces can work in one- and two-storey spaces since, in those circumstances, the rooflight becomes the 'window' and the building becomes a 'narrow section' building rather than narrow plan. These projects demonstrate different approaches to the creation of a flexible working environment, allowing for the provision of open plan as well as cellular space, but giving careful consideration to the paths for daylight and ventilation through the building, as well as the conventional routes for pipes, wires and cables.

The deeper the office floor plate the more difficult it is to provide adequate natural light and ventilation. Rules of thumb suggest a height-to-depth ratio of about 1:4 for double-sided naturally ventilated spaces.[6] This also allows for reasonable penetration of natural light. At the New Environmental Office for the BRE these proportions provided us with a building that was calculated to have a daylight factor of between two and five per cent, with the former confined to the central corridor area. In practice however, because of the introduction of furniture and partitions, this turned out to be somewhat less. Natural lighting can obviously reduce electrical loads (lighting is responsible for more than half of the carbon dioxide emissions of a typical low-energy workspace) and natural ventilation can remove the requirements for fans and ducts. More importantly however the proximity of a window provides a view, a source of relaxation for eyes that are focused on computer screens, and a sense of the outside environment. Atria and lightwells can provide some of these benefits in terms of both ventilation and daylight but they don't provide real contact with the outside world.

Daylight is essential to the healthy office, but care must be taken to avoid potential problems from solar gain and glare, particularly in the face of a warming climate. East and (particularly) west elevations are more difficult to protect from direct sunlight and almost always need movable blinds. On the inside they will control glare; on the outside they can also keep out solar gain. South elevations can be protected by fixed blinds, though at the BRE we introduced movable ones that also enabled us to control glare too. North elevations are obviously easier to control, though one has to be wary of the low-altitude afternoon sun from the north-west. The science of excluding direct sunlight requires careful work with either com-

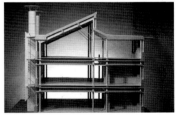

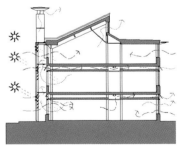

New Environmental Office, Building Research Establishment

puter models or physical models in an artificial sky. Either way we find that the fine tuning provided by an internal roller blind is extremely useful, particularly in the sense of control that it gives the user but, again, care has to be taken that these do not block ventilation routes and that blinds do not remain lowered leading to the classic 'blinds down, lights on' syndrome, that negates the energy saving potential of a well daylit design.

With increasing internal heat gains from people, lighting and computer loads, the need for additional heating is considerably diminished. A more significant architectural and environmental challenge is to reduce the need for cooling. Increasing summertime temperatures through global warming – and our decreasing tolerance of them – is exerting a pressure to increase energy use by resorting to air conditioning to give more guaranteed control of temperature and humidity but this is creating a vicious energy-intensive cycle. The brief for the New Environmental Office defined the allowable comfort parameters for naturally ventilated office buildings, specifying that internal temperatures would be allowed to exceed 25°C for no more than five per cent of the working year, and 28°C for one per cent of the working year.[7] Lengthy discussions led to 1990 being chosen to be the year to provide benchmark weather data. The year the building opened, 1997, turned out to have record summertime temperatures (and it was subsequently adopted as the new datum year) but the building nevertheless remained within the temperature constraints.

Computer loads can be cut by improving efficiency (eg the adoption of flat screens and laptops) while daylighting, together with high efficiency luminaries and controls, can reduce the heat output from the lighting system. Nonetheless the move towards higher densities of occupation provides an increased load that is more difficult to mitigate. Natural ventilation can deal with loads of around 20W/m². Controlled ventilation run during the night to cool down exposed thermal mass within the building can cope with 30-40W/m², typical of an office floorplate with an average occupancy of around eight square metres per person. But increasing loads beyond this, for instance in meeting rooms and seminar spaces, requires imaginative solutions if we are to avoid the standard split-unit air conditioning systems. At the Rare headquarters we used borehole water from 60 metres below ground (supplied at a constant temperature of around 12°C) to feed into fan convectors located at each workstation. These same units were supplied with hot water in winter and allowed for personal control at each workstation of filtered outside air, heated or cooled to the occupant's requirement. Borehole cooling was also installed at the BRE building for the seminar rooms, and pipes were built into the floor screed of the office areas, although they have never been needed.

With increasing standards of insulation, the principal component of winter heat load has become the requirement for fresh air. Relying on air leakage was the traditional solution. Increased airtightness has led to the incorporation of 'trickle vents' but these tend to be left open, providing continuous and excessive infiltration. Calculations for the National Trust building showed that it was almost cost effective to incorporate a ducted fresh air system with heat recovery to provide the necessary eight litres/second/person of fresh air to satisfy the requirement in winter.

Corporate clients are becoming more concerned about their public image and their green credentials. The New Environmental Office for the BRE very consciously displayed its environmental credentials. The facade was composed of architectural elements all of which contributed towards the control of natural light and ventilation, as well as the small area of photovoltaics adjacent to the front entrance. The design of the National Trust building is based around the roof, rather than the south facade, as the prime energy moderator. The repetitive ridge and furrow profile allows for both north light to be optimised and provides a south-facing photovoltaic collector area, a design that enables a building theoretically to approach carbon neutrality.

If incorporating photovoltaic collectors on buildings is going to form part of a long-term energy future, it is likely that roofs and canopy structures will provide the location roof for PV installations. In terms of the overall annual collection rate, south-facing walls are only 65 per cent as effective as a 30 degree southerly roof slope. On the other hand wall cladding is more visible and the offset costs against the cladding are higher. The symbolism of low-energy design is still likely to have iconic value. Understanding the relationship between this symbolic aspect, the actual (measured) carbon dioxide emissions and a healthy working environment will continue to provide challenges for the next generation of office buildings.

New Central Office for the National Trust

Notes
1 Royal Academy of Engineering: Long-term costs of owning and using buildings, Richard Haryott et al.
2 Natural Capitalism: Creating the next Industrial Revolution, Paul Hawken, Amory B Lovins, L Hunter Lovins (Earthscan Publications 1999). See also www.epa.gov.
3 People and lighting controls, AI Slater, WT Bordass, TA Heasman (BRE 1996).
4 Amory Lovins (ibid).
5 The Green guide to Specification, Jane Anderson, David Shiers with Mike Sinclair, Cosignia (Oxford Brookes/BRE Blackwell Science 2002).
6 Natural Ventilation for Offices, BRE for NatVent Consortium (BRE 1999).
7 EOF figures now incorporated into British Council of Offices data. BRE General Information Report 30 – A performance specification for the Energy Efficient Office of the Future.

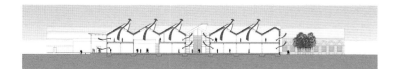

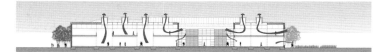

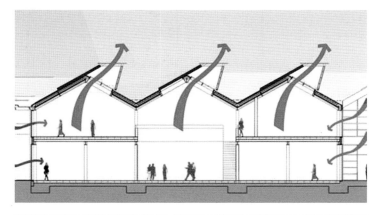

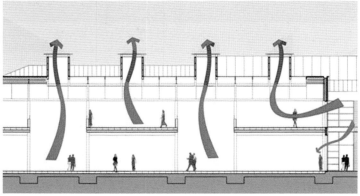

Max Fordham: Heat, light and air – some simple mathematics

On any working day you can look at office buildings which claim to be naturally lit and are six metres deep from the window wall, and see that the electric lights are on. The reason is simple. The electric lights are designed to provide something between 400 and 500 lux while the light level at the back of a six metre deep building can hardly be more than one per cent daylight factor. One per cent of an overcast sky of 5000 lux is 50 lux.
A person sitting at the back of a 'naturally lit' building with the electric lights off will be sitting in a light level of 50 lux and looking towards people sitting by the window in around 2000 lux. If they switch the electric lights on, they will have 400 to 500 lux. So that is what happens.

If we look at the energy used by office buildings, we find that electricity used for lighting is responsible for around half the carbon dioxide emissions of the building. Clearly what is needed is much more natural light. On an overcast day, passive solar energy provides $50W/m^2$ of energy (equivalent to 5000 lumens/m^2 of light) on a horizontal roof light or $20W/m^2$ of energy (2500 lux) on a vertical window, no matter what the orientation. 1000 lumens of light is equivalent to 10W of energy. 1000 lumens of light provided by an efficient fluorescent source takes 10W of electricity or 30W worth of carbon emissions from fossil fuel. If an incandescent light source is used then the figures are nearly 10 times as great – 100W of electricity or 300W worth of carbon emissions from fossil fuel.

It is actually worse than this, because the passive solar heat energy received by a window practically never equals the heat loss through a window – whereas the passive solar energy received as light easily saves the energy lost through the glass. On an overcast day, natural light can be organised to provide enough light for the building but it cannot be organised to provide enough heat. A square metre of glass window on an overcast day admits about $20W/m^2$ of energy, which can replace between 60W and 600W of fossil fuel used as light but can only replace about 20W of fossil fuel used as heat. On a cold day a double-glazed window loses about $40W/m^2$ and so the heat from light cannot offset the heat loss from the window, whereas the light easily replaces the fossil fuel it uses.

Rooflit buildings can easily be bright enough. The indoor cricket school at Lords by David Morley Architects is a recent example. When we received the enquiry for the new central office for the National Trust, we suggested a plan for the office where the plot ratio was about 1.5:1, so that two-thirds of the office could be directly rooflit and the remaining third could be generously lit under mezzanine floors. Thus electrical energy for lighting the building will be needed only when working hours exceed outside daylit hours, ie in the early morning and late afternoon in winter.

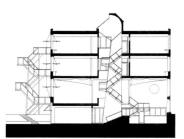

Greenpeace headquarters Islington

1991
with Synergy

Greenpeace secured the lease on a 1920s factory building in Islington for its UK headquarters in 1990. The four-square, four-storey, relatively deep-plan building had brickwork outer walls and a cast-iron internal frame. The large windows on three sides gave the potential for high quality daylighting but the single-glazed metal-framed windows needed replacing. Untreated Douglas fir frames were used with low-emissivity double glazing, providing what was then a relatively high level of specification. Light shelves fitted to both the inside and outside of the south-facing glazing bounce direct sunlight deep into the plan and shade the workspaces adjacent to the window. The upper floor level has a 4.2 metre floor-to-ceiling height. To produce a more intimate scale of space at low cost, a series of fabric canopies was stretched between the cast iron columns and the window walls, the shape of the canopies giving identity to each team-based workspace and bringing a sense of light and movement to the main floor space.

At that time high frequency fluorescent fittings were extremely expensive, and so metal halide uplighters were used to illuminate the ceiling (or, in the case of the upper ground floor, the fabric canopies). In retrospect this proved a mistake, because of the difficulties with the re-strike time on the bulbs when they were controlled by photocells.

The major planning move was to create a new central staircase linking all four floors by removing one of the central bays and suspending a stair within the resulting void. The lightweight structure, suspended from a central rooflight, acts as a counterpoint to the terracotta tile treads which form the floor finish on the lower ground floor, connecting to the courtyard garden. The new staircase

brings light and ventilation deep into the plan and provides a symbolic connection between earth and sky, as well as improving social communication through the building.

The Greenpeace headquarters was one of the first projects where the environmental agenda of materials began to emerge. The plastics industry tried to encourage us to use their windows, with the catchphrase 'save a tree, use pvc'. In the end our analysis led us to develop our own frames, using untreated Douglas fir with aluminium cill section beads and a water-based wood preservative stain. Coir carpets (which didn't stand the test of time very well), linoleum floors, clay tiles and furniture and screens made from mdf and hardwood with natural paints and stains provided the language for the interior fit-out. The CHP system was felt to be justifiable on the rather dubious grounds that the electrical and heating loads could be balanced by dumping some excess heat into an insulated workshop building at the back of the site. Although CHP technology has improved since that time, it would still be doubtful as to whether there was sufficient heat load to warrant the system running for a few months each year. What did emerge from the project was an exemplar of creative re-use where the materials, details and the whole of the interior architecture was an aesthetic that was derived from environmental considerations.

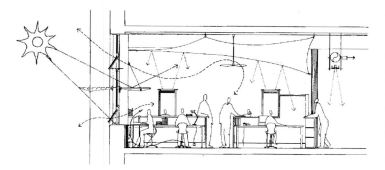

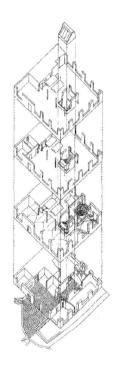

New Environmental Office Building Research Establishment Garston

1996
with Max Fordham

The brief for the New Environmental Office was both to create a new landmark building at the centre of the Building Research Establishment campus and to provide a replicable exemplar office building designed to stringent new low energy standards. The environmental brief called for dramatic reductions in energy consumption compared to the guidelines in the DETR's Energy Consumption Guide 19 and required temperatures to be maintained below 28 degrees C for at least 99 per cent of the working year, and below 25 degrees C for at least 95 per cent of the working year. The functional brief was to provide flexible office accommodation for 100 people capable of both open plan and cellular subdivision, plus high quality seminar facilities to complement the existing provision on the BRE campus.

The outcome of a fruitful collaboration with environmental engineers at Max Fordham, the building is arranged simply, with offices on three floors facing north/south separated from a stack of seminar spaces to the west by a glazed stair and entrance space. On the ground floor, a single-storey wing extends to the north to house a seminar space for 100 together with exhibition and reception areas. The fairly shallow office plan (13.5 metres) with substantially glazed facades exploits natural daylight. It is well suited to cross ventilation via BMS (building management system) controlled windows at high level, with manually openable windows at lower level.

Cross ventilation is a natural choice for open-plan arrangements, but a degree of ingenuity is required to deal satisfactorily with cellular offices which normally interrupt a simple cross-building air path. The approach taken here was to split the plan asymmetrically into a 4.5 metre deep zone on the

north side of the building (which is better suited to cellular offices with single-sided ventilation), a circulation zone 1.8 metres wide and a 7.5 metre deep zone on the south side best suited to open-plan workspace.

The southern zone was too deep for the given comfort criteria to be met by single-sided ventilation. To maintain cross ventilation of this area while avoiding acoustic problems between offices, a wave-form floor slab design was developed that incorporates ventilation routes passing over the ceilings of cellular spaces. The high points of the 'wave' have corresponding high-level windows and daylight can thereby penetrate deep into the plan. At the low points, large ducts are formed within the overall floor depth, by bridging across the tops of the wave with precast concrete planks. The wave-form floor structure is interrupted by the circulation zone, which has a thin slab at the level of the planks over the floor ducts. This forms a crossover zone for air from the occupied spaces to pass into the ducts in the floor structure. The high-level windows, set at the same level as the floor zone, are arranged to coincide with the undulations in the slab, ventilating the ducts in the low points and the occupied spaces at the high points.

The wave form increases the spanning capacity of the slab. It also increases the exposed surface of the concrete and, therefore, the available thermal mass. This is further expanded as, thanks to the ducts within the structure, both sides of the slab and the inner faces of the ducts are available to help reduce peak temperatures. The floor spans between integral lattice beams at column lines which allow partitions to be positioned against flat soffits.

While the design team was confident that the brief could be met without the

need for additional cooling (and results over the unusually hot summer of 1997 confirmed this), the opportunity was taken to test a further step of elaboration of the floor structure.

The floor surfaces at each level are divided into 1.5 metre strips of raised access floor (for flexible servicing). This alternates with screeded areas incorporating pipework that can be used both for heating in winter (in combination with radiators for quick response) and for cooling in summer. The cooling source is a new, 70 metre deep borehole cut into the chalk below. This supplies water at 10-12 degrees C, which is passed through a heat exchanger and returned to a second borehole 20 metres deep, and is calculated to deliver an estimated 8.6kWhrs of cooling energy for every 1kW of electrical pump energy. It is anticipated that this will reduce peak temperatures in the offices by about 2 degrees C and the source is also used for the main seminar space, where cooling in addition to ventilation was needed to meet comfort criteria.

A building that uses cross ventilation as its principal ventilation strategy requires alternative measures to deal with hot still conditions in summer. The approach taken here was to incorporate ventilation stacks on the south facade, connected to the lower two floors. To maximise their usefulness, the tops of the stacks are placed clear of ridge and eaves eddy zones. They contain low resistance propeller fans (80W each) mounted at top-floor level. This gives them a predictable minimum performance if required and also means that they can be used for other ventilation scenarios, eg to pull air through the floor ducts and across the office spaces on still nights.

The stacks are glazed with etched glass blocks. The interior vents into the

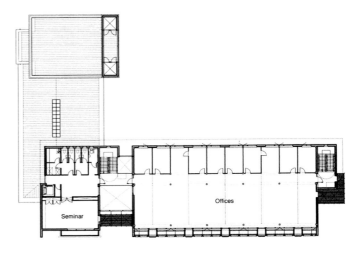

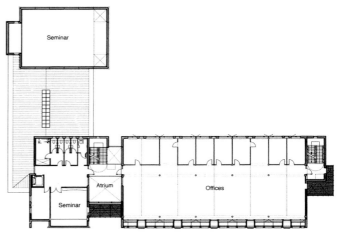

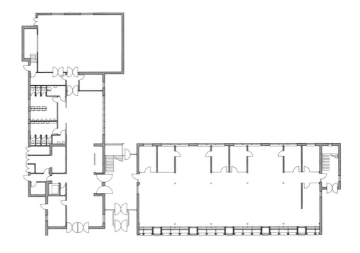

stacks are bottom-hung windows, also of etched glass, allowing daylight to be admitted through the stacks themselves to contribute to the natural lighting of the office area. The stacks also fulfil a variety of functions: in addition to ventilating the lower two floors in hot still conditions, they provide shading against low-angle oblique sun from the east and west. They also provide a support structure for horizontal maintenance access grilles at each floor level and for external shading systems.

The top floor differs from the lower levels, exploiting the possibilities of daylighting and ventilation through the roof. The section is stepped along the line of the circulation zone, with the south-facing roof rising to provide clerestory light and cross ventilation over the northern cellular office zone.

Substantially glazed facades in combination with high ceilings and a relatively shallow plan depth mean that the need for artificial lighting and the consequent electrical load will be significantly reduced as compared with a conventional office building. However, the need to control glare and solar gain becomes correspondingly more important. These factors are controlled by using BMS-controlled external motorised glass louvres, set 1.2 metres from the facade, with the lowest blade on each floor at 1700mm above floor level. The louvres are extremely slim

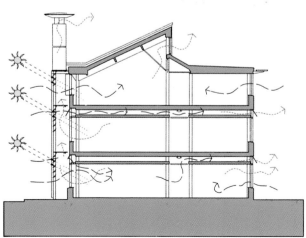

119

(10mm) when rotated to their horizontal position but, being wide, are set well apart so that an excellent view out is maintained when they are not required for shading. It is also possible to rotate the blades beyond the horizontal to a position where they act as adjustable lightshelves, reflecting direct sunlight onto the ceiling deeper into the plan. Unlike fixed horizontal lightshelves, they have a minimal impact on the diffuse light from an overcast sky entering the building. The louvres are controlled by the BMS specifically to deal with solar gain. However, being made from fully fritted white glass, they can also be used for glare control. Occupiers can override the automatic setting to reduce glare if they wish but the BMS will reset them to an optimum position at the end of the day.

Control of daylight is mirrored in the careful control of artificial lighting (and thus a significant part of the building's electrical load) using T5 fluorescent lamps linked to presence and light sensors but, again, with occupier override, using infrared controllers. These provide general lighting at around 300 lux, which is supplemented by task lighting where required, with an uplighting component to wash the wave form ceiling to provide a balanced visual environment. Each of the lamps is separately addressable by the BMS to allow different light output levels to be assigned across the floor plan and thus take maximum advantage of daylight.

Electrical loads are further reduced by the incorporation of an array of 47 square metres of thin-film amorphous silicon photovoltaic cells on the south facade with a peak output of approx 1.5kW. This is fed directly into the general electrical supply for the building via inverters and, over the year, should provide some 1,500kWhrs – approximately two per cent of the total electrical load or seven per cent of the total anticipated artificial lighting load.

While energy efficiency formed a major focus of the project, the environmental aspects of the materials used to construct the building were also considered in some detail. Secondhand bricks were sourced from a reclamation company near Cambridge. Lime mortar was used for the internal crosswalls of the entrance area, which do not take wind loading, to allow the bricks to be reclaimed once again. Crushed concrete from an office building being demolished in London was used as concrete aggregate for the foundations, ground slab and much of the in situ superstructure. Internally, woodblock flooring from London's County Hall was reused in the reception and exhibition areas. Gyproc screeds, based on gypsum from power station de-sulphurisation waste, were used throughout the building.

The building has been occupied since the spring of 1997 and it has been monitored extensively by both the BRE and the University of Westminster. The summertime performance has been exemplary and the comfort criteria have been met. Hourly average temperatures in the August 1997 peak recorded over a week when external temperatures

went well above 30 degrees C on five consecutive days showed internal temperatures just below 25 degrees C, giving a remarkable 5 degrees C of free night-time cooling.

Monitoring shows that the stacks actually contribute very little to the cooling of the thermal mass, since wind-driven cross ventilation has always been available during the monitoring period. The borehole cooling has only been called on infrequently but, in view of expected increasing summer temperatures, this provides useful spare cooling capacity for the future.

Measured electrical consumption has been 48kWhrs/m²/yr, considerably more than the 36kWhrs/m²/yr given in the brief. This is due to a number of factors, including a major computer installation on the ground floor, higher than anticipated artificial lighting requirements (resulting from the higher partitions and furniture installed on the ground and first floor) and problems with the automatic control of louvres. Heating energy consumption was far higher than anticipated (127kWhrs/m² as against a target of 47kWhrs/m²), largely due to unanticipated levels of air leakage. When first tested the rate was more than double the design target of 7.5m²/hr at 25 Pascals. Some improvements have been made, but the seminar room is still a major source of infiltration heat loss.

Overall however the building's energy performance, at 46kg CO_2/m², still compares favourably with the ECON 19 benchmark of 40 CO_2/m² for a good practice open-plan naturally ventilated office. But the real success of the building is its summertime performance, achieving more than a 5 degree C temperature reduction without any form of mechanical cooling.

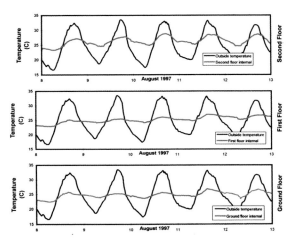

Rare headquarters
Manor Park
Twycross

2001
with Battle McCarthy

Manor Park is a 3,500 square metre corporate headquarters for the 200 staff of computer software company Rare. Both the client and the design team were committed to developing a low-energy design that minimised its environmental impact and enhanced the site ecology. The project provided the opportunity to adopt a site-wide approach to the environmental design of a new building, demonstrating that there are reasonably reliable sustainable solutions to the environmental design of highly loaded situations with extended working hours.

A masterplan was produced for the whole site, including construction of a new entrance road and extensive landscaping based on an ecological survey. An existing pond was integrated into the scheme and connected via a rill and ditches to a new lake, forming an integrated surface water disposal system. A reedbed system has also been included as a final polisher to the new sewage treatment plant.

Shared facilities, including restaurant, administrative offices, a small recording studio, creche and specialist technical areas, are located in the main administration building. This is connected by glazed links to the development 'barns', which house most of the workstations.

The materials chosen reflect the client's preference for using traditional materials and pitched roof forms, together with an interest in the use of contemporary materials that emerged during design development. The barns are clad in natural cedar with exposed Douglas fir posts and trusses and prepatinated copper-clad gutters, while the administration building is clad in prepatinated copper on its south side with brick elevations to the north. Westmoreland slate is the predominant roofing material, with copper used for

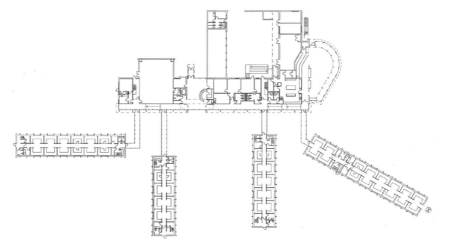

lower pitched areas. The roof of the administration building is of stressed skin construction, giving clear spans across the building and resting on composite timber and steel columns integrated into bands of windows on each side.

Internal finishes are simple with beech joinery, ash-faced doors, a combination of opaque and clear glass screens, stainless steel ironmongery and details, plus beech, granite and carpeted floors and plastered walls. Purpose-designed fitted desks are integrated with the environmental systems.

The buildings are naturally ventilated and daylit. Exposed concrete ceilings provide high thermal mass that is exploited for night cooling by the BEMS (building energy management system). This is a low-energy solution in spite of the onerous demands made on the internal environment by significant equipment heat loads (some workstation computers can generate up to 2kW of heat).

External sliding timber and aluminium louvered screens provide protection from unwanted solar gain and glare. There are motorised windows at high level under BEMS control (with manual override) and manually operable windows at low level for direct occupant control. All windows are fitted with screens to avoid problems with insects, particularly when working at night.

Individual fan-coil units serving each pair of workstations are connected to louvres under the windows, with a damper arrangement to enable them either to pull air in from outside or to operate in a recirculating mode. These are also controlled by the BEMS but occupants can override the fan. They operate in a variety of ways depending on internal and external conditions. For heating they operate in recirculating mode to provide rapid warm-up time.

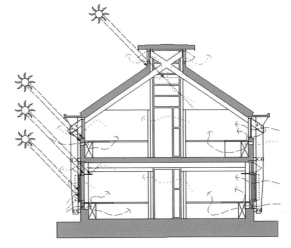

For cooling they can open up to the outside air to provide fresh air, both with and without the fan running, or operate in recirculating mode with the fan running to provide active cooling, using the borehole as a cooling source. The borehole also feeds the water features and it was originally intended to use the same source to provide all water for non-potable uses. Unfortunately, the extracted water has proved to be too hard for this.

Buildings with automated control of natural ventilation require an integrated approach to their design, construction and operation. They combine lessons from the past on how a carefully designed building fabric can assist in providing comfortable conditions with minimum energy input, together with services control experience drawn from the world of fully automated highly serviced buildings. The challenge is how best to provide draught-free ventilation to satisfy the very different requirements of summer and winter conditions in an economical manner.

Neal's Yard Remedies
Dorset

2006
with Max Fordham

Neal's Yard Remedies makes health and skin care products that are carefully prepared from natural ingredients and beautifully packaged. The organisation decided to move from south London to the Dorset countryside to bring it closer to the horticultural ingredients that provide its raw materials. The new factory, warehouse and office building are set in a hinterland of herb and flower cultivation on a site that slopes gently to the south west from where it overlooks open countryside.

The 'works canteen' has always been the focus of Neal's Yard, and in the new design it is centrally placed between offices for 80 people and a much larger factory and warehouse building for a further 20. The cafeteria space opens out onto a south-facing courtyard garden, a 'captured' piece of the productive landscape.

The ingredients used in Neal's Yard's products are natural and wholesome; the building follows the same principle. The frame uses substantial glulam beams and structural insulated panels which comprise polyisocyanurate foam sandwiched between two layers of oriented strand board (OSB) – ie compressed wood fibres. The manufacture of the sandwich does not involve adhesives but simply heat and pressure. Although the foam has a high embodied energy from its petroleum sources, butane is used as a blowing agent and it therefore has a zero ozone depletion potential (ODP).

This simple structural system allowed us to fabricate big single-storey shed-like spaces using organic materials, some of them at virtually the same cost as steel but with a dramatically reduced embodied energy. The resulting structure is lightweight thermally but very well sealed and insulated. Adding thermal mass to dampen temperature fluctuations was achieved with unfired clay bricks using the Kimmeridge clay from the site as the base material, and adding imported sand and local quarry waste to provide appropriate constituent mixes. The floors and walls comprise clay plasters, terracotta tiles and timber floors with Hessian-based carpets.

The office wing is a simple 12 metre wide cross-ventilated monopitch structure. The manufacturing and warehouse building is a wedge-shaped element extending to a height of 13 metres, with its roof tilted at 10 degrees facing virtually due south. Various options for electricity production, including an array of photovoltaic panels were researched but unfortunately budgetary constraints precluded their use. Calculated output for a standard polycrystalline array indicates that, if the entire roof was covered, almost three times the predicted electrical requirements of the building (for lighting, cooking and small power) could be met, allowing a substantial margin to meet process loads (which are less predictable). By comparison, even a less efficient but cheaper amorphous silicone array would generate more than one and a half times the predicted electrical load whereas a hybrid crystalline and amorphous silicone array could

produce more than three and a half times the predicted load. The roof has been structured to allow retrofitting of panels when costs fall.

Similarly, space and infrastructure are provided to allow the later installation of a biomass boiler plant for heating. At present this is provided by the oil-fired boiler that would be required as back-up for the biomass system.

The project therefore has the potential to be developed into a zero carbon manufacturing facility in the future.

Heelis
National Trust central office
Swindon

2005
with Max Fordham

For its new central office, the National Trust chose an intriguing site close to the centre of Swindon that had once formed part of Brunel's Great Western Railway works. It was the adjacent nineteenth-century engineering sheds that provided us with a precedent for the office. Lofty, two-storey structures with good daylighting and ventilation through a regular rhythm of pitched roofs, these buildings were designed before the days of artificial light. Our design uses a similar form, with the ridge turned to provide south-facing roof slopes for solar collection and north-facing lights for daylighting.

A key client requirement was that all the disparate parts of the organisation that were coming into the new building needed to feel part of one organisation. The regular rhythm of an all-embracing roof supported on slender columns, visible from all workstations on the ground or mezzanine floors, seemed to fulfil this objective. The deep plan initially seemed to be counter-intuitive, although redefining the building with the roof as the major connection to the environment means that in effect each workstation is no more than seven metres from daylight and ventilation. Internal courtyards were added to provide private garden spaces and a greater connection to the outside.

The design concept also derived from Max Fordham's belief that in office environments it is important to maximise natural lighting and that the most efficient way to do this is to use roof apertures. The goal was that each workspace should be able to see the sky. The most difficult zones in which to achieve this were under the mezzanine floor areas, which were designed to be nine metres wide. Various geometrical analyses were carried out to generate voids between mezzanine floor plates of six

1 Kemble Drive
2 Car park
3 Car park/Service entrance
4 Churchward House
5 Steam Museum
6 Outlet Centre

0m   50m

128

metres and floor-to-ceiling heights on the ground floor of 3.75 metres, providing an even distribution of daylight to the ground floor. Anticipated daylight factors range from three per cent at the centre of the underside of the mezzanine floors to an average of nine per cent on the mezzanines.

The rooflights are shaded in two ways. The leading edge of the south-facing photovoltaic panels is extended over the ridge to provide shade from high-level summer sun; and ventilators at a minimum of nine metre centres with a raised enclosure provide shading from both east and west low-level elevations.

The ventilators at roof level are designed to operate independent of the wind direction and to provide rain protection to the opening sections of rooflight. Both these vents and the vertical openings around the perimeter of the building are automated to provide night cooling in summer and daytime ventilation from spring to autumn.

One of the problems with naturally ventilated buildings is providing the very low rates of ventilation required to maintain oxygen levels during the winter – casement windows or even trickle vents tend to admit too much air and cause draughts. To address this a very low level mechanical ventilation system has been designed with an integral heat recovery system; this introduces air to raised floor plenums and provides a single point of extraction adjacent to the fan unit itself in order to provide heat recovery. This should have a dramatic effect on the overall heat requirement, reducing it from 49 to 13kWhrs/m²/yr with minimal fan power.

Naturally ventilated buildings often incorporate 'safety net' measures to deal with excessive summertime conditions. Rather than providing extensive cooling, the solution here is to incorporate an

CO₂ Cost/Benefit of Various Energy Strategies

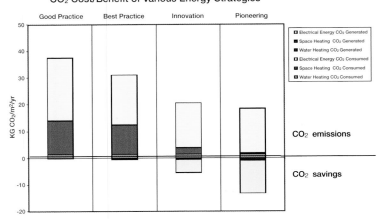

	Good Practice	Best Practice	Innovation	Pioneering

☐ Electrical Energy CO₂ Generated
■ Space Heating CO₂ Generated
■ Water Heating CO₂ Generated
☐ Electrical Energy CO₂ Consumed
☐ Space Heating CO₂ Consumed
☐ Water Heating CO₂ Consumed

KG CO₂/m²/yr

CO₂ emissions

CO₂ savings

extract ventilation system in five of the roof ventilation 'snouts' which can enhance cooling potential and air movement if absolutely necessary. It is not anticipated that these would be used other than in exceptional summer-time circumstances.

Power consumption by office equipment however is more difficult to control and in a low-energy office building will remain the largest source of carbon dioxide emissions. The only way to meet this electrical load without importing electricity is to incorporate on-site photovoltaic generation. The roof form of the building maximises this with a total potential area of 1,400 square metres of collection area facing due south at 30 degrees to the horizontal.

Various photovoltaic options were considered, each with different capital costs and outputs, and the most cost-effective solution was a thin-film amorphous silicon panel. However desktop studies which looked at the use of high-efficiency polycrystalline silicon cell showed that the maximum installation over the roof area would result in an annual contribution of 82 per cent of

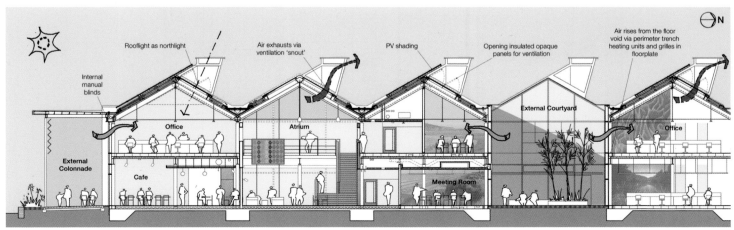

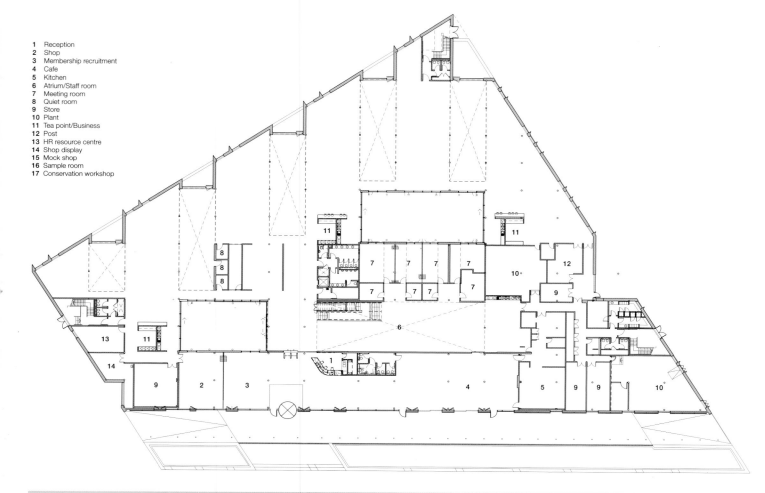

1 Reception
2 Shop
3 Membership recruitment
4 Cafe
5 Kitchen
6 Atrium/Staff room
7 Meeting room
8 Quiet room
9 Store
10 Plant
11 Tea point/Business
12 Post
13 HR resource centre
14 Shop display
15 Mock shop
16 Sample room
17 Conservation workshop

the total electrical load of the building, reducing carbon dioxide emissions to almost zero. This doesn't necessarily imply that one- and two-storey buildings are optimal, because of the impact on land take and urban design, but it does show that commercial buildings in which the roof area dominates the wall area are more likely to meet the elusive target of zero carbon dioxide emissions.

The National Trust was very keen to benchmark the building against 'good practice' and to push the boundaries of innovation in terms of sustainability. We therefore developed a matrix of sustainability issues which was used throughout the design process to track our progress in meeting targets. This is reproduced on page xxx, but updated to show where the final building design ended up. Studies of water usage showed that by installing 4-litre flush wcs and waterless urinals, spray taps and class-A kitchen appliances, it would be possible to reduce water consumption by 60 per cent. Because of this, rainwater recycling systems were shown not to be cost-effective. But the site is subject to flooding and attenuation of surface water was required by the Environment Agency. This was achieved by creating a bunded tank under the car park, using the natural clay of the ground to retain the water prior to discharge into mains drainage. An alternative system was examined that took rainwater from the roof and car park, passed it through a series of wetland swales that ran down one side of the building (to provide natural filtration) and thence into a tank from which it was pumped back into the building to flush wcs, but this proved too expensive.

The materials selected for use in the building were also subject to scrutiny by, among other things, checking against the ratings in the Green Guide Specification. Blue engineering bricks,

chosen for the outer walls, are laid in lime mortar to facilitate recycling. Both the roof and windows are made from aluminium, which today has a very high percentage of recycled stock. Various options were examined in relation to the superstructure frame, with timber solutions evaluated against steel. Surprisingly, studies showed that the choice between timber and steel sections with a high percentage of recycled steel made very little difference to the overall embodied energy. The refinement of the steel frame and the reduction in thickness of the slab were of greater consequence.

The National Trust is very keen to utilise materials from its estates, and one of the more significant undervalued products is the sheep's wool from the Herdwick flock on the Lake District fells. This was incorporated in a contract grade 80:20 carpet, demonstrating a commercial use for a product which to date has been difficult to process viably. Elsewhere internal fittings use timber from nearby National Trust estates.

The Trust's sustainability policy also extends to its transportation strategy. The site was selected because of its proximity to the mainline station, and the number of car spaces provided has been reduced below what commercial developers might expect and the planning authority might accept. The provision of just one car space for every three workers will mean that a green transport plan will be needed, helping to reduce car dependence.

Thorough post-occupancy evaluation is proposed, and a display of the building's energy consumption will be available in the reception area. Such an approach should ensure maximum benefit from feedback from what ought to be the lowest energy consumption office building in the country.

		1. GOOD PRACTICE	2. BEST PRACTICE	3. INNOVATIVE
Operational Energy Consumption and CO_2 Emissions	1. CO_2 Emission Target	40kgCO_2/m²/yr	30kgCO_2/m²/yr	15kgCO_2/m²/yr
	2. Heating Load Target	79kWhr/m²/yr	47kWhr/m²/yr	30kWhr/m²/yr
	3. Electrical Load Target	54kWhr/m²/yr	43kWhr/m²/yr	35kWhr/m²/yr
	4. U Values: Wall / Average Window / Roof / Ground Floor	0.35 / 2.20 / 0.20 / 0.25	0.25 / 1.80 / 0.18 / 0.22	0.20 / 1.40 / 0.15 / 0.20
	5. Airtightness	<10m³/hr/m²	<8m₃/hr/m²	<5m₃/hr/m²
	6. Ventilation	Natural ventilation where possible. Mechanical where not.	Designed natural ventilation with automatic openers, mechanical ventilation to WCs etc.	Mechanical ventilation with heat reclaim in winter and BMS controlled natural ventilation in summer.
	7. On Site Energy Generation		Solar domestic water heating to WCs.	Cost effective PV installation using PVs to shade rooflights
	8. Daylighting	"Reasonable" to BS8206 part 2. A 2% daylight factor	80% office space daylit to meet criteria of BS8206: part 2.	100% of office space daylit to BS8206 part 2.
	9. Artificial Lighting Controls	PIR detectors in WCs etc. Low energy fittings throughout.	Luminance and presence detectors throughout building. No dimming.	Luminance and presence detection at all fittings with dimming to zero and BMS override.
	10. Cooling Systems/Sources	Zero ozone depletion refrigerants in high efficiency comfort cooling/air conditioning systems.	Night time structural cooling with automatic window vents.	Evaporative cooling to rooms with high internal heat gains.
	11. Embodied Energy in Structural Materials	Steel and concrete frame engineered to minimise mass of materials.	Use of cement replacements eg GGBFS in concrete. Use recycled steel.	Timber structure in lieu of steel or concrete but retaining concrete floors. Use of recycled aggregates in structural concrete.
Water and Waste Systems	12. Water Usage	Low flush WCs (4 litre), spray taps and 'A' rated kitchen appliances. PIR detection on urinal flushing systems.	Waterless urinals. Hand PIR on tap operation.	Mains water only used for drinking water. Rainwater harvesting for WC use.
	13. Drainage Systems	Conventional mains stormwater drainage for areas around building.	Use Sustainable Urban Drainage Systems soak aways etc to reduce burden on sewage system.	Integrate S.U.D.S. with wetland swales to provide attenuation on site.
Materials Used in the Construction Process	14. Toxicity of Materials	Avoid high VOC content paints sealants etc and all ozone depleting materials.	Eliminate PVC cabling, change to LSF. Avoid all 'C' rated materials in BRE design guide.	Eliminate PVC drainage - change to Cast Iron. Avoid all 'B' and 'C' grade materials in BRE design guide.
	15. Materials Sourcing	State preference for locally sourced materials. All timber to be FSC certified.	Specify all heavyweight materials to be from local sources. Consider recyclability and lifecycle costing of materials.	All materials to be UK sourced with preference for N.T. timber etc.
	16. Insulation Materials	Zero ODP insulation	Use non petro-chemical based insulation materials wherever possible.	Prohibit use of petro-chemically based insulants.
	17. Recyclability of Materisals	Avoidance of potential problems with dismantling e.g. using pre-stressed elements.	High grade materials e.g. bricks to be designed for recyclability e.g. using lime mortar.	Avoid composite materials to allow for recyclability.
	18. Waste Production during Construction	Contractor to comply with industry standards on waste separations/minimisation. EPI 10.58m²/100 m². Avoid all export of excavated material.	Contractor to commit to targets on waste production from site. Encourage prefabrication.	Apply for financial constraints to reduce waste production from site. Maximise prefabrication.
Transport Issues	19. Biodiversity in Landscaping	Maximise areas for tree planting and soft landscaping.	Give preference to local species and select from local seed sources.	Increase intensity/diversity of planting around the building (creating a protected garden space). Specify green roofs/green exterior wall covering (creepers and climbers etc)
	20. Transportation	Covered cycle storage to encourage bycycle use.	Lockable covered secure cycle storage and provision of showers. Incentivisation of car sharing and public transport use.	Minibus service to and from station. Employment/car parking policy to discourage (prevent) local employees to use their car to go to work.
Management and Monitoring Issues	21. Commissioning and Staff Training/Feedback/and Monitoring in use	User involvement in commissioning and staff training. Normal 12 month monitoring.	Commissioning company retained to monitor over the first year. Full post-occupancy evaluation of building and energy use patterns.	Staff involvement in ongoing monitoring or performance. Improved monitoring facilities - more user-friendly BMS.
	22. Facilitating Waste Recycling	Adequate space for storing recyclable waste.	Managed recycling processes involving space for separating and collecting recyclable waste.	

4. PIONEERING	NOTES
"Carbon neutral" 0kgCO$_2$/m	Industry standard EEO targets
20kWhr/m²/yr	Industry standard EEO targets
25kWhr/m²/yr	Industry standard EEO targets
0.10 1.90 0.10 0.10	Good practice=current building regulations. Pioneering=Bedzed values.
<3m³/hr/m²	5.5m2/hr/m2 achieved following site test.
Solar water heating to kitchens. Maximum PV installation using most efficient PVs. Wood/waste fired CHP.	Obtained 65% grant for PV installation.
Borehole/ground water cooling to rooms with high internal heat gains.	
All timber structure with thermal mass provided using minimum amount of concrete.	
Grey water recycling for WC flushing. On site sewage treatment with vortex separation and filtration.	Decision during construction to change to manual lever handle taps to allow user responsibility. Currently considering reminder notices.
Eliminate all use of VOCs in paints and timber. 80% of materials to achieve 'A' rating in BRE Green Guide.	
All materials to come from 50 mile radius from site.	Used NT timbers and NT sheep wool for carpet.
Use only insulation materials from regenerative sources eg cellulose/wool/cork.	
Prefabrication and erection to allow for easy dismantling.	
All superstructure to be fabricated off site to reduce wastage.	
Electric vehicle "taxi" available for visitors coming by rail, (capable of using Brunel Tunnel).	Green transport plan provided only uncovered cycle storage provided.
Instigation of one/five year monitoring and evaluation programme to reduce energy use etc year on year.	
On-site composting for vegetation and office paper waste.	Ongoing informal and formal information gathering between design team and staff.

Gathering

Gathering

Shared space is a key aspect of social sustainability; but over the last 50 years, as we have moved towards more private ownership of land and buildings, the quality of shared space has declined. Its revival is a vital part of the challenge facing us today. Many of the buildings that we have worked on in this category are privately owned but accessible. They are designed to serve, as well as represent, the community and help foster social cohesion. Often they have a retail or commercial aspect which means they need to consciously invite the public in.

One of the first community buildings we worked on was the McLeod Centre for the Iona Community, an ecumenical religious group who wanted to develop a hostel for the numerous visitors coming to the magical island of Iona, off the west coast of Scotland. The building consisted of bunk-bedded dormitories, communal kitchen, dining room, craft workspace and a shared community courtyard – an outside space enclosed on two sides by the building and on the other two by rocky outcrops in the surrounding landscape.

The hierarchies of space, from the public outdoor realm to indoor public (or semi-public) space, are often a key determinant in these buildings. At the Earth Centre for instance the entrance canopy provides both a gathering space and a sheltered public arena, its roof a major statement of sustainability both as an energy collector and in terms of materials from which it is constructed. By contrast the visitor facilities at Painshill are linked by a simple linear covered route, which provides a transition from the twenty-first century car park and new entrance bridge to the eighteenth-century garden that the visitors have come to see. At Yorkshire Sculpture Park a similar axial route leads from the car park to a formal garden that provides an enclosed heated and ventilated concourse, connecting a range of facilities.

An intermediate solution would be to create an unheated buffer zone, such as we have constructed linking the two major buildings at the Oxstalls Campus at the University of Gloucestershire. This consists of a two-storey glazed link bridging a water feature and providing a gathering space that is largely heated by extract air from the buildings which it serves. Providing an easy transition between inside and out often results in high energy use. Over-complex lobbies and revolving doors detract from the immediacy of the connection between inside and out, although a single plate glass door of the high street shop type, more often open than closed, creates a huge energy burden in winter.

There is a very obvious psychological connection between transparency and 'openness'. Government buildings, whether national, regional or local, often use and abuse architectural languages to create buildings which symbolise power and authority. There was a time in the 1970s when an over-reaction to this authoritarianism led to council offices that looked like sheltered housing schemes, desperate to create a sense of friendliness. We believe that truly 'public' buildings need a sense of civic dignity, but also need to be open and inviting. The obvious transparency that glass provides can be used to symbolise this, as in our initial proposals for the civic offices at Runnymede. There is an easy transition from external piazza to internal atrium, which in turn both contains and exhibits the council chamber as the embodiment of local democracy. The symbolism and legibility are appropriate from both an architectural and an environmental perspective. The atrium is an inherent part of the ventilation strategy. The more enclosed and acoustically and environmentally controlled council chamber is more highly insulated and introverted.

Symbolism is important to community buildings and we are intrigued by using form and detail suggested by environmental design to give the building a symbolic identity. At the local area housing offices at Fishponds in Bristol, the entrance is marked by a visual tower which also drives the natural ventilation of the offices and public spaces below. At the Oxstalls Campus at the University of Gloucestershire, where public access was regarded as a major consideration, the three-storey entrance canopy also shades the central atrium from unwanted solar gain. Icons can emerge from the sustainability brief.

Community buildings also present a challenge in terms of variable use patterns. Meeting spaces require acoustic enclosure and can generate high heat gains. Gallery and exhibitions spaces often require acoustic isolation and mechanical ventilation. High internal heat gains can come from display lighting and a large through-put of people. These were the conditions that led us to develop the underfloor labyrinth system at the Earth Centre, which increases the thermal mass for night-time cooling in summer. Other

Iona community

Fishponds Area Service Office

Runnymede Civic Centre

spaces rely on daylighting; in a culture that yearns for sunlight, it is important that major public spaces do not exclude it. It is also important to recognise that many visitors to public buildings retain their outdoor clothing if they are simply passing through, and will therefore be dressed for the exterior climatic conditions. Staff however require different treatment. One of the most difficult categories of people to keep environmentally happy are those who provide reception functions to public buildings, often located in draughty areas only one door away from the outside environment.

Retail specialists demand focused and high intensity artificial lighting, an effect achieved better with high energy tungsten rather than highly efficient fluorescent fittings. Catering facilities are major consumers of energy both in the process of cooking and the ventilation of odours and heat gain; annual energy consumption figures are more than twice those of office buildings. These are often specific problems that need specific technical solutions. Services engineers are generally unwilling to take risks with low-energy insulations when guaranteed and instant performance is essential. We can modify buildings to deal with high heat loads by using such devices as the labyrinthine floor, but a low energy commercial kitchen design requires dedicated services engineering.

These problems are further exacerbated by fluctuations in usage. Low thermal capacity 'lightweight' buildings must be able to adapt very quickly to increases in occupational heat load. 'Heavyweight' buildings can soak up the fluctuations more easily, but need to be maintained at close to comfort conditions. Patterns of use will dictate a decision on thermal capacity, but in general higher cooling loads will tend to suggest a more heavyweight internal structure. We are considering various strategies for a recent public arts building, a competition for an arts and cultural centre in Derby, including a heat recovery ventilation system, utilisation of borehole water and the possibility of incorporating a photovoltaic skin.

Community buildings more than any other building type allow us both to reflect the aspirations of society and develop an architecture that engenders social interaction and responsibility. It is in these buildings that we hope to bring together both the social and environmental aspects of sustainability, producing buildings that are an internal extension of the outdoor public realm.

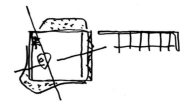

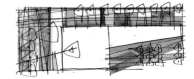

Derby Quad

Solar Canopy, Earth Centre

The Lantern Centre
Ringwood

1992

with John Willoughby

The design of the Lantern Centre at Ringwood reflects in its form the philosophy of the Sheiling Community. This was inspired by the ideas of the German expressionist sculptor, architect and philosopher Rudolf Steiner. From his early-twentieth century perspective, Steiner believed that the form, colour and materiality of our surroundings have a strong influence on our behaviour.

The Sheiling Community is a village providing curative education and training for mentally handicapped children and young adults. In designing the new building we sought a solution that addressed the specific nature of the woodland site and provided spaces of sufficient variety and diversity to meet the needs of the older 'trainees', who would be able to meet and serve members of the wider community.

The centre forms a new focus for the 20 hectare Hampshire estate, where community members live in family houses. It comprises two highly articulated forms that make a clear distinction between the served and servant components of the brief. A simple two-storey 'barn' contains a workshop, kitchen, toilets, stockroom and a warden's flat. These serve the more flexible and free-form public areas that share the space enclosed by two curved protective brick walls, with a lofty mono-pitch roof that rises up on timber 'trees' to create a high-level south-facing clerestory.

As an expressive composition the contrasting forms and elevations resolve the meeting of several significant routes across the estate. Externally the building reads as a secure enclosed shelter, with strong brick walls and an all-encompassing cedar shake roof. Internally attention is focused on the edges of the space. Shelving and seating provide a variety of intimate niches within the depth of the convex perimeter wall while a concave timber screen breaks the containment, creating a sheltered external courtyard space that mediates between the interior and the landscape.

The articulation of the two forms is resolved internally by a high-level mezzanine, clerestory and rooflight, which not only flood the space with daylight

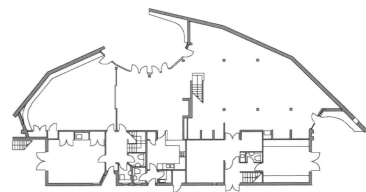

and southerly sun, but also provide a quieter retreat above the more expansive spaces. Visitors and staff can use the shop and cafe (both staffed by trainees) and the meeting room, which can be isolated from the space with a movable acoustic screen; or they can retreat to the reading area above.

The benefits of natural light and cross-ventilation are simply harnessed by the building's form and orientation. Natural materials are used throughout, with Douglas fir, beech and terracotta as the predominant internal finishes. A rich palette of brick and timber boarding, cedar shingles and shakes and copper are used externally. Organic in form, materials and setting, the Lantern Centre is also a highly specific response to the philosophy of its user clients.

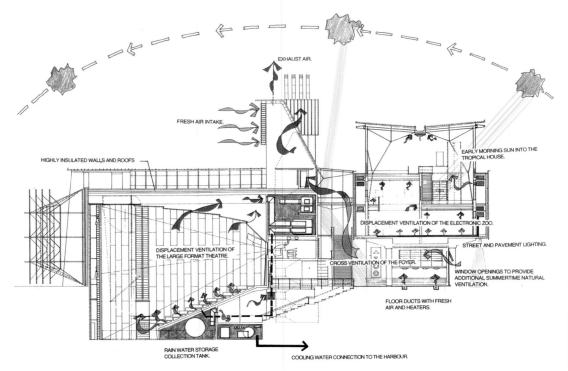

EXHAUST AIR.

FRESH AIR INTAKE.

HIGHLY INSULATED WALLS AND ROOFS

EARLY MORNING SUN INTO THE TROPICAL HOUSE.

DISPLACEMENT VENTILATION OF THE ELECTRONIC ZOO.

DISPLACEMENT VENTILATION OF THE LARGE FORMAT THEATRE.

STREET AND PAVEMENT LIGHTING.

CROSS VENTILATION OF THE FOYER.

WINDOW OPENINGS TO PROVIDE ADDITIONAL SUMMERTIME NATURAL VENTILATION.

FLOOR DUCTS WITH FRESH AIR AND HEATERS.

RAIN WATER STORAGE COLLECTION TANK.

COOLING WATER CONNECTION TO THE HARBOUR.

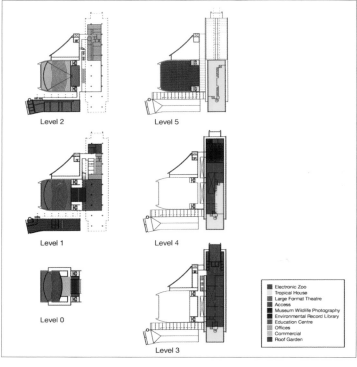

Level 2 Level 5

Level 1 Level 4

Level 0

Level 3

Electronic Zoo
Tropical House
Large Format Theatre
Access
Museum Wildlife Photography
Environmental Record Library
Education Centre
Offices
Commercial
Roof Garden

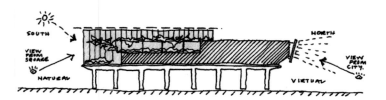

SOUTH NORTH

VIEW FROM SQUARE

VIEW FROM CITY.

NATURAL VIRTUAL

EMERGING FORM.

Wildscreen World Bristol

1996
with Buro Happold

142

Developed around the BBC's wildlife department in Bristol, Wildscreen World was conceived as a visitor attraction that would represent the natural world though film and photography.

Our competition entry explored the idea of an 'ark', carrying knowledge about the world around us, organised as a sequenced exhibition internally and represented in an iconic way externally. The project sought to integrate a combination of electronic media and natural exhibits to provide a unique educational facility, combining highly specific uses with substantial areas that would change significantly both during the design development process and during the life of the building.

Wildscreen World consists of three principal spaces: 'electronic zoo', tropical glasshouse and a large-format Imax cinema. The electronic zoo and the tropical house are treated as an integrated element, allowing a direct connection between the man-made world of the electronic zoo and the more natural world of living plants and insects in the tropical house. As the most important element of the building, it is lifted up above street level, with foyer and exhibition spaces below, achieving maximum daylight and sunlight for the tropical house and providing visual impact externally.

The external envelope of this combined form – a layered skin of woven copper and glass – orders the public elevation while allowing a flexible arrangement of window openings behind for the electronic zoo. The screens admit filtered daylight into selected gallery spaces in the lower levels of the tropical house. The elevational screens form an abstract representation of the edge of a forest or the skin of an animal, with the glass element of the tropical house emerging from behind to reveal the beauty of the glazed envelope with its exotic contents, like a butterfly emerging from its chrysalis.

The primary design objective of the tropical house was to achieve views out with minimal cleaning, by providing an energy-efficient transparent skin enclosing an environment with up to 100 per cent relative humidity without causing condensation. To this end we developed a double-skin solution. Cleaned and filtered hot air is passed through a cavity between the outer and inner layers of the glass, with single glazing on the inside and double-glazed units on the outside. The cavity is large enough for the inside to be accessed and cleaned on a maintained basis.

The Imax cinema is partially buried into the ground, with the underside of the raked seating area acting as a pre-view space and forming a link with the ground-floor foyer. This conditioned

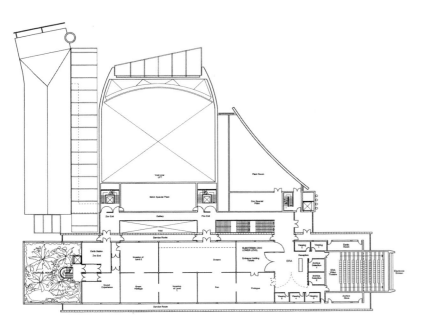

black box space is accessed via sub-foyer 'locks' that adjust the levels of daylight from the natural outside to the artificial inside. The roof becomes a terrace and a wildlife garden with a rooftop cafe, accessed from the electronic zoo/ tropical house circulation space.

The competition scheme provided valuable insights for the later visitor buildings at the Earth Centre and the Yorkshire Sculpture Park. It also led to an interest in the layered translucency of external materials which was to feature in later projects such as the London Centre for Nanotechnology and Haverstock School.

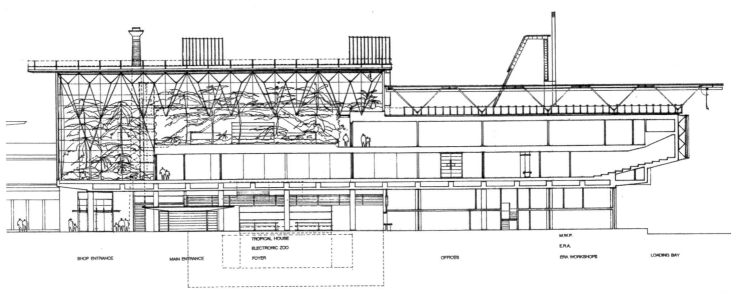

Earth Centre
Doncaster

2001

with Atelier Ten and ECOFYS

Conceived as a visitor attraction providing education and entertainment on environmental issues, the Earth Centre is located on a 122 hectare site in one of the most environmentally devastated areas in the UK: the coalfields of South Yorkshire. We were appointed initially to work on the masterplan and thereafter as one of four architects working on the project, with the task of designing some of the major buildings, including exhibition spaces, a cafeteria, shop and an information point forming the entrance to the Earth Centre site. The strategy was to integrate a low energy building with a highly visible solar generator, the

first component in a strategy to make the site self-sufficient in terms of power.

The buildings are located at the edge of a limestone escarpment and a number of the major exhibition spaces, particularly those which do not require daylight, are buried into the hillside, with the limestone of the escarpment, quarried less than a kilometre away, forming the retaining wall to the new buried buildings. Founded on poor quality ground, these buried buildings required very strong raft foundations. This led to the concept of a basement 'labyrinth' which is used to store heat from internal gains in winter and benefits from night-

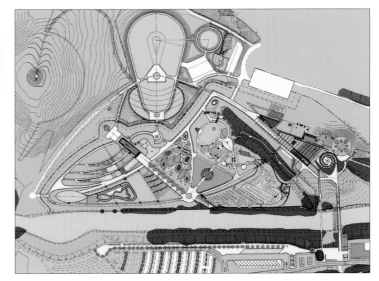

time cooling in the summer. A building with potentially very high internal heat gains is thereby able to operate without air conditioning.

While the bulk of the buildings are built into the earth, one simple rectilinear building floats free from the hillside, defining a funnel-shaped arena which forms the entrance to the site. A canopy stretches across this trapezoidal space and shelters the ticket booths and main entrance area. It consists of a distorted timber space frame constructed using roundwood poles of Scottish-grown larch with galvanised steel connectors. The elaborate geometry created by the

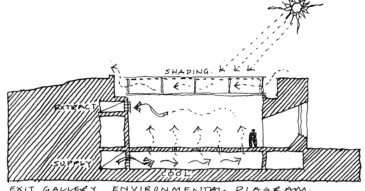

EXIT GALLERY ENVIRONMENTAL DIAGRAM.

trapezoidal frame and the almost random supporting posts forms a dynamic contrast with the purity and simplicity of the adjacent building forms.

The canopy is roofed with photovoltaic cells embedded in glass. The cells are spaced 4mm apart with a 60mm space round the edge so that approximately 25 per cent of the daylight striking the canopy penetrates through it – the dappled light and complex geometry of the timber structure creates an abstract representation of a forest. Processed timber forms the trunks and branches of the 'trees' with photovoltaic cells capturing the transforming sunlight, as do leaves.

Studies were carried out looking at various configurations for the arrays of cells. Ridge and furrow solutions, while benefiting from increased irradiation due to the steeper angle, also meant a reduced collector area and a more complex structural arrangement of guttering. The individual arrays would have to be spaced further apart, particularly where collector angles were steeper, in order to avoid overshading in winter. In the end the configuration chosen was to provide a flat plate to the entire roof sloping at an angle of 5 degrees towards the south. Water collects at the front edge of the canopy in a single large gutter which also acts as a wind deflector, with the water discharged into a holding tank in the earth bank.

The 1000 square metre array is rated at 107kW peak, yielding a potential of 77,000kWh of generated electricity per year. This would provide about 20 per cent of the annual electrical consumption of the entrance building. Sadly, declining visitor numbers led to the closure of the Earth Centre in 2004 and various options for its reuse are now being considered.

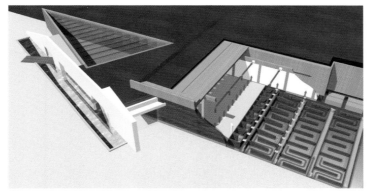

Daytime cooling Incoming air is cooled by passing through the labyrinth, then it is fed through floor grilles.

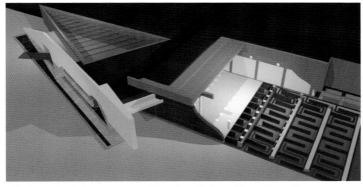

Night-time cooling Cold air enters from outside, cools the labyrinth, and is vented to ouside.

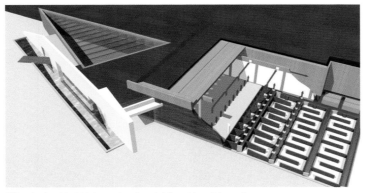

Winter heating Labyrith is bypassed and heat is delivered through heat grilles.

The Earth Centre Labyrinth: Patrick Bellew – Atelier Ten

The galleries at the Earth Centre sit over the largest thermal storage labyrinth in Europe. The labyrinth is a series of concrete and blockwork passageways through which warmed or cooled air is distributed to provide conditioning to the space above. The defining design issues were the desire of the client to have a very low energy building. The poor ground conditions and the presence of an old fault line beneath the site were leading the structural engineer towards a thick raft foundation solution. The predicted high occupancy loads required considerable ventilation to the tall gallery spaces, and there was a need for flexibility in the air delivery method as the exhibition arrangements had not been determined when the design was being developed.

The inspiration came from a number of sources including the Palladian Villa Schio at Costozza in Italy where air is precooled through caves and introduced at floor level – an early example of passive cooling. Also, I have always been a fan of the Barossa termite, a creature that provides close environmental control of its nest using ground coupled night cooling and evaporative cooling controlled by blocking and unblocking air passages with mud.

The use of thermal storage for environmental control has increased in the past two decades. As building envelopes have increased in insulation quality the proportion of energy that is expended on ventilation in winter has increased, with a corresponding focus on heat recovery systems. In the summer the use of diurnal temperature variations as an integral part of systems to reduce or eliminate the reliance on mechanical cooling is also key. The labyrinth thermal storage system is intended to address these two principal issues and to deliver a good quality conditioned environment with excellent air quality at a fraction of the energy consumption of conventional air conditioning systems.

So the labyrinth, located beneath the gallery space, provides a means of decoupling thermal storage from the exhibition volume, allowing surface temperatures that are lower than can be used for room or integrated structural cooling systems to be retained and thereby increasing the efficiency over conventional room storage techniques. The labyrinth system is mechanically driven but it is designed for very low pressure drops so that specific fan power is minimised and indeed can be provided from the photovoltaic system for much of the year. The use of indirect evaporative cooling could have further enhanced the performance of the labyrinth in sustained periods of hot weather; detailed thermal analysis showed that it was not necessary in the climate of Doncaster.

The labyrinth is cooled at night by the operation of fans. Air is delivered into the exhibition spaces until the design conditions are met and then it is diverted by the operation of a number of dampers to be dumped to the outside at roof level. During the day warm outdoor air is passed through the passageways of the labyrinth and it is cooled if required by conductive and convective heat transfer with the walls. Almost as clever as those termites!

Visitor Centre
Painshill Park
Cobham

2001

with Atelier Ten

Visitor centres can detract from the attraction that they seek to promote, and there was always a danger that this building would be an intrusion rather than an insertion into the existing landscape. Here the solution was to break down the bulk of the accommodation into a series of spaces, some underground, some cut through the ground and some elevated above the ground. To ensure easy accessibility the buildings share a common ground-floor level and the landscape is allowed to flow over, though and under them.

The visitor centre building sits on a concrete plinth, which emerges from the sloping ground, giving the sense of a light structure sitting firmly on a solid base. The principal axial route leads from the twenty-first century visitors' car park and entrance bridge through to the eighteenth-century landscape via an external covered 'loggia' cut into the rising ground. On one side of this the

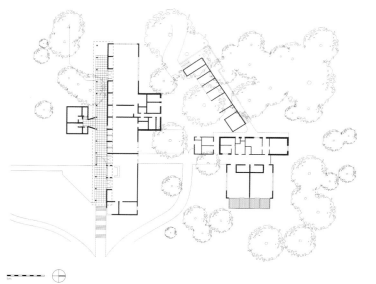

toilets are buried into the ground; on the other the shop, cafe and meeting room sit just above it. In contrast, the education facility reads as a timber structure floating above the river bank, with its cantilevered balcony reaching out towards the river.

The principal buildings are substantially of timber construction, clad in untreated oak (imported from France following the major storm of 1997) while the service areas are in a natural earth-red coloured render. Floors are stone and tile. Large areas of glazing link each of the major public spaces to dedicated outdoor areas: the tearoom has a terrace, the meeting room a courtyard and the classrooms have balconies. All the main spaces share access to the stone-paved walkway running beneath the loggia.

The building is extremely highly insulated – 20 per cent better than the then current building regulations. It uses low-emissivity glass and a high-efficiency underfloor heating system with a condensing boiler. The spaces all benefit from high levels of daylight while being protected from glare. It was originally intended that the primary buildings should be all-timber construction using Masonite beams. Interestingly, value engineering led to a change to a less purist steel roof structure with higher embodied energy.

Like Hamilton's original eighteenth-century landscape creation, the buildings are built to last and designed to create a statement that is both bold and functional, as well as respecting the 'genius of the place'.

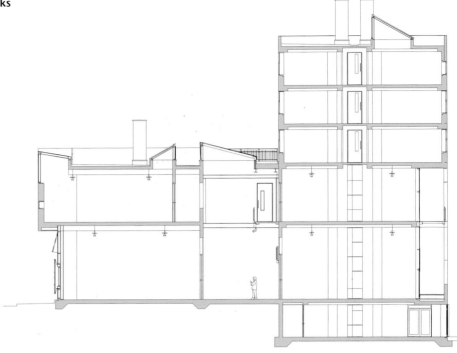

Persistence Works
Sheffield

2001
with Buro Happold

Persistence Works is the UK's first purpose-built studio complex for fine art and craft. It is run by Yorkshire ArtSpace, a charitable organisation that provides studio space to artists at affordable rents.

The building is located on a prominent site at the intersection between the cultural and industrial areas within Sheffield's old cutlery industry quarter. The building is arranged as two parallel elements: a two-storey street frontage facing north and a six-storey element to the rear. The two parallel forms are linked by an internal covered space.

Concrete is used throughout, both as a loadbearing and as a finished building material. The aspiration was to use a robust and 'ordinary' material in a unique way, which seemed fitting for a building where fine arts and crafts were to be produced. The building explores the use of concrete in the basic shutter work, the large cantilevered overhang at the public entrance and the twisted curved wall to the reception area.

The environmental concept is to optimise the performance of the fabric of the building so as to minimise capital and running cost expenditure on mechanical and electrical systems. Rent is charged on a floor-area basis and covers operating costs of the building (including common areas), together with a minimum background heating within studios to prevent condensation. This allows a degree of control on overheads by individual artists while ensuring that the basic needs of the building are met. Services such as water, gas and boost heating (supplied through the Sheffield district heating system) are metered individually to each studio.

Passive features of the architectural concept include a well insulated building envelope with a relatively high proportion of glazing to provide good natural daylight. The building is naturally ventilated with individual ventilation extract chimneys to each studio, which increases flexibility in use.

From a sustainability perspective, concrete has a high embodied energy both through the steel reinforcement

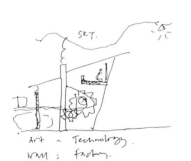

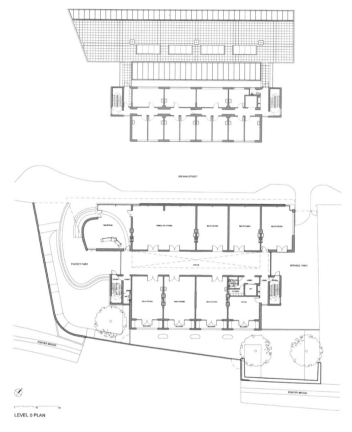

LEVEL 0 PLAN

(although in the UK virtually all steel is produced from recycled sources) and because of the high energy content of the cement. We were however able to replace 60 per cent of the normal Portland cement content with ground granular blast furnace slag (GGBFS), a waste material from the steel industry that can provide a low-cost cement substitute derived from an industrial waste product. This resulted in a lighter concrete finish, which was then coated with a mineral finish surface treatment to reduce its porosity. This provides a weather-resistant finish to the concrete which should prevent long-term staining to the facade.

The thermal mass of the building is exposed throughout, with very few finishes. This keeps the fabric of the building cool in the summer and retains heat in the winter. It also gives the building a raw but healthy appearance, appropriate to its use and reminiscent of the old industrial buildings that once populated the area.

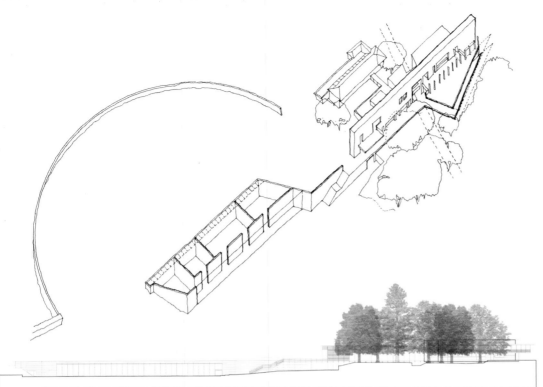

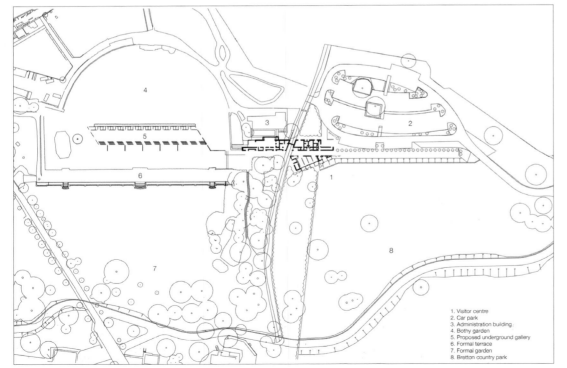

1. Visitor centre
2. Car park
3. Administration building
4. Bothy garden
5. Proposed underground gallery
6. Formal terrace
7. Formal garden
8. Bretton country park

Visitor Centre and Gallery
Yorkshire Sculpture Park

2001-05

with RW Gregory and Ernest Griffiths & Son

The new visitor facilities at the Yorkshire Sculpture Park, located at West Bretton near Wakefield, grew out of a lottery-funded masterplan which was designed to conserve the eighteenth-century landscape and provide a new entrance, car park and visitor centre.

The visitor centre is intimately connected to its site and provides both an entrance and a focus for the visitor. It is organised along a linear route or 'bridge' through the belt of mature trees, crossing a ha-ha that separates the formal gardens from the parkland. The route is itself an extension of the formal terrace, a theatrical piece of landscape that separates what was originally the productive Bothy Garden to the north from the ornamental gardens to the south. The concourse provides gallery space for sculptures and two-dimensional works. It also provides access to the shop, cafe, meeting rooms, education spaces and toilets. Following the precedents of the Louisiana Museum of Modern Art in Denmark and the Burrell Collection in Glasgow, the concourse provides views into the woodland and opportunities for viewing sculpture in nature. The axis of the concourse, parallel with the terrace walkway, extends out into the landscape, where it forms a new entrance terrace overlooking the Henry Moore sculptures in the park.

Underfoot it provides an opportunity for a fundraising 'walk of art' by Gordon Young comprising the names of donors cut into 10mm checker-plate, extending 100 metres into the landscape.

Running parallel with the concourse is a stone spine wall, two metres thick, containing lifts, circulation, service spaces and lobbies, and providing a vertical termination to the building as it emerges from the tree belt east and west. The remainder of the accommodation grows out of the spine and the concourse, mainly to the north, where the spaces that do not require light – toilets, kitchens, lecture room and plant room – are buried into the rising

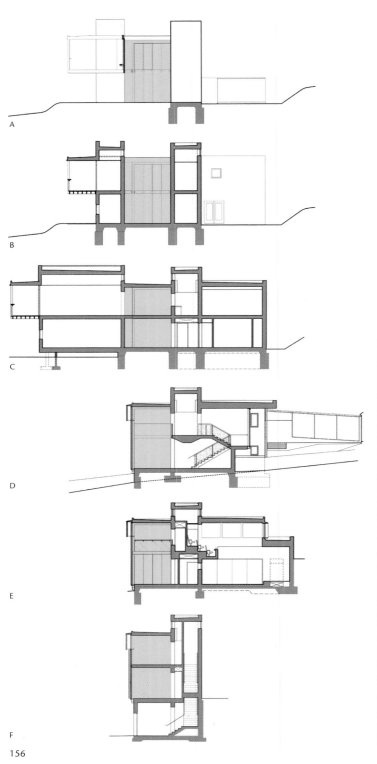

A

B

C

D

E

F

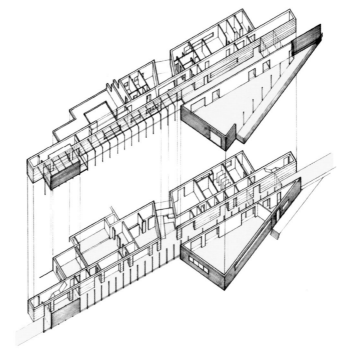

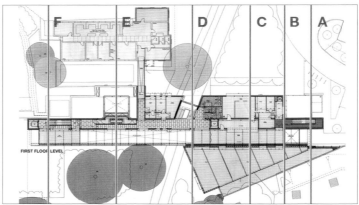

FIRST FLOOR LEVEL

GROUND FLOOR PLAN

LOWER GROUND

F E D C B A

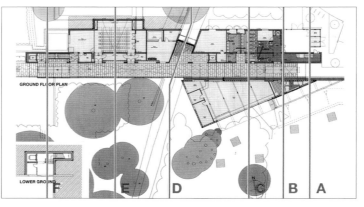

ground. South of the concourse, near the entrance, a timber wedge emerges which contains the shop on the ground floor and the cafe above, from which a continuous balcony, angled out towards the parkland, provides spectacular views down into the valley. As the new concourse crosses the ha-ha, the main staircase realigns to reflect its geometry beneath the building.

The building has a strong environmental brief and energy costs were reduced by working to standards in excess of the current building regulations. Being sheltered by trees and partially buried in the ground also helps reduce heat losses. The six metre high south-facing glazing in the concourse provides a daylit exhibition space. Heat losses are minimised by using the highest performance glazing then available (U-value 1.2W/m²K) which also has a high visible light transmission (65 per cent) and a relatively low solar transmission (35 per cent) in order to minimise summer overheating. Shading is provided by the mature oak trees immediately adjacent to the glazing, as well as fixed aluminium sun shading that forms an 'eyelid' at the top of the glazed wall.

The result is a space which will rarely require artificial lighting during daytime hours and, with 4.5 metre high panes of glass fixed directly to slender T-section columns at two metre centres, provides as far as possible the idea of being within the woodland glade it overlooks. The potential for overheating is also minimised by careful attention to natural ventilation in all the major spaces, as well as the use of heavyweight thermal mass both in the concourse and the main lecture room. The latter also incorporates a hybrid natural/mechanical ventilation system that can be used to achieve night-time cooling via BMS controls.

Environmental considerations also informed the choice of materials. The sandstone for the concourse floor and spine wall comes from the nearby Pennine quarry in Derbyshire and is a good match with Bretton Hall itself. The timber 'wedge' began life as English oak but to achieve a substantial cost saving this was changed to cedar, which has a similar durability and will weather to a silver grey. The black self-coloured render to the service spaces behind the spine wall allows these elements to recede into the woodland backdrop.

The final piece of the YSP jigsaw was the Underground Gallery in the Bothy Garden. The 700 square metre sculpture gallery is partially buried in the historic landscape, earth sheltered on three sides with 300mm of earth on its roof, it consists of three gallery spaces two of which are naturally ventilated and the third air conditioned to provide temperature and humidity control for sensitive exhibits. The galleries can be enclosed and isolated or open and linked to a fully-glazed concourse with south-facing glazing looking onto the lower terrace of the Bothy Garden.

Cross ventilation of the galleries is via BMS-controlled louvres above the concourse glazing and also at high level in the rear wall of the galleries. The four metre square gallery doors are left open during the day, allowing unrestricted air flow across the building, and closed at night for security. The doors are clad in slatted maple and perforated steel to allow air to pass freely through to allow night-time cooling.

The environmental strategy of the building also addresses both the landscape and its historical setting. In its new form the rationalisation of the landscape within the Bothy Garden re-establishes a historic link between the

upper semicircular enclosure and the lower rectilinear space. The division is marked by a new ha-ha, part of the Bretton landscape tradition. The ha-ha will eventually be filled with a triangular hornbeam wedge, providing a dark green vegetation strip against the reflective horizontal glazing of the rooflight. Taking the building into the sloping site of the garden preserves distant views from the Bothy itself, as well as providing enhanced settings for sculpture on the grass roof, and results in the loss of a minimal amount of the existing lawn. As with the visitor centre, it is a case of maximum volume, minimal exposure.

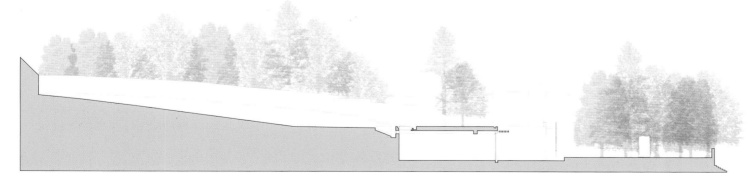

Milestones of Flight
RAF Museum
Hendon

2003
with Buro Happold

The Royal Air Force Museum in Hendon required additional space in order to house its new Milestones of Flight exhibition, a collection of classic aircraft drawn from aviation's 100-year history. The new building is located at the focal point of the site, bridging the gap between the disparate existing museum buildings. It takes the form of a simple barrel-vaulted structure enclosing the maximum possible volume and providing a structurally efficient frame from which to suspend aircraft. Its entrance, the new main reception for the museum, is marked by the 25 metre high Skydance sculpture by Kisa Kawakami.

The barrel vault is clad externally in stainless steel, reflecting the sleek fuselages of modern aircraft, and internally in semi-translucent fabric panels, evoking the fabric construction of early aircraft. The two ends of the building are entirely glazed in cast glass channels which glow at night and provide diffuse light during the day. A low strip of glazing runs along the length of the west elevation providing a new 'shop window' for the museum.

Internally a series of staggered mezzanine boxes and walkways form a building-within-a-building. These provide the museum with a series of smaller scale exhibition and audio visual spaces and give the visitor a number of different vantage points from which to appreciate the display. From ground level the aircraft are seen against the artificial sky of translucent fabric panels, but from the uppermost level the backdrop is provided by an abstracted 'fields of England' pattern in the resin floor.

The museum houses exhibits made from photosensitive material such as paper and wood and, to a lesser degree, paints and metals, so an annual exposure limit of 500klux hours was identified and an intensity limit of 10mW per lumen was set for the ultraviolet content of the daylight falling onto the exhibits. However, given these constraints, and unlike all the other museum buildings which are essentially black box spaces, the new building has a strong emphasis on natural light. A central barrel-vaulted rooflight at the apex of the roof allows daylight and sunlight to fall onto the back of the fabric panels at certain times of day, creating huge scalloped shadows. The fabric also acts as an environmental filter, preventing ultraviolet light from damaging the exhibits. Pollution, temperature and humidity levels are regulated by means of an air-conditioning system. After numerous environmental studies examining the potential use of passive controls this was seen as the only option, given the fragile (and often priceless) nature of the aircraft.

The building structure comprises mild steel arched trusses at six metre centres which sit on top of four metre high cantilevered concrete fins. The barrel vault achieves an internal height of 14 metres and a span of 26 metres. The ends of the vault are clad in cast glass channels spanning 4.5 metres between transoms which in turn are supported off vertical trussed wind posts. The internal mezzanine structures are formed using in-situ concrete clad in plasterboard or glass.

The skin of the barrel vault is made up of several layers. Zed purlins (spanning between arched trusses) support a profiled metal roof comprising two layers of 32mm deep trapezoidal deck with insulation between. This structure provides all of the thermal and waterproofing requirements of the building, while zed bar spacers support a separate stainless steel rainscreen. Open joints between the 1200mm by 3000mm panels allow water to flow into a hidden gutter that runs the length of the building, discharging into a series of gargoyles. There is therefore no need to break up the facade with downpipes and the system helps reduce staining as rainwater only ever travels across one panel.

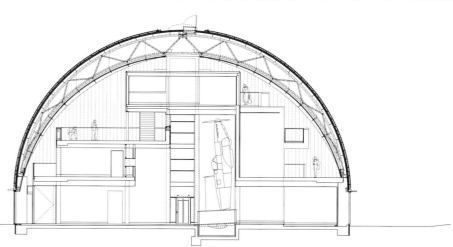

Auditoria

Our definition of auditoria covers all manner of spaces designed for listening, so it includes spaces for theatrical and musical performance as well as lecture theatres and school halls. All these are gathering spaces, where the focus is on the group or community rather than the individual. It is self-evident that the acoustic requirements in the space are paramount, as are the thermal and spatial characteristics of spaces where people may be seated from one to three hours, Nonetheless the shaping of such spaces, particularly those designed for musical or theatrical performance, is also critical, not only to create a successful relationship between performer and audience but to help mould the audience into what Tyrone Guthrie, one of the great directors of the last century, called 'that great single collective personality'.

Many auditoria have to be flexible enough to provide space for theatrical performances 'in the round' as well as forward-facing or lecture format. But acoustic flexibility can be even more difficult to achieve, ranging from the higher reverberation times required for acoustic music to the lower figure required for the human voice or amplified sound.

The key environmental issues in the design of auditoria derive from two main considerations. First, the building environment needs to be able to cope with very significant variations in heat load generated both by the audience and artificial lighting systems. Second, the space often requires acoustic isolation as well as internal acoustic treatment, both of which impact on the ability to use natural cooling and ventilation strategies.

A seated audience occupies between 0.9 and 1.2 square metres per person. With each individual providing around 100 watts per person, there is more than enough energy to heat a well insulated space whatever its volume. With 100 watts per square metre, heat load engineers turn to air conditioning and it is necessary to work hard to avoid it. Add to that the further 20-50 watts per square metre of lighting in a theatre and the problem becomes even more serious. Both the capital and running costs of an air conditioning system can be very dramatic. At the theatre for Bedales school our engineers, Max Fordham & Partners, estimated that during a four hour performance in summer energy consumption for a naturally ventilated building would be 5kW, compared with 190kW for a conventional air-conditioned theatre of the same size.

The challenge of avoiding air conditioning is both helped and hindered by the fact that heat load on the building changes dramatically when the audience enters. Exposed high thermal capacity wall and roof surfaces will help dampen down the environmental 'shock'. At the Wiltshire Music Centre we designed an extremely well insulated and heavyweight enclosure using a concrete structure for the floor, walls and roof. The space was designed primarily for acoustic music, with height and volume providing a long reverberation time and little need for acoustically absorbent surfaces.

The concrete structure of the control room at Real World Studios, which is also designed as a listening environment, required more acoustic absorption. In some areas of the ceiling the acoustic absorption effectively isolates the concrete structure, although the absorbers in the side walls are freestanding (to allow the air to transmit the room's heat to the walls behind) and the back wall consists of a row of glass diffusers, which add to rather than detract from the thermal capacity of the space.

In the new theatre at Bedales, however, we were asked by the school to design an all-timber building, which inevitably resulted in a low thermal capacity. Here we introduced mass into the space by sitting the whole building on a semi-basement of concrete block walls, a labyrinthine structure beneath the central auditorium which provides the air inlet path for the natural ventilation system.

At the seminar room for the New Environmental Office at the BRE, we used borehole water to provide a nominal amount of cooling to a naturally ventilated incoming air stream. Combined with high levels of exposed thermal mass and a natural ventilation system, this can cope with the internal gains. The area of both intake and extract ductwork seems large, but not when compared to the plant space required for a mechanically ventilated solution.

Natural ventilation in auditory environments automatically creates acoustic problems. Removing sound from incoming air – and indeed preventing noise from escaping to disturb the neighbours – requires very careful attenuation. The isolated rural environment of Bedales meant that these problems were discounted at an early stage. There is therefore no acoustic attenuation on either the low-level intake vents or the high-level exhaust. We have had no complaints of any problems, although at one performance the piercing song of the blackbird outside was somewhat distracting. Low exter-

A theatre architect who manipulates audience density, comfort and sight lines will find it easier to design a dynamic space animated by cross currents of energy. In a fan-shaped auditorium where all are comfortably equal, the show on offer is less likely to ignite the conflagration of communication and more likely to seep from the stage like a slowly radiating stain.

Iain Mackintosh
Architect, Actor and Audience
(Routledge 1993)

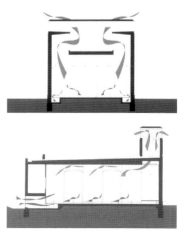

New Environmental Office, BRE

nal ambient noise levels make particular sounds more intrusive.

At the Wiltshire Music Centre it was essential to achieve a relatively high noise reduction level of NR25, which meant that both the low-level and high level openings to the outside air needed careful attenuation. This was achieved by a three metre length of acoustic attenuators, involving a fibreglass lining to each side of a series of airpaths which effectively meant doubling the cross sectional area of the airflow path. Containing this in the area underneath the raked seating was relatively easy but making space for it in the ventilating 'lantern' that surmounts the roof was more complicated. It was air leakage through high-level glazing however that caused most problems in sealing the building acoustically.

Airflow paths need very careful consideration. At Bedales, we started out with a 'guesstimate' based on Max Fordham & Partners' experience that the cross-sectional area of both inlet and outlet air paths should be around five per cent of the building floor area. The critical issue throughout the design development was maintaining this free area despite the addition of grilles, insect screens and structure around all the ventilation air paths. The same principles were used at the Wiltshire Music Centre.

Spaces for theatrical and musical performance tend to rely on artificial lighting, and therefore on blackout during daytime performances. In most auditoria one would not think of introducing daylight, but in multi-functional spaces that are also used for rehearsal and teaching, the psychological impact of daylighting as well as the potential energy savings are highly significant.

The brief given to us by Peter Gabriel for Real World Studios was to create studio spaces that were, as far as possible, daylit. Conventionally, recording studios tend to be rooms within rooms, buried in buildings, usually in cities, and cut off from the natural world. The site for Real World Studios at Box Mill allowed us to create an extension to the mill pond, thus enhancing the natural setting for the key studio space on the site. This was to be not just a control room that would operate in tandem with the studio in the adjacent mill, but also a listening environment in its own right, a space where the creativity of the recording engineers and musicians could come together in a synthesis of acoustic and technically manipulated music. The demand for maximum light and view was at odds with the requirements for very high acoustic isolation

and, to a certain extent, with the requirement to minimise air conditioning loads. The control room is shaped to optimise the listening environment from the control desk and provide musicians with a panoramic view to the north across the mill pond, as well as admitting a strip of diffused sunlight from a central rooflight (complete with internal louvre blinds). The cockpit-shaped 'nose' of the building is therefore substantially glazed but, since it faces north, it is not subject to solar gain.

At the Wiltshire Music Centre the main daylighting concern was to illuminate the orchestral stage during daytime rehearsals and so the design of a rooflight 'monitor' that dealt with both ventilation and daylighting was the subject of a series of modelling simulations. The principles are similar, in that we ended up with an acoustic outer double-glazed unit, a substantial inter pane void lined with absorbent material, and an inner layer of heavyweight glazing. The space also contains blackout blinds.

At Bedales the solution is somewhat simpler. The theatre lighting system and high-level gantries precluded the use of rooflights at the centre of the space, but a 'doughnut' of glazing halfway down the roof provides background daylighting onto the central stage and allows the stage to be used without artificial light for rehearsals. Louvred blinds were initially installed along the inside, but an additional layer of blackout blinds were found to be necessary to provide daylight exclusion for day-time performance.

Most theatre spaces rely on the magic of the black box transformed by light and colour and this often conflicts with use of daylight in the space. But for multipurpose spaces natural light adds humanity as well as the potential to reduce energy costs. The same can be said for lecture theatre spaces, where the tendency towards providing the comfort-cooled conditioned black box environment needs to be resisted in favour of an architecture which is more closely connected to the outside microclimate.

Seminar room ventilation chimney, BRE New Environmental Office

Bedales auditorium

Real World Studios
Bath

1989
with Buro Happold

Industrial buildings clustered around Box Mill provide evidence of a working environment that stretches back to Tudor times, with new buildings added each century. It was the tough industrial nature of these buildings as much as their idyllic setting that convinced Peter Gabriel to convert them into the headquarters of his recording company, Real World. Some questioned the logic of constructing a recording studio so close to the steepest section of the Great Western Railway, where the engines are at their noisiest before they enter Box Tunnel; but with recording studios, noise has to be kept in as well as out and the acoustic isolation standards had to be of the highest quality, irrespective of the ambient noise levels.

The brief was to create a studio that related closely to its environment. Natural light was important, as was the potential to escape to the outside world in mid-session. The client was convinced that lack of daylight and view not only proved uncreative but, when combined with the air conditioning of studio spaces, created an unhealthy working environment. So it was the psychological aspect of environmental concerns that steered the design of this building.

But the brief also called for a radically new type of space. Conventional recording studios consist of a small control room dominated by the control desk, with musicians acoustically isolated in a separate studio space. Peter Gabriel wanted to bring these disparate activities together, so that musician and recording engineer could work together in an environment that allowed alike for recording, listening, sampling, mixing and listening. Because of the equipment and paraphernalia required by a whole group of musicians, this space needed to be very large – and certainly more

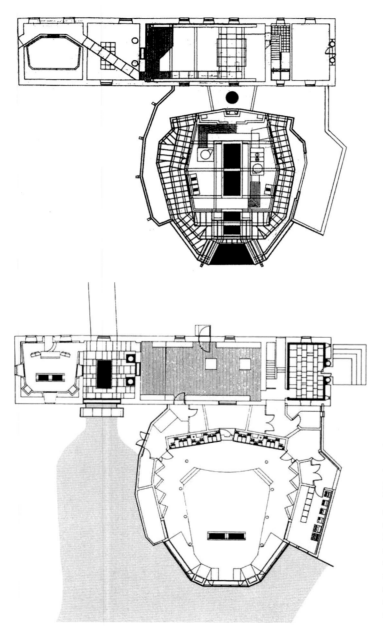

substantial than the spaces in the existing eighteenth- and nineteenth-century mill buildings. So a new space was born, which grew out of the 'back' of the mill and into an enlarged mill pond.

Acoustic isolation required that the whole building be set on a system of rubber turrets. Some 500 tonnes of building are supported on 50mm rubber turrets at 1.2metre centres, effectively isolating any of the base sound vibrations from the adjacent railway. The shape of the building was determined by its acoustic requirements as a listening space, resulting in an organic ovoid form with its glazed nose projecting northwards into the mill pond. The substantial areas of north-facing glazing give an intimate connection to the mill pond and the landscape beyond, while admitting very little sunlight which would add to the air conditioning load, or noise, due to the acoustic specification of the glazing. Additional daylighting comes from a strip of glazing that runs the full length of the studio space but this did require solar protection – blackout blinds preclude glare and provide flexibility in the way the space can be used. The strip of daylighting runs centrally through the roof plantroom with air handling units located to each side, immediately above the space that is conditioned.

The existing buildings were converted to form a variety of studio spaces, each with a particular acoustic. Wherever possible, the original character and materials were retained, generally as a rough and unfinished appearance. New interventions were conspicuously new but again used a language of robust and ordinary materials, often in a raw and unfinished state. There was also a presumption in favour of natural materials. But the environmental concerns also impacted on the language of

the conversion. The client was convinced that air delivered through plastic or metal ducts produced negative ions in the air, and insisted that the air should be delivered through ducts constructed of natural materials. In the main studio spaces clay pipework was used, suspended from stainless steel cables. In the top floor 'wooden room', hollow timber ducts were used to deliver the air. Daylighting was also of paramount importance, whether in the studio spaces or in the main staircase. This was constructed using industrial stair tread units made from a galvanised steel mesh; this meant that the rooflights at the top of the stair brought daylight down three floors below.

Real World is an exercise in creating a new building type, achieved by working closely with acoustic designer Harris Grant and services engineer Buro Happold. Despite being sealed, isolated and air conditioned, the building still has the qualities of natural light and natural materials that were at the forefront of the client's brief.

The Olivier Theatre
Bedales School
Petersfield

1996

with Max Fordham

Bedales is steeped in the arts and crafts tradition. The process of 'making' is an inherent part of the creative curriculum of the school. The 1926 oak-framed library was designed by arts and crafts architects Gimson and Barnsley and two other buildings on the site grew out of local timber-framed barns that were rescued and rehabilitated. For the new theatre the school approached Roderick James of Carpenter Oak & Woodland and we were brought in to co-ordinate the design team.

The challenge that grew out of this tradition was to make the entire building out of timber and to use only indigenous species. Precedents discussed in the early stages included Norwegian stave churches and Japanese temples – structures built entirely in timber, from roofs and walls to floors and window frames. What emerged was an essay in the use of UK timber: framing was oak and Douglas fir, the cladding was Douglas fir and larch. But the timber is enhanced by use of metals such as zinc for the flashings and gutterings. Stainless steel acts as a counterpoint to the massive oak sections, providing cross bracing and triangulation to the pyramidal roof structure and supports for the suspended balconies.

The brief called for a very flexible rehearsal and performance space, with the auditorium most commonly used as a theatre 'in the round' (or, as prescribed by the pyramidal geometry, 'in the square'). Audience seating can vary between 260 and 300.

The building's structure is derived from the barn-like forms of the traditional buildings on the site, but it also provides a sense of unity to the enclosure of audience and stage. More significantly from the point of view of the environmental performance, it provides additional height to enable the stack ventilation and night cooling system to work.

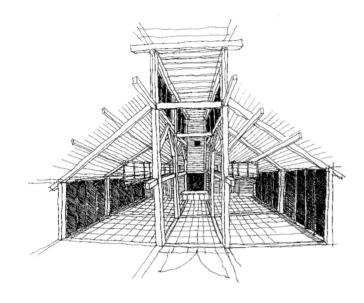

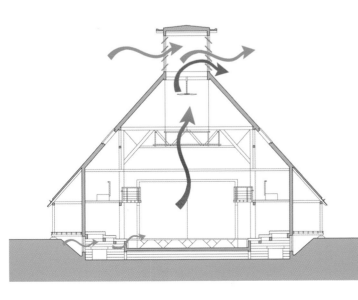

167

The brief called for a naturally ventilated and daylit rehearsal and theatre space. But the theatre is also used for public performance. Fortunately, being away from major noise intrusion, a naturally ventilated system was felt to be appropriate. The building is designed around a very simple naturally driven displacement ventilation system, whereby air enters the building beneath the external balconies into a sub-floor labyrinth of reinforced block walls which support the timber structure above. The driving force for this ventilation air is a combination of both wind and stack effect, with the air being exhausted at high level in the centre of the pyramidal structure 18 metres above the stage.

During the winter, with the vents closed, there is enough fresh air coming through the openings at low level to supply the audience's requirements, with the air pre-heated by fin tube convectors underneath the seats. In summer, however, when overheating from people and lighting can occur, high- and low-level vents are opened at night to charge the basement area with 'coolth'. Closing the vents during the day and opening them only during the performance means that cool air is delivered at the audience's feet and hot air exhausted at the top of the building.

As with the ventilation stacks at the BRE's New Environmental Office, a ceiling fan is mounted at the top of the auditorium to provide some mechanical assistance, should the natural systems not be able to cope. The fan has never been used. The low- and high-level dampers are operated by a building energy management system, which is also provided with information from wind and rain sensors so that the vents can close in inclement weather. The operation of the system has proved successful, although initially some leakage occurred around the vents open to the prevailing wind, and since there was no shortage of high-level ventilation openings, these have been permanently closed.

An oak frame is prone to considerable shrinkage over the first three years of its life. This would have resulted in the 250mm square external post sections shrinking by almost 10 per cent in each dimension. The infill studwork panels between the posts were therefore designed with both slip joints on the flashings and flexibility in the vapour barrier, to accommodate this movement.

Because the principal requirement of the space was for rehearsal purposes, the school was keen to have natural light in the auditorium. This was achieved by a 'doughnut' of glazing which runs all the way round the auditorium beneath the level of the lighting gantry. Fabric insulation values are very high, with a principal layer consisting of 150mm studwork frame and rockwool infill and an internal layer comprising 50mm studwork and insulation on the inside of the vapour barrier (allowing wiring and pipework to be run in this zone without puncturing the vapour seal). The resulting U-value is 0.15. A similar construction is used in the sloping roofs. The floor is uninsulated, and only a lean-mix slab is used beneath the building, thus providing a direct connection to the ground for additional 'coolth' storage.

The building is heated from a boiler plant in an adjacent building and so unfortunately it has not been possible to monitor energy use. Steady state calculations however showed that, for a four hour performance in summer, the energy consumption for the naturally ventilated building would be 5 per cent of what would be required if it was fully air conditioned.

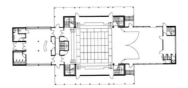

Randall Thomas – Max Fordham LLP

With the advantages of experience gained and time passed since the completion of Bedales (1996) and the BRE Environmental Office (1996), let me set out a brief theoretical and aesthetic framework.

Traditionally, the m&e engineer designed services which were installed in an unsightly fashion in unseen risers and above false ceilings. As services became exposed (in part to facilitate use of the building's thermal mass) in some of the more innovative buildings of the 1980s and 1990s, great care was given to their appearance (this is true of Bedales where, for example, cables to the stage lights were beautifully detailed to suit the oak frame).

But the real accomplishment of Bedales (and the BRE Environmental Building and a number of other projects) is the creation of a building that is an integral part of the environmental control system and, thus, the basis of the thermal, visual, olfactory and acoustic comfort of the occupants.

The essence of the solution is simplicity itself and can be traced back to Taoist philosophy: 'go with the flow'. Or, more scientifically, air is heated by the audience and stage lighting, becomes less dense, and rises. If one allows sufficient fresh air in at low level and if the exhaust air can easily exit at high level, the natural ventilation process can be optimised.

Bedales started with a number of advantages. The natural slope of the countryside site meant that aesthetically it was relatively easy to incorporate at low level the large area required for incoming air (five per cent of the theatre's floor area). Note that the solution with its timber louvres under a walkway is both aesthetic and functional. And the high pyramidal form provides ample height for a low-level comfort zone to be created for the audience. Above this sits a layer of hot air which is constantly being removed through the tower by the forces of buoyancy and wind.

Of course, backing up this artful simplicity is a great deal of science. Quantitative techniques in architecture are of increasing importance. Computational Fluid Dynamics (CFD) was used to study air movement and temperature in the auditorium and to develop the design. For example, entering air in the sub-floor structure was modelled and it was determined that a central divider was required to provide uniform air distribution to the audience. The quantitative analysis carried out also indicated that it was possible to provide comfort with very low energy consumption and without the need for air conditioning, which often involves environmentally unfriendly refrigerants.

Thermal mass was also a key issue in the design. As is readily appreciated, thermal mass at high level has costs, both economic and environmental; a robust structure is needed to support it and this is more expensive and requires more embodied energy. The question was whether sufficient mass would be provided by the sub-floor structure. Modelling indicated that this would be so and that the comfort criteria would be met. The result is a (fairly lightweight) structure sitting on a (heavyweight) base in direct contact with the (very heavyweight) earth.

Wiltshire Music Centre
Bradford-on-Avon

1997

with Halcrow Gilbert Associates

The Wiltshire Music Centre provides a home for young musicians from throughout the county of Avon. At its centre is a 300-seat auditorium for both the rehearsal and performance of acoustic music, with a stage area that can accommodate a full symphony orchestra. This is surrounded by a series of music practice rooms which double as green rooms. A separate linked wing accommodates two music classrooms that are used on a day-to-day basis by St Laurence School, in whose grounds the building lies.

The acoustic and environmental aspects of the main auditorium space, designed with Halcrow Gilbert, provided a real challenge. The building had to achieve a high degree of isolation (NR25), both to stop outside noise coming in and the music generated inside leaking out to the surrounding housing estate. The client was also keen to reduce energy costs.

Acoustic musicians hate fan noise, so an acoustically attenuated natural ventilation strategy was adopted. This involves an air intake underneath the raked seats of the auditorium and an extract at high level, with both air paths incorporating a two metre length of acoustic attenuation. With natural ventilation, the volumes of the air paths need to be much bigger than with mechanical ventilation and so the attenuators are much larger, but on the other hand there is a considerable saving on both ductwork and fans.

Thermal modelling carried out with Flovent showed that the stack effect over the 20 metre high building produced an adequate ventilation rate (six air changes per hour) to deal with the heat build-up from the audience, orchestra and lights during a summertime performance. In addition the heavyweight thermal capacity of the

building (including concrete block walls and a precast concrete tiered floor and faceted roof) meant that the peak summertime heat load was absorbed into the structure and so comfort conditions could be maintained even with relatively high external temperatures. The volume of the hall (four cubic metres for each member of the audience) guaranteed a high reverberation time and added to the overall height and thermal capacity, both of which helped diffuse the summertime cooling problem.

There is also an alternative air intake path through two ducts, built into the diaphragm walls, that form the primary structure of the auditorium. These ducts, eight metres high, provide natural acoustic attenuation and deliver air through a series of registers at the back of the stage. In order to reduce excessive heat loss in winter through the natural ventilation systems, the ducts also provide a return air path which is fan assisted and provides a degree of warm air re-circulation.

There was also a desire that the hall should be naturally daylit, particularly when used for rehearsal purposes, with the daylight concentrating on the stage area. The design of the top of the roof therefore became an exercise in resolving the competition between glazing (to admit daylight) and attenuators and louvres (to provide natural ventilation). The final design gave approximately equal areas to both, with a zone of rooflight and a zone with sound attenuators and electronically controlled dampers. It was calculated that the daylighting would displace 36 per cent of annual electrical lighting costs for the auditorium, and the natural ventilation system would reduce the energy consumption to only five per cent of what it would be with an air conditioned alternative, based on the Energy

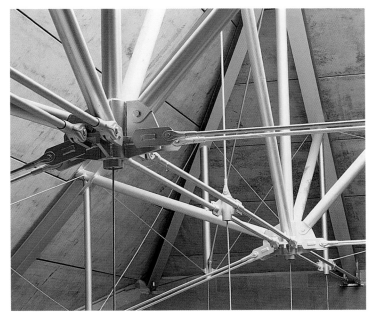

Efficiency Office benchmarks.

Monitoring the energy consumption of the auditorium in isolation has not been possible since it is part of a much larger building with a variety of different hours of occupancy. Looked at in relation to energy consumption benchmarks for schools, however, the building operates very well. The benchmarks for public entertainment buildings are generally much higher because they are normally air-conditioned or at least mechanically ventilated; the music centre has a carbon dioxide emission that amounts to only 20 per cent of the EEO Good Practice guidelines.

One aspect of the learning process on this building involved the importance of air-tightness, particularly with a natural ventilation strategy. We found that the sealing around the extremities of the dampers needed much more care than the subcontractors initially gave, and the dampers themselves were leakier than had been imagined. It is possible to get a reasonably good seal between the blades but seals at each end present more of a challenge. The high-level roof lantern also required re-sealing for air-tightness. Until this was done, the noise from wind whistling through gaps around the glazing was more significant than the fan noise that we had managed to avoid! Acoustic isolation and low-energy design both require extremely careful attention to the constructional detailing to achieve effective airtightness.

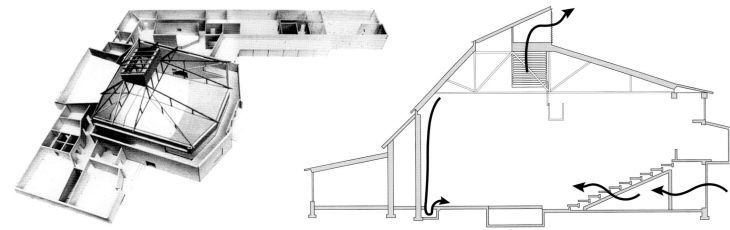

Place-making

Urban design, like architecture, is an exercise in analysis and synthesis enhanced by intuition. But uniting a building with its immediate hinterland, creating a community of buildings, or recreating a part of a city provides greater opportunities for beneficial environmental design and allows us to address the wider aspects of sustainability. Whereas a masterplan often ends up as a conceptual model of physical infrastructure buildings and landscape, it is the design of the life support systems that link them that lies at the heart of holistic environmental design. Flows of heat, light and energy, air and water, material and waste and most importantly the movement of people are all issues that need to be considered, mapped and modelled.

Design at any level requires consideration of the local and the global, addressing the specific and the present as well as the general and the future. Recognising the boundaries of the systems that we are designing for often presents the greatest challenge. With university masterplans for instance it is easy to constrain one's thoughts to the physical boundaries of the site, but the economic and social consequences of the influx of thousands of young people into a community need to be considered, as do the movement patterns that they generate.

Other systems come under stress. The capacity of water supply, energy, infrastructure and drainage systems need to be able to cope with increased load. There is a continual import and export into servicing systems beyond the constraints of the site. But the plans for a new community, like the plans for a building should follow the same systemic principles of environmental design, ie as self sufficient as possible in terms of energy, water, material and waste, using the site and its microclimate, sun, wind and rain, in preference to 'bought in' alternatives; and closing loops around energy and water flows rather than creating a dependency on outside systems.

Any planning exercise begins with an analysis of the existing context, its history and archaeology, its landscape and ecology. These provide raw material within the design process; positive features to develop and enhance, and negative aspects that require remediation. A simple reductive analysis of the constraints on development such as we undertook for the Falmouth College of Arts at Tremough (now the Combined Universities of Cornwall), can lead directly to a design concept. Elsewhere, at Morlands in

Glastonbury for instance, the question of what to retain and how to integrate it is more complex. In other areas such as the Shipton Quarry development, the topography and shape of the land became the starting point for the design.

Landscape and ecology

The tremendous opportunity afforded by masterplanning and urban design is the integration of landscape and buildings. Valued resources in either category can help define future possibilities. An innovative input from landscape designers on large-scale planning projects is essential but the role of the landscape can vary. In some schemes it is vital to protect and enhance historical landscapes such as at the Yorkshire Sculpture Park and Falmouth. But landscape design provides more than historical continuity. Sustainable planting has many possibilities: it can filter out air- and water-borne pollution; provide acoustic and privacy buffers; generate shelter, humidity and shade to modify microclimate; protect and enhance biodiversity; raise temperatures in winter and lower them in summer; help with rainwater attenuation and sewage purification; provide a food or energy resource; and provide a communal or educational resource.

The built environment

Built form, density and patterns of use emerge from an understanding of the brief, the environmental capacity of the site in terms of built form, and economic sustainability. In most of the featured projects we have increased densification, often building higher and deeper in plan than pre-existing developments, concentrating built form where possible to relieve the pressure on green space elsewhere. This often results in a more urban scale which is particularly evident for instance in the proposals for Emerson's Green, where the concept of a science 'park' is turned upside down and results in a built development of three- and four-storey streets and squares to form more of a science 'city'.

Increasing densities obviously leads to higher block ratios (the ratio of internal floor space to site area) and taller, often deeper buildings. The table gives some useful density rules of thumb based on a case study analysis of the London Planning Advisory Committee (2000) exploring the housing potential of larger sites.[1] The key issue here is the reduction in car space provision in high density areas where more environmentally appropriate means of transport are more workable.

Flexibility of form is a key environmental issue. Recognising the limitations of shallow-plan, low-ceiling buildings with loadbearing walls, one begins to realise the value of 3.7-4.2 metre floor-to-floor heights and 12-15 metre deep buildings. Flexibility for workspaces, teaching spaces and dwellings will hopefully reduce the need for replacement and prolong the use of the embodied energy in the structure. New communities of buildings however require a balance between the ordinary and the unique, the urbane background against which the landmark building, a social or communal focus, will emerge. Our urban diet needs to have a preponderance of bread, potatoes or pasta, but adding only a small portion of meat or spicy sauce creates a wholesome meal.

The holistic balance between building forms is as important as the spaces we create between buildings. The balance between three dimensional urban space and form, however, needs to be influenced by the design of the systems of energy and material flow that interact with them. And it is the movement of energy, air, water, waste and above all people that needs to be considered in terms of overall environmental design.

Integrated energy management

The location of buildings with respect to sun and wind can be reduce energy consumption in very simplistic terms. North and south aspects are easier to design for in terms of institutional use: housing that faces east and west can ensure that the maximum number of habitable rooms benefit from sunlight. Naturally ventilated buildings need to be designed to suit prevailing wind directions, but equally the use of existing topography or new earth berms, trees and hedges to deflect or reduce the impact of wind can dramatically reduce heat loss by infiltration. The larger the site the greater the opportunities to create a microclimate to suit the building, and to use the building to provide sheltered outdoor spaces.

Larger sites also provide the opportunity for integrating renewable energy systems such as solar power, wind, and biomass. Larger building volumes and different building types can also produce a more balanced load between the demand for heat and electricity thus making combined heat and power systems more viable.

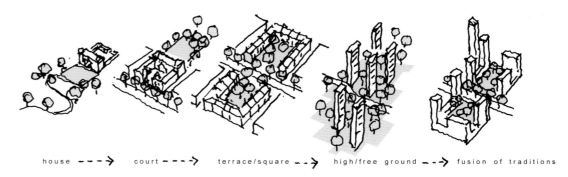

house ----> court ----> terrace/square --> high/free ground --> fusion of traditions

King's Cross housing project

Combined Universities of Cornwall

University of Gloucestershire

A matrix giving guideline density ranges for sites with different levels of accessibility to local facilities and public transport

Definition of site setting			Car Parking Provision		Option 1 High 2-1.5 spaces per unit	Option 2 Moderate 1.5-1 space per unit	Option 3 High Less than 1 space per unit
Central	very dense development, large building footprints and buildings of 4-6 stories and above, e.g. larger town centres and much of Central London.		Predominant housing type		Detached & Linked houses	Terraced houses & flats	Mostly flats
			location	Setting			
Urban	dense development with a mix of different users and buildings of 3-4 stories, e.g. town centres, along main arterial routes, and substantial parts of inner London.		Site within town centre 'pre-shed' 6	Central			240-1100 hr/ha 240-435 u/ha Ave. 2.7 hr/u
				Urban		200-450 hr/ha 55-175 u/ha Ave. 3.1 hr/u	450-700 hr/ha 165-275 u/ha Ave. 2.7 hr/u
Suburban	Lower density development, predominantly residential buildings of 2-3 stories, e.g. some parts of inner London, much of Outer London.		4	Suburban		240-250 hr/ha 35-60 u/ha Ave. 4.2 hr/u	250-350 hr/ha 80-120 u/ha Ave. 3.0 hr/u
Key			Sites along transport corridors & sites close to a town centre 'pre-shed' 3	Urban		200-300 hr/ha 50-110 u/ha Ave. 3.7 hr/u	300-450 hr/ha 100-150 u/ha Ave. 3.0 hr/u
hr =	habitable rooms		2	Suburban	150-200 hr/ha 30-50 u/ha Ave. 4.6 hr/u	200-250 hr/ha 50-80 u/ha Ave. 3.8 hr/u	
u =	unit		Currently remote sites 2	Suburban	150-200 hr/ha 30-65 u/ha Ave. 4.4 hr/u		
ha =	hectare		1				
u/ha =	dwelling units per hectare						
hr/ha =	habitable rooms per hectare						
Ave =	average number of habitable rooms per dwelling						

Integrated transport management

Transportation is responsible for approximately 25 per cent of carbon dioxide emissions in the UK and the percentage is rising (the adjacent table gives the relative energy efficiencies per passenger kilometre in different forms of transport). Average journey lengths are increasing as we become more dependent on car travel. On a typical urban housing site the primary energy usage for transport is approximately equal to that used in buildings or in the provision of food to the inhabitants. In the design of buildings we have responsibility to reduce operational consumption; in the planning of communities we have responsibility to encourage people out of their cars. A classic study of 32 cities by Newman and Kenworthy [2] concluded that if a city was going to reduce its car dependence the five most important factors would be to: increase density of urban development; provide better alternatives – for pedestrians, cyclists as well as public transport systems; restrain car speeds; increase clustering of densities around public transport nodes, schools and shops; and improve public transport systems, in terms of speed, efficiency and cleanliness etc.

This means giving precedence to pedestrians and cyclists, and to shared transportation systems. But it does not necessarily mean spatial segregation. Removing kerbs to combine roads and pavements, and designing for traffic-calmed shared surfaces to enforce 20mph speed limits can ensure that streets remain people friendly and also allow for disabled and service access. The new type of urban development proposed for Emerson's Green is based on this concept. The primary public transport route is designed in accordance with the principle of a maximum five minute walk (about 400 metres) to a bus stop. Dedicated routes and spaces are necessary in some areas however either for bus routes to by-pass rush hour cars, or to create pedestrian-only zones in the heart of an institutional development such as the university environments.

All of the featured projects involve the expertise of a transportation consultation and the production of a green transport plan, essential to determine how the scourge of the car is dealt with, not only in terms of masterplan design but the future site management.

Integrated water management

The conventional approach to water management in planning terms has been to deliver vast quantities of high quality water to our buildings which then disappears down drains, whilst at the same time creating non-porous surfaces in our buildings and landscape which again surcharges the drainage system and rivers downstream. A more environmental approach is to reduce water usage, and either to collect rainwater to offset some of this requirement or to provide porous surfaces to reduce run-off. All of these measures will reduce imports and exports from the site and close the cycle of water usage. Once again it is easier to contemplate cost effective environmental systems with larger site areas and building usage. Integrated water management can also offer up other opportunities. At the headquarters for RARE, the hydrological system was designed around extracting ground water to be used for cooling the building in summer, flushing toilets, and feeding a series of water features, before it all returned to the ground via a sewage treatment with reed beds discharging into a lake. The land take was quite considerable but the landscape area was available to enable this to work. In more urban situations, the collection of rainwater for flushing toilets and irrigation, and the attenuation of run-off by the use of green roofs or porous paving are more likely to provide cost-effective environmental solutions.

Integrated Waste and Resource Management

Despite the increased popularity of recycling and legislation to control waste, the volume of waste we generate is still growing. These issues are in many ways dealt with at the level of local and regional government, but planning for recycling and closing the loop of material used on a site does impact on the design and planning of communities. At a fundamental level it impacts on the materials used in the building and the recyclability of those materials, particularly relatively short life components such as carpets and furnishings. It also impacts on the design of waste management systems in the building, allowing for separation of organic waste and recyclable materials at the point of use, and providing sufficient space for storage of recyclable materials, typically glass, aluminium, paper and cardboard.

The separation of materials for ease of recycling needs to feed into every aspect of manufacturing. As McDonough and Braungart point out in Cradle to Cradle,[3] we need to think about materials either as part of a biological cycle of substances that occur in nature and are biodegradable, or part of a technological cycle of man made resources which need to be preserved for recycling and reuse.

We also need to value human waste as a resource which in some cases can be recycled on site rather than piped for miles using valuable water as an aid to transmission. At the Earth Centre the use of a vacuum sewage system is part of the educational process of recycling human waste through a 'living machine' where biological ecosystems break down human waste and turn it into fertiliser. Such systems need very careful management and may not be appropriate for other large scale developments, but precedents do exist for instance for the use of biogas generators to recycle organic wastes, and carefully controlled incinerators to convert mixed waste into energy.

Air quality and the acoustic environment

The dramatic improvements in air quality in our cities since the 'Great Stink' of London's sewers in 1858, and city smogs fuelled by the burning of coal, have been replaced by the problems of air-borne pollution and noise resulting from the internal combustion engine. Most of the key air contaminants, carbon monoxide, carbon dioxide, nitrous oxide, hydrocarbons and particulates result directly from road traffic. Noise is also obviously a major issue. Whereas planting can help considerably with both forms of pollution, more solid acoustical barriers combined with absorption are required to mitigate excessive traffic noise. The location of building openings in relation to both traffic pollution and noise needs careful consideration, particularly in respect of naturally ventilated buildings.

The social component of sustainability

Urban design allows us to create the public realm – the shared communal space between buildings which is representative of our society and social ideals. If one of the principles of sustainability is social equity, then those spaces need to be humane and accommodating spaces which allow for individual expression and communal values. Many of the featured projects have involved extensive stakeholder consultation – public exhibitions, workshops and consultations. At its worst public consultation can result in lowest common denominator solutions, designing for a rose tinted view of the past rather than a more dynamic and creative future. At best it can provide genuine shared ownership of a scheme – and a desire to make

the vision work long after the design team has departed.

Urban structures can last a thousand years whereas buildings might barely last a hundred, often outlived by well positioned and well loved trees. Services in buildings tend to be replaced every 25 years, but the location of underground service infrastructure can be as constraining as legal boundaries when it comes to creating the physical environment. The invisible and intangible is often as important as the physical. But the most important aspect of a design process is vision and clarity – a clear concept of the scale and nature of spaces that provide for the wealth of human activity, interaction, celebration and delight. Too often over the last half century city spaces have been designed for vehicles rather than people, and reversing that trend pronounces with our greatest challenge.

Rare headquarters

Chart from Towards an Urban Renaissance (DETR 1999)

Creating a walkable neighbourhood: all "local hubs" should be within easy walking and cycling distance (12)

Possible facility – Catchment population		
4–10km radicals	City facilities	Stadium — City
		Cathedral — City
		City hall — City
		Theatre — City
2–6m	District or town	Sports centre — 25,000–40,000
		District centre — 25,000–40,000
		Library — 12,000–30,000
		Health centre — 9,000–12,000
400–600m	Neighbourhood	Community offices — 7,500
		Community centre — 7,000–15,000
		Pub — 5,000–7,000
		Post office — 5,000–10,000
150–250m	Local hubs	Primary school — 2,500–4,000
		Doctor — 2,500–3,000
		Corner shop — 2,000–5,000

This chart is indicative and is based upon city-scale urban areas. Catchments will vary in specific areas.

Notes
1 London Planning Advisory Committee, Sustainable Residential Quality: exploring the housing potential of large sites (2000).
2 P Newman and JR Kenworthy, Sustainability and Cities: overcoming automobile dependence (1999).
3 W McDonough and M Braungart, Cradle to Cradle: remaking the way we make things (2002).

Andrew Grant – Grant Associates
People and Nature

It is through landscape that our relationship with nature is most clearly expressed. In the landscape we directly experience life, seasons, weather and the abundance of other species that share the earth. Landscapes also have the capacity to endure way beyond the life of a building and provide a physical and spiritual link to the continuum of history.

Consequently, sustainability in landscape design is not a simple scientific issue but must also involve an understanding of natural life-forms and the rhythms, scale and poetry of habitats and places. It must bind the 'art' of landscape with the 'ecology' of landscape. It must also engage people and communities. To be sustainable, people must cherish and nurture these landscapes and work with them as they evolve over time. At the same time, they must work as balanced ecosystems that can sustain wildlife and demonstrate a balanced use of natural resources. Designing for sustainable landscape must also involve consideration of the following:

Heart and identity
A sustainable landscape is a living, breathing and breeding environment. It has a heart and an identity that is rooted in the ecology and community of its place. It is special and memorable. The identity is drawn from a thorough understanding of the site. The smallest details can bring the big picture to life and define the 'genius' of the place.

Productivity and play
Sustainable landscapes are hard working, highly efficient and beautiful. Economies can derive from combining productive landscapes such as food, timber and water management with those of play, recreation and sensory delight. The design process must also explore the human response to a site and the spaces within it. How do we experience and respond to a site? How do we move through it, use it, see it, smell it, sense it?

Connection and integration
A sustainable landscape connects its various parts to become an integrated whole. It is essential to understand how these often invisible and complex patterns (including water flows, energy, people movements and wildlife systems) link together to form a site ecosystem. Providing a space for nature and designing for biodiversity is fundamental to this inclusive approach. This is about the creation of communities and the connections between human management and nature's systems.

Teamwork and innovation
Working sustainably means seeing the big picture and linking the minutiae of detail to big ideas, visions and strategies. This will involve working closely with clients, architects, thinkers, engineers, scientists, artists and the public so as to generate new ideas for each project and to discover the integrated 'big picture'. From this stems innovative conceptual and technical solutions that make each project special and sustain its heart and identity.

Masterplanning projects offer important opportunities for landscape and environmental integration in both urban and rural areas. The objective is to achieve a fully integrated three-dimensional landscape and site ecosystem that is tuned to the specific environmental and cultural issues relevant to each site. At Shipton Quarry, inspiration developed from the extraordinary geological and ecological setting of the site. At Falmouth College of Art, the masterplan was built around a sensitive understanding of the historic importance of site features, the opportunities of working with the granite geology, the potential for significant habitat enhancement for wildlife and the need for a fully integrated water management system for the site. These themes followed through into the detailed design of the new access road, car park and the digital media centre. At Emerson's Green in Bristol similar factors influenced the planning of the site. The design sought to take optimum advantage of level changes and local views by creating a new site infrastructure that established positive links with the surrounding areas in terms of pedestrian, cycle and vehicle movement as well as wildlife corridors, drainage patterns and views.

Using this integrated approach to masterplanning the proposals are informed by and inspired by the environmental parameters of the site. This mix of creativity and scientific rigour is the key to more sustainable design.

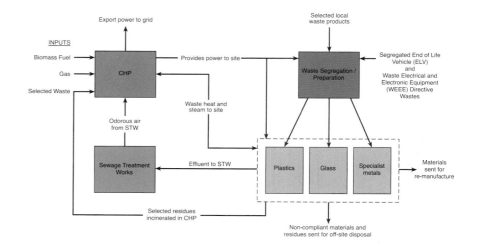

Morlands Glastonbury

2002-

with RPS Chapman Warren

Our work on the proposed redevelopment of the Morlands site between Street and Glastonbury illustrates how achieving economic sustainability in any new development can present a major challenge to the design process. We were appointed to provide urban planning and architectural advice for the masterplanning of this 16 hectare contaminated industrial site, formerly a municipal waste tip, tannery and sheepskin factory and located adjacent to a large sewage works. The site has an extraordinary history and includes a number of listed buildings.

Working with the South West of England Regional Development Agency, and following an extensive local consultation, the principles for sustainable development came very much to the fore. Initial ambitions to create a mixed development were thwarted by the practical and economic difficulties of reducing the environmental impact of the sewage works. Detailed negotiations then led to a strategy to explore the potential of industrial development, particularly integrated industrial

processes involving combined heat and power together with industries that require heat, water and waste disposal facilities.

A CHP facility could use either local authority horticultural waste, straw or biomass crops, and potentially it could also benefit by using polluted exhaust air from the sewage sludge drier as combustion air, thus reducing odour as well as producing heat and power for on-site industries. An industrial ecosystem could thus be developed on site for process industries such as laundry, catering and food processing, taking advantage of cheap heat and power, a plentiful supply of grey water from the sewage works and the ability to dispose of waste back into the sewage treatment plant. With the decline of conventional agriculture on the Somerset Levels, the planting of biomass crops such as willow could also help recreate the link between the town and its hinterland.

In addition to the concept of a sustainable industrial park, the design study also explored the opportunities for green tourism. Despite the industrial decay and the presence of the sewage works, the history of the site could offer educational potential for various aspects of sustainability. The idea of incorporating a small eco-museum on part of the site was developed; this would present the history and archaeology of the area, the long history of the tanning workshops themselves, and the vision of a more sustainable future. The facility could be linked to a display of the new green industries on the site, presenting and explaining the concept of combined heat and power. The agricultural history of the Somerset Levels could also be recreated by redeveloping part of the site as a wetland resource, sealing over the deposits of sewage sludge with a layer of clay to create a lake

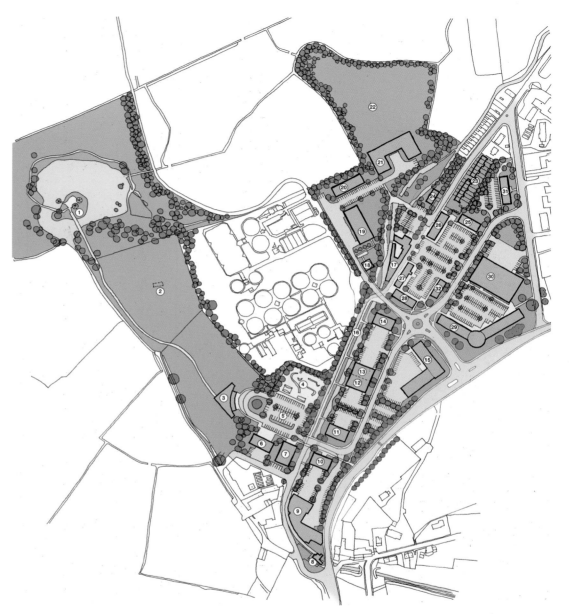

which could then be used to recreate the wetland environment.

The location – midway between the communities of Glastonbury and Street – also offered an ideal site for a new combined fire, police and ambulance service station, providing a landmark communal building as part of the urban regeneration of the site. Some of the existing tannery buildings were

well suited to conversion to small scale industrial and commercial workspaces – incubator units and serviced offices which could provide low-cost workspace for the two communities.

The proposals arose from a detailed consultation exercise and a series of workshops which instigated lateral thinking into the issue of how a difficult site could be given a new series of

sustainable uses. The final vision is a long way away from the initial somewhat idealistic vision of a mixed community of houses, workshops and communal facilities, but it does provide an economically realistic base for future development, and addresses some of the wider needs of society such as the requirement for locations for the renewable energy and recycling industries.

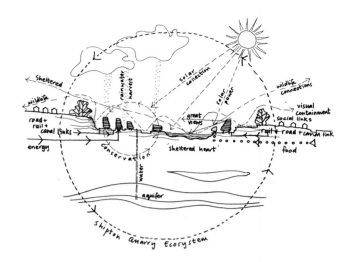

Shipton Quarry Ecosystem

Shipton-on-Cherwell Oxfordshire

2005-
with Arup

The masterplan of this substantial mixed-use development aims to transform an unsightly disused quarry, occupying 66 hectares in north Oxfordshire, into a new settlement as a genuine exemplar of a sustainable community. The site offers a real opportunity to create a unique place to live and work, and would form part of the government's 20 year plan to build sustainable communities in the UK, including 300,000 new homes in the south of England.

Shipton-on-Cherwell quarry is a distinct landform with a kidney-shaped bowl whose boundaries are formed by steep rock faces and scree slopes. The quarry is a redundant brownfield site currently housing an old cement works. The site is physically discreet; despite its scale, it is all but invisible when viewed from beyond its perimeter.

A significant factor is the extent to which the development benefits from the existing infrastructure of road and rail connections. The proximity of the River Cherwell and Oxford Canal and the related network of footpaths and cycleways offers the opportunity for the creation of enhanced recreational facilities both within and beyond the site. The presence of water is a major asset, both as a feature of the scheme and as an integral part of its resource management and recycling strategy. The masterplan seeks to utilise the existing waterbodies on site, connecting them with the river and the canal with a dramatic slice through the embankment.

The community will provide 3,000 new homes in three identifiable zones: canalside village, lakeside terraces and town centre, at a density of about 60 dwellings per hectare, split equally between houses and apartments. A hierarchy of streets and terraces steps up the bowl, tiered into the landscape beyond.

The scheme includes a new mainline

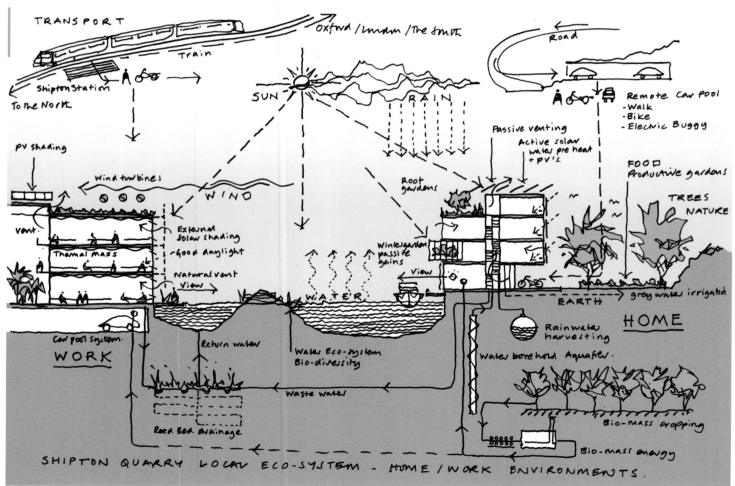

SHIPTON QUARRY LOCAL ECO-SYSTEM - HOME/WORK ENVIRONMENTS.

station, a research development park, shops, school, church and community facilities. A 45,000 square metre office precinct would provide employment for up to 1,500 people. A new heart to the quarry is built around the water and the distinctive site contours. Paths, public squares, open spaces and communal private gardens provide opportunities for circulation and a sense of ownership. There are three key public open spaces: the new urban square, which forms an arrival from the station; the village green on the opposite bank; and to the north, parkland with undulating topography covered in grassland and trees, providing a buffer zone between the site and the countryside beyond.

The scheme offers a significant opportunity to develop energy efficient forms of building technology, recycling, waste and resource management. The landscape and natural features provide many starting points: solar collection, rainwater harvesting, water supply from natural aquifers and active renewable energy, with the ultimate aim of zero demand and zero carbon dioxide emissions.

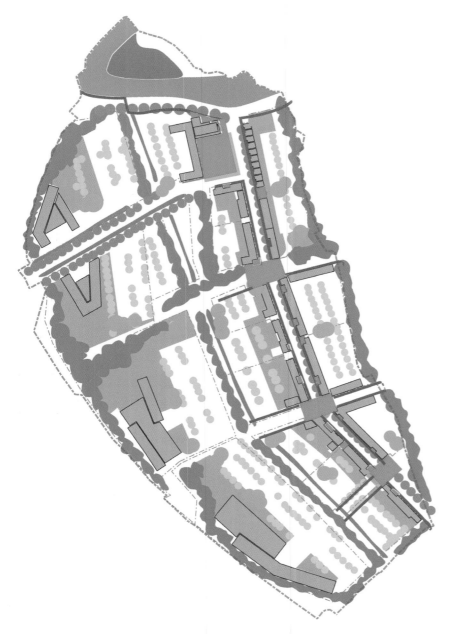

Emerson's Green
Bristol

2003-

with Grant Associates

The South West of England Regional Development Agency appointed FCBa to undertake a masterplanning exercise looking at a major development north of Bristol of around 50 hectares with a 23 hectare science park in the first phase. This scheme will be developed on a similar timescale to, and be integrated with, an adjoining residential development. The appointment included the design of a new innovation centre.

Emerson's Green is planned to be a centre for knowledge exchange, a concept devised in North Carolina and subsequently trialled by Cambridge, Warwick and York universities. It will act as a focus for science and technology industries in the south west and

beyond, a region which already supports several key companies within the aerospace, defence, biotechnology and digital technology sectors. The centre will have close links with the universities of Bristol, Bath and the West of England, and it is intended that the innovation centre will capture local scientific research and expertise and act as a channel between the business and academic worlds. The South West RDA is making an initial investment of £30 million to develop the scheme, which is expected to create up to 6,000 skilled jobs over the next decade.

The concept, developed with Grant Associates, was to create a more urban framework for the development with

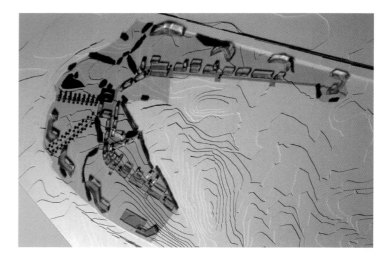

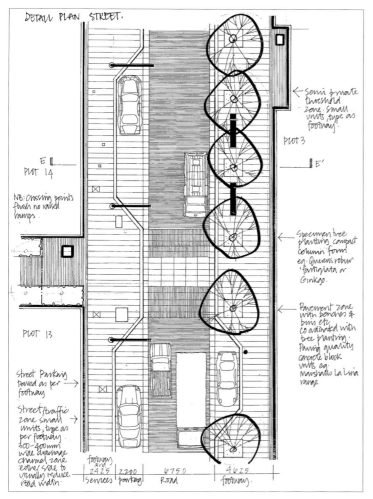

DETAIL PLAN STREET.

PLOT 14

E

PLOT 13

← Semi private threshold zone. Small units, type as footway.

PLOT 3

E'

NB: Crossing points flush no raised bumps.

← Specimen tree planting compact column form eg. Quercus robur 'fastigiata' or Ginkgo.

← Pavement zone with benches & bins etc. co ordinated with tree planting. Paving quality concrete block units eg. Marshalls La Lina range

Street Parking paved as per footway →

Street/traffic zone small units, type as per footway. 300-400mm wide drainage channel zone either side to visually reduce road width. →

footway and Services 2425 | parking 2200 | Road 6750 | footway 4625

the primary route based on linked streets and squares rather than boulevards and roundabouts. Three- and four-storey buildings would reduce the frontage of this street providing science-related workspace buildings – a science city rather than a science park.

The key to the concept is to provide a shared road surface that can contain primary bus routes and reduce speed limits to 20mph, with provision for cycles, slow moving cars and pedestrians. While the principal circulation route with its streets, squares and urban buildings provides the core of the workspace development, the masterplan also provides for taller landmark buildings outside this perimeter, facing the ring road and motorway. Taller buildings, particularly to the north, would provide some buffer to motorway traffic noise and provide a counterpoint to the dense three- and four-storey buildings fronting the primary street. Between the perimeter buildings and the street is a series of green spaces, recreation areas and car parks, the latter often cut into sloping ground or decked to reduce land take, providing a green route parallel to the inner route encircling the site.

What emerges is a high density form of urban workspace development – 4,500 square metres of workspace per hectare – almost double that of conventional science parks. The flexibility of use, densification, a transport strategy that gives precedence to non-car travel,

and an urban structure that provides communal identity are all indicators of a new form of sustainable urban development that can take place in greenfield sites such as this.

The plan of the principle road is influenced both by the shape of the site and topography, but it also gives links to secondary east-west routes. A study of potential renewable energy strategies suggested that the most promising were solar, ground source

heating and cooling, and combined heat and power which would enable loads to be balanced between residential and workspace development. It remains to be seen whether commercial interests will allow consideration of the latter but, as part of the master-planning study an academic innovation centre was designed as a centrepiece and entrance building, using both photovoltaics and ground source pump technology, to set a precedent.

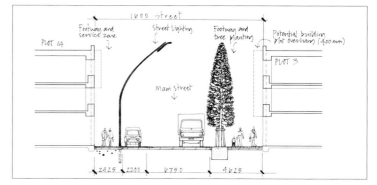

Exchange Greengate
Salford

2004-
with Whitbybird

We were commissioned to undertake the masterplanning of 13 hectares of Salford, close to the city centre of Manchester. Historically this key inner city site forms the gateway between the two cities and has always been a place of markets and exchanges. It is dominated by two prominent physical features: the river, which curves around the Manchester city boundary, and a magnificent railway viaduct, a prime example of heroic Victorian engineering. The site offers extraordinary potential and could provide a city sector of European significance.

The new plan is for a major high density mixed use development providing up to four million square feet of mixed use floor space, with potential for a significant public building, major retail and commercial provision, leisure facilities, workplace and residential accommodation. The client is a joint partnership of Salford City Council, Network Rail and property developer ASK, all of whom own significant parts of the site. The brief was to produce a development plan, with FCBa leading a team with Aitkin Leclerq (urbanists), Grant Associates (landscape architects), Whitbybird (engineers and transportation) and Davis Langdon.

The proposal comprises the New Exchange, a model zero-energy sustain-

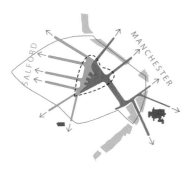

able community: 1,700 new homes, 13,000 square metres of public open space, a new 6,000 square metre water space, and a new bridge linking the two cities – all in all comprising a new community of 12,000 people.

The sustainability strategy focuses on the reduction of carbon emissions for the site as a whole. The ultimate goal is of a carbon neutral urban development. Options for realising this include:
• Building fabric performance will surpass anticipated Building Regulations requirements. BREEAM and Ecohomes assessments will be carried out for all developments, with the attainment of 'very good' rating as a minimum standard. Proposals for both commercial and residential developments will also be subject to wind, sun/daylight and solar access studies during design development. Air-conditioning in residential buildings will not be permitted, in favour of passive ventilation design strategies.
• A combined heat and power (CHP) plant could generate a substantial proportion of electricity requirements for the site locally and thus avoid the inherent inefficiencies of the electricity grid. Surplus heat from the plant will be distributed around the site in mains provided as part of the new site infrastructure. The use of such a centralised plan will allow for easier, site-wide upgrades to ensure compliance with future energy consumption directives.
• The creation of water features and the integration of the Irwell Riverside walk ensures that water is a dominant theme of the redevelopment. The river offers the opportunity as a low-energy source of cooling and the provision of a site-wide cooling mains will be considered. Sustainable urban drainage systems will be installed. Grey water recycling will be encouraged as well as the harvesting of rainwater, in particular from large

footprint roof spaces and urban block raised courtyards.
• Photovoltaic cells are to be installed on the high level roof and they will be considered for all major roofscapes and where appropriate vertical building/ infrastructure facade elements.

• Vertical axis wind turbines may be considered for mounting on higher level roof areas. Orientation will be carefully considered to ensure actual benefits are achieved rather than superficial performance.
• A sustainable approach is encouraged

in relation to both demolition of existing fabric and the sourcing of new-build materials. Demolition and excavation materials will be retained on site, and incorporated into new build/landscape elements. Heavy new-build materials will be sourced locally to reduce the embodied energy cost of remote production and long distance transportation.
• The development benefits from good public transport connections so the site has the opportunity to excel as a sustainable urban quarter. Improvements to Victoria Station and the reconfigured bus provision to the site will be promoted over private car use. Cyclists will be well catered for with the provision of secure and covered storage spaces. Connections by rail and MetroLink to out-of-town park-and-ride facilities should also be actively encouraged.
• The prospect for the Exchange, Greengate being a highly regarded 'Food Quarter' will be combined with an emphasis on local produce. The success of farmers' markets throughout the UK could be capitalised upon to create a place renowned for its sustainable attitude to quality produce.

Houndwood Housing
Street
Somerset

2004-
with ESD

The prosperity of Street has been inextricably linked with the manufacture of Clarks shoes for more than a century. By the end of the twentieth century, the pressures of operating a global business made relocating manufacture to the Far East an inevitability, but the company decided to consolidate its position in the town by building a large distribution centre on a site next to its existing factory. This released the large factory site for the development of a new urban quarter immediately adjacent to the town centre that also linked to the landscape of the Somerset levels. FCBa was appointed, with landscape architects Grant Associates and energy consultant ESD, to develop a sustainable masterplan for the site.

The approach builds on the experience of the Accordia project in Cambridge to create a series of significant shared public spaces that have different characters, with landscaped 'mews' spaces providing intermediate semi-private space and private space provided by courtyards. The concept is that courtyard houses which exploit their relatively small plots as a 'terrace of gardens' have considerable advantages, in terms of privacy and the relationship between internal and corresponding external spaces, over the standard model of a mat of narrow frontage terraced houses with gardens that are significantly overlooked.

Grant Associates' landscape strategy took as its starting point the topography of simple landscape features associated with the Levels while building on the existing structure of mature trees and exploiting the existing culverted water course as a reed bed spine to a sustainable urban drainage system running through the site. Further layers of new planting, green roads, shared surfaces and open space are added to

exploit the irregular edge conditions of the site and to create a rich mosaic of private and public landscapes in counterpoint to the efficient orthogonal planning of the built form.

ESD investigated a range of strategies for reducing carbon dioxide emissions based on first reducing energy demand, then considering options for community heating or combined heat and power systems, and then using renewable energy to supply any residual demand. Dwelling carbon dioxide emissions were modelled, broken down by end use, against three scenarios: B1 (a 2005 Building Regulations house), B2 (Best Practice based on a Carbon 60 Strategy – ie 60 per cent reduction in emissions) and B4 (an Innovative Standard of energy efficiency incorporating mechanical ventilation with heat recovery). It was evident that, as heat losses are reduced by adopting higher standards, electrical usage tends to dominate carbon dioxide emissions, and this then led to the investigation of cost effective systems for the supply of electricity on site.

The study concluded with an analysis of three options. The first, based on the 'best practice' standard plus a gas-fired CHP system, met the initial brief of a target carbon dioxide emission of 2,450 Kg/dwelling/year. This option had 25 per cent lower emissions than the Building Regulations base case but could also be adapted to enable biomass to replace gas in the future.

The second solution was based on the Innovative Standard with a biomass CHP sized to deliver all hot water plus 60 per cent of the space heating. Natural gas back-up provided residual heat requirements. This option had emissions about half of the Carbon 60 climate change target for 2050 ie 1,300 Kg of carbon dioxide/dwelling/per year.

Full carbon neutrality (ie zero net carbon dioxide emissions) could be provided by the above strategy by adding a 300kW wind turbine within two kilometres of the site to meet the residual electricity demand. Given the proximity to the Somerset Levels and the availability of wind energy close by, this strategy was felt to deserve further consideration.

Below Carbon dioxide emissions for heating and hot water, calculated by SAP.

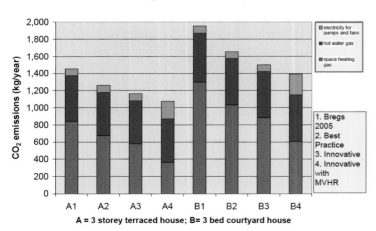

Below Comparison of three sustainable energy options with benchmarks.

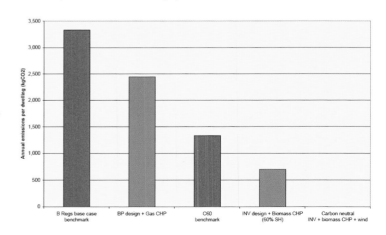

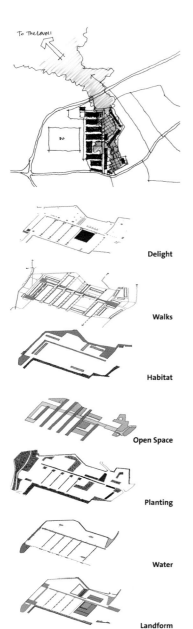

Delight

Walks

Habitat

Open Space

Planting

Water

Landform

Ben Hamilton-Baillie – Hamilton-Baillie Associates
Reconciling Place, People and Traffic

Conventional approaches to urban traffic engineering have been based on establishing clear segregation between vehicles and people. This approach was central to Colin Buchanan's report 'Traffic in Towns' of 1963, which advocated the use of clear hierarchies for traffic movement and the idea of traffic-free pedestrian precincts. Over the intervening years this has led to our all too familiar urban landscape of kerbs, road markings, traffic signs, pedestrian crossings, barriers and signals – an urban environment where vehicles clearly dominate and pedestrian movement and social activity remain subservient.

In recent years a radically different approach has started to emerge across Europe, based on integrating urban design and landscape principles into traffic engineering and highway management to accommodate vehicles, cyclists and pedestrians more equitably.

The approach has its roots in the Woonerf or Home Zone design principles developed in Holland, which established the concept of 'shared space' for traffic and social activities in residential streets (see 'Improving Road Safety through Urban Design', Ben Hamilton-Baillie and Phil Jones, 2005). It has since been extended to apply similar counter-intuitive design principles to city centres, town squares, main streets, rural roads, and the focal points of communities. The ideas are partially covered by the draft 'Manual for Streets'. However to date there are still few examples in place in the UK.

The key principles underpinning the approach are:
• Clear gateways to emphasize the transition between the highway and the public realm.
• Avoidance of standardized highway engineering elements.
• Low speed (under 30kph) regime based on contextual road design, blurred boundaries and an emphasis on 'place' over 'roadway'.
• The use of ambiguity, variety and intrigue to influence vehicle movements, with a strong emphasis on the use of eye contact and social interaction.
• The use of a palette of surface treatments and street furniture to inform movement and define spaces, and to create places from points of traffic intersection.
• Multi-use road design with integral parking and landscaping.
• Punctuation of roads with squares and spaces related to surrounding buildings.

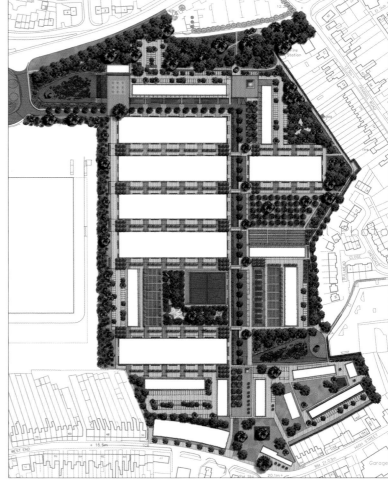

187

This part of the book is about the pragmatics of environmental design. It is based on a number of papers which summarise FCBa 'received wisdom' learnt over the last 25 years. Each section is intended to provide a basic introduction to key principles, as well as a gateway to more detailed information.

The first part presents key environmental facts and figures, particularly in relation to carbon dioxide emissions from buildings and global warming. It also looks at benchmarks, from the scale of a building through to local and global. Most of the information in this section is relevant specifically to the UK climate, building typology and regulations but FCBa is developing the principles and methodology to suit the different climates in which the practice is beginning to work.

The principles of low-energy design are subdivided into the key areas of heat, power, light and air, addressing the principles of environmental control that help reduce carbon dioxide emissions. Also, there are sections on materials, water and waste systems and plants.

Elements of the primer are available on www.feildenclegg.com, and these will be constantly updated, so that by the time you read this the 'virtual' document will have changed. FCBa has tried to be rigorous about the accuracy of sourcing information but would welcome any corrections and clarifications through the website message board. It is only by easy access to relevant information, pooling our resources and sharing our experiences that we will have any chance of reversing the potentially disastrous environmental problems that have been generated over recent decades.

Primer

Carbon dioxide:
facts and figures

Peter Clegg

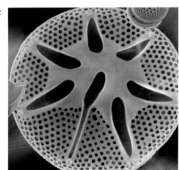

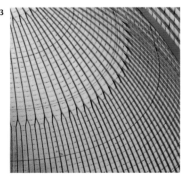

1,2,3 Greenhouses at different scales: the Earth, an algal diatom and Bicton conservatory.
4 Increase in atmospheric carbon dioxide concentration (source: Bruges 2000)

Greenhouses come in different sizes. Our planet exists within one made of gases (primarily carbon dioxide, water and methane), which are transparent to solar radiation but absorb the longer wavelength infra-red radiation from the earth's surface. Without the greenhouse gases the earth would be 33 degrees Celsius cooler than its present average temperature of 14 degrees, and we would not be here. But increasing concentrations of greenhouse gases are making the earth get warmer.

Greenhouses also exist at the micro scale of algal diatoms (2000 would fit on a pin head). These form transparent silicone shells which help fix atmospheric carbon dioxide from the surface of the ocean and eventually deposit it as calcium carbonate on the ocean floor.

A third sort of greenhouse is the man-made greenhouse found in gardens. Glass, like greenhouse gases, is transparent to solar radiation but opaque to infra-red. Its magical transparency allows us to create shelter, absorb solar energy and produce naturally heated protected microclimates.

The earth greenhouse is changing rapidly. Concentrations of carbon dioxide (4) have increased dramatically in recent centuries – particularly since we started taking the fixed carbon buried in the earth's crust and re-releasing it to the atmosphere by burning first wood, then coal, and then oil and gas. Global temperature closely follows carbon dioxide concentrations, which are now considerably greater than at any time in the past 400,000 years.

At the 1997 Kyoto summit, 100 countries, mainly from the northern hemisphere, agreed to reduce their greenhouse gas emissions to 5.2 per cent below 1990 levels within 15 years. The UK government has gone further and committed to a 10 per

cent reduction by 2010 and aspires to a 60 per cent reduction by 2050. The US senate voted unanimously not to ratify the Kyoto treaty. The problem is one of ecological equity. Figure 5 shows how carbon dioxide emissions have grown throughout the world since the beginning of the industrial revolution. The graph shows the enormity of the problem. The hypothetical line drawn for 2030 shows what needs to happen if carbon emissions increase proportionally with population, while the lower line suggests what needs to happen by 2080 if carbon emissions are to contract to a sustainable level (about 20 per cent of current levels).

Figure 7 shows current rates of carbon dioxide emissions per capita around the world. On average, everyone in the world is responsible for 4200kg of carbon dioxide emissions per year but an average American emits nearly 20,000kg, an Indian emits 800kg and a UK citizen 9600kg.

So how do we in the UK produce all this carbon dioxide? Figure 8 shows the total UK delivered energy consumption and related carbon dioxide emissions for the year 2000. 28 per cent is generated by housing and 19 per cent by the commercial and industrial sectors.

Figure 11 shows the commercial and industrial sector average energy consumption per square metre of floor area, broken down by end use and sector. This shows data from all existing buildings and, since older buildings are a lot less well insulated than modern ones, heating energy predominates.

Figure 12 shows the dramatic increase in the proportion of delivered energy that is provided by electricity, as we move towards heating our buildings by increasing our usage of lighting and appliances and increasing mechanical ventilation and air conditioning.

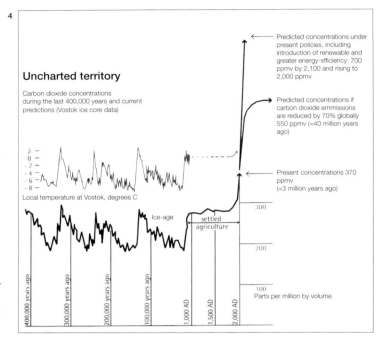

Uncharted territory

Carbon dioxide concentrations during the last 400,000 years and current predictions (Vostok ice core data)

Predicted concentrations under present policies, including introduction of renewable and greater energy-sfficiency: 700 ppmv by 2,100 and rising to 2,000 ppmv

Predicted concentrations if carbon dioxide emmissions are reduced by 70% globally 550 ppmv (=40 million years ago)

Present concentrations 370 ppmv (=3 million years ago)

Local temperature at Vostok, degrees C

Ice-age   settled agriculture

Parts per million by volume

Although there has been a dramatic decrease in carbon emissions from UK electricity generation since 1950 – a trend likely to intensify as renewable energy comes on stream – one kWhr of delivered electricity still produces 2.5 times that of delivered gas (9).

A kilogram of carbon dioxide occupies 0.54 of a cubic metre – about the volume of a coffin. In rough figures we generate this every time we:
• leave on a 100 watt tungsten light bulb for a day;
• use a 13 watt fluorescent tube continuously for a week;
• use a gas cooker to make a decent Sunday lunch;
• drive a two-litre diesel car for 11km;
• travel 16km on an intercity train;
• fly 2.4km on a short-haul flight;
• consume, in London, half a kilogram

of strawberries from Israel or six kilograms of strawberries from Scotland or 60 kilograms from Kent (from Pooran Desai and Sue Riddlestone, Bioregional solutions for living on one planet, 2002).

Interestingly, that same coffin's worth of carbon dioxide is what a square metre of forested land absorbs in a year. We need a lot of trees to offset the carbon in our current lifestyle.

To architects, historical analysis of data (12) is less useful than benchmarks against which our buildings should be tested. Data on these is more difficult to obtain but we have compiled what we can into the spreadsheet (10) and illustrative bar chart (13). The BRE Energy Efficiency Guides provide most of the targets, with further data available from FCBa's design work or from monitored

5

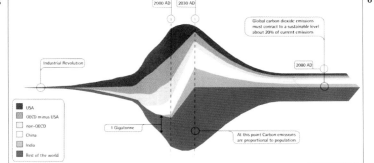

5 Proportionate responsibility for global atmospheric carbon dioxide (source: Bruges 2000)

6 Greenhouse gases and their contribution to global warming (source: Bruges 2000)

7 Carbon dioxide emissions per capita worldwide (source: UN Development Programme)

6

	Pre-industrial concentrations ppm	Present concentrations ppm	Possible 2030 concentrations	Warming contribution %	Warming effectiveness	Human sources
Carbon dioxide	280	350	360-500	49	1	Combustion of fossil fuels (coal, oil and gas), deforestation and changing land use, biomass burning
Methane	0.7	1.7	1.85-3.30	18	25	Wetland agriculture, enteric fermentation in cattle and termites, leakages from gas/oil exploitation, biomass burning
CFCs	-	CFC-11: 0.0002	0.0005-0.0002	14	CFC-12: 10,000	Refrigeration, air conditioning and plastic foam; also used as propellant, solvent and sterilant
	-	CFC-12: 0.0004	0.0009-0.0035			
Nitrous oxide	0.28	0.31	035-0.45	6	150	Nitrogen-based fertilisers, fossil fuel combustion, biomass burning

7

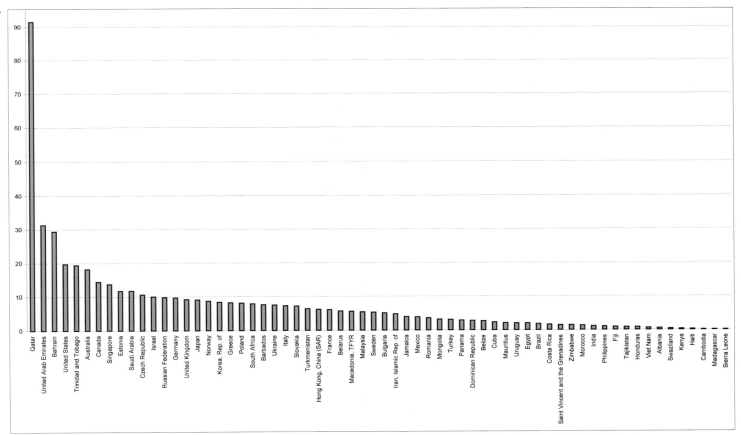

buildings. With all data it is important to recognise the assumptions made in terms of hours of use for each building type (offices are typically occupied for 2000 hours per year whereas Breeam for Schools works to 1040 hours) and any monitored data has to take into account climate conditions over the measured year (available from the Met Office in terms of 'degree days').

We need to know how our buildings perform and to become as familiar with kgCO2/m^2/year for a building as we are with miles per gallon for a car. From 2006 all new and existing buildings had to have a certificate of energy performance in accordance with the EU's Energy Performance of Buildings Directive. Buildings will be labelled just like fridges: benchmarking will be a significant part of the design process.

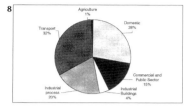

8 Total UK carbon dioxide emissions by sector (source: Carbon dioxide emissions from non-domestic buildings).

9 Emissions in kgCO2/kWhr for different fuels (sources: Energy Saving Trust, SAP-XCO2).

10 Commercial energy consumption rates by end use and sector (source: as 8).

9

Gas	0.19
Electricity	0.46
Oil	0.25
LPG	0.25
House coal	0.29
Wood pellet and chip	0.03

11 Energy consumption by fuel type in non-domestic dwellings 1950-2000 (source: as 8).

12 Energy costs and carbon dioxide benchmarks for various building types (source: Energy consumption guides: best practice pogramme).

13 Carbon dioxide benchmarks for various building types (source: as 12).

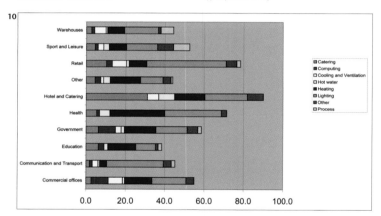

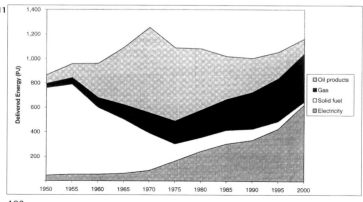

12

Building Type			Costs £/m²		KWhrs/m²		CO2 Emmissions kg/m²			Assumptions	References
			Fossil Fuel	Electricity	Fossil Fuel	Electricity	Fossil Fuel	Electricity	Total		
Housing	Conventional 1985	Average			200	40	38.0	18.4	56.4	Full time occupation.	GIR 53
	2000 Building Regs	Average			90	30	17.1	13.8	30.9	Gross Floor Area.	XCO2
	Intermediate FCBA Target	Average			30	25	5.7	11.5	17.2		BEDZED
	Bedzed	Average			42	33	8.0	15.2	23.2		
	Low Heat X CO2	Average			35	20	6.7	9.2	15.9		
Schools	Primary School	Typical	2.4	1.9	171	24	32.5	11.0	43.5	Occupancy based on 45	EEB 1
		Good Practice	1.7	1.4	121	17	23.0	7.8	30.8	hours/week.	EEB 5
	Secondary School	Typical	2.6	2.2	186	26	35.3	12.0	47.3	Gross Floor Area.	BREEAM for
		Good Practice	1.9	1.6	135	19	25.7	8.7	34.4		Schools
	Exemplar Schools	Without PV						2.4	7.3	9.6	M&E operation 1500hrs/yr.	
		With PV					2.4	4.3	6.7	Occupancy 1040hrs/yr.	
	Further Education	Typical	2.4	3.2	171	45	32.5	20.7	53.2	Occupancy 50 hours/week.	
		Good Practice	1.6	2.2	114	30	21.7	13.8	35.5	Gross Floor Area.	
Higher Education	Academic Buildings	Typical	1.8	3.8	180	76	34.2	35.0	69.2	Occupancy 50 hours/week.	EEB 5
		Good Practice	1.5	3.3	150	66	28.5	30.4	58.9	Gross Floor Area.	ECON 54
	Residential Buildings	Typical	2.3	4.4	230	88	43.7	40.5	84.2	Occupancy 168 hours/week.	
		Good Practice	1.9	3.8	190	76	36.1	35.0	71.1	Net Floor Area.	
Offices	Air Conditioned Prestige	Typical	1.9	17.9	211	358	40.1	164.7	204.8	Occupancy 55 hours/week.	EEB 6
		Good Practice	1	11.7	111	234	21.1	107.6	128.7	Treated floor area (excluding	ECON 19
	Air Conditioned Standard	Typical	1.8	12.4	180	225	34.2	103.5	137.7	areas not directly heated).	
		Good Practice	1	7	100	127	19.0	58.4	77.4		
	Normally Ventilated Open Plan	Typical	1.7	5.5	154	85	29.3	39.1	68.4		
		Good Practice	0.9	3.5	82	54	15.6	24.8	40.4		
	Normally Ventilated Cellular	Typical	1.8	4.1	150	55	28.5	25.3	53.8		
		Good Practice	1	2.5	83	33	15.8	15.2	31.0		
	BRE Energy "EOF" Brief	Best Practice			47	36	8.9	16.6	25.5		
Manufacturing	Light Manufacturing	Typical	1.9	3.2	211	76	40.1	35.0	75.1	Based on Building Energy costs	EEB 13
		Good Practice	1.1	2	122	48	23.2	22.1	45.3	only Double Shift. 5 Day week.	ECON 18
	Storage & Distribution	Typical	1.5	2	166	48	31.5	22.1	53.6	Gross Floor Area.	
		Good Practice	1.1	1.3	122	31	23.2	14.3	37.4		
Public Buildings	Libraries	Typical	2.4	4.4	171	62	32.5	28.5	61.0	Occupancy: 63 hours/week.	EEB 8
		Good Practice	1.7	3.2	121	45	23.0	20.7	43.7	Gross Floor Area.	
	Museums	Typical	2.1	7.9	150	111	28.5	51.1	79.6		
		Good Practice	1.5	5.7	107	82	20.3	37.7	58.1		
	Churches	Typical	1.7	1.3	121	18	23.0	8.3	31.3		
		Good Practice	0.9	0.6	64	8	12.2	3.7	15.8		
Leisure	Dry Sports Facilities	Typical	3.5	5.2	292	84	55.5	38.6	94.1	Dry Sports 98hours/week.	EEB 7
		Good Practice	2.3	4.6	192	74	36.5	34.0	70.5	Gross Floor Area.	EEB 11
	Sports and Pool	Typical	5.8	12.6	483	203	91.8	93.4	185.2	Pools 119/hours/week.	ECON 51
		Good Practice	3.9	9.2	325	148	61.8	68.1	129.8	Gross Floor Area.	
	Swimming Pool Only	Typical	12.1	14.4	1008	232	191.5	106.7	298.2	Pools 119/hours/week.	
		Good Practice	8.4	10.1	700	163	133.0	75.0	208.0	Gross Floor Area.	
	Theatre	Typical	0.4	0.9	33	15	6.3	6.9	13.2	Theatres 56 hours/week.	
		Good Practice	0.3	0.7	25	11	4.8	5.1	9.8	Gross Volume.	
	Cinema	Typical	0.6	0.9	50	15	9.5	6.9	16.4	Cinemas 56 hours/week.	
		Good Practice	0.5	0.7	42	11	8.0	5.1	13.0	Gross Volume.	
Retail	Supermarket	Typical	3.6	64.7	257	911	48.8	419.1	467.9	Based on 55 hours per week.	EEB 3
		Good Practice	2	47.1	142	663	27.0	305.0	332.0	Sales Floor Area Only.	
	Department Store	Typical	2.8	20.4	200	287	38.0	132.0	170.0		
		Good Practice	1.9	16.9	135	238	25.7	109.5	135.1		
	Non Food Retail	Typical	1.6	18.3	114	258	21.7	118.7	140.3		
		Good Practice	1	14.1	71	198	13.5	91.1	104.6		
	Small Food Retail	Typical	1.3	35.1	93	494	17.7	227.2	244.9		
		Good Practice	1	28.1	201	396	38.2	182.2	220.4		
Health	Large Active Hospital	Typical	4.7	3.7	470	74	89.3	34.0	123.3	Full time operation measured on	EEB 4
		Good Practice	4.2	3	420	60	79.8	27.6	107.4	gross floor area	
	Nursing Home	Typical	4.6	2.8	460	56	87.4	25.8	113.2		
		Good Practice	3.6	2.2	360	44	68.4	20.2	88.6		
Hotels	Public House	Typical	4.6	13	418	224	79.4	103.0	182.5	Based on Full Time operation and	EEB 2
		Good Practice	2.8	7.8	255	135	48.5	62.1	110.6	average occupancy	EEB 9
	Holiday Hotel	Typical	3.6	7.2	327	124	62.1	57.0	119.2		
		Good Practice	2.3	4.1	209	71	39.7	32.7	72.4		

Further information

- CH Pout, F Mackenzie and R Bettle, Carbon Dioxide Emissions from Non-Domestic Buildings, 2000 and beyond (BRE 2002)
- James Bruges, The Little Earth Book (Bristol 2000)
- Energy Consumption Guides: Best Practice Programme; offices (19), sports and recreation buildings (51), further and higher education (54), hospitals (72); www.actionenergy.org.uk

- James Lovelock, The Gaia World Atlas (London 2002)
- www.undp.org: United Nations Development Programme
- www.industrialbuildingsbenchmark.info: benchmarking tool for industrial buildings: heating and artificial lighting
- XCO2 Conisbee, Low Carbon Heating with Wood Pellet Fuel; www.britishbiogen.co.uk
- www.est.org.uk

12

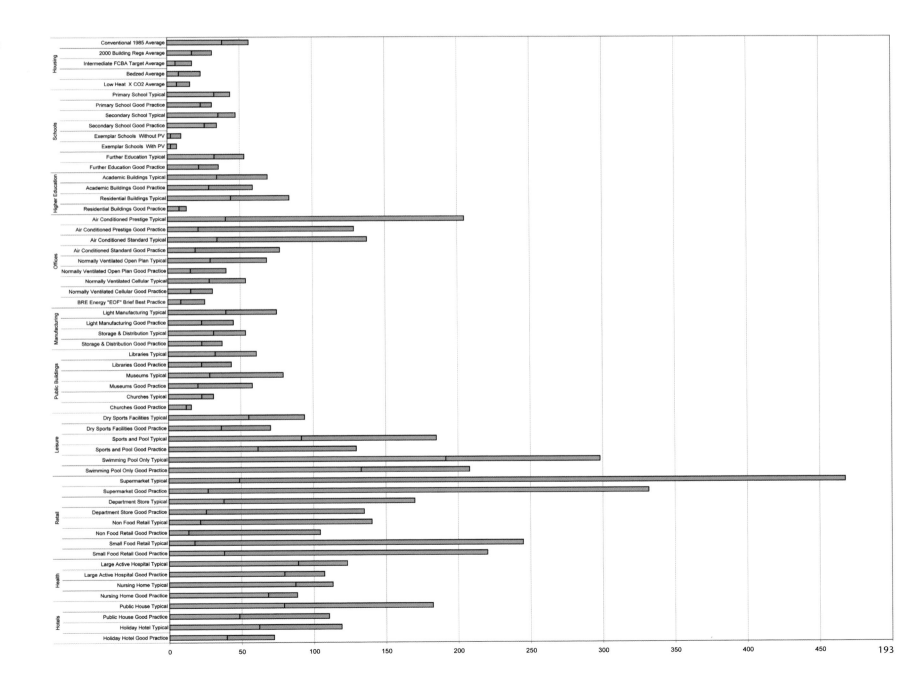

Principles of heating and cooling

Peter Clegg

Thermal comfort depends on a variety of factors – air temperature, radiant temperature, humidity and air movement, as well as clothing. The psychometric chart (1) illustrates these parameters. But there are also psychological aspects to thermal comfort and one of the most significant is the relationship between external and internal conditions. We tend to be more tolerant of lower temperatures in winter and higher temperatures in summer. A simpler version of the psychometric chart which combines the dry bulb temperature, mean radiant temperature and the cooling effect of airspeed results in a concept of the 'operative temperature'. Figure 2 shows how this varies with relative humidity between summer and winter.

As insulation standards improve, heating loads go down, to the extent that buildings become self-heating by their occupants and solar and equipment gains. But cooling becomes more of a problem. For comfort, the human body has to get rid of 70-100 watts per hour by convection, radiation or transpiration. This energy is useful in winter but in summer has to be dissipated.

Ten key points

• With a well-insulated building it is always more difficult to design for summer cooling than winter heating.
• Set comfort parameters for winter and summer with the client and engineers.
• Question blanket limits to summer temperature below these levels and try to persuade clients of the benefits of a flexible approach. The brief developed for the BRE New Environmental Office set a range of acceptable summertime temperatures: above 25 deg C for up to five per cent of the working year and above 28 deg C for one per cent of the working year (BRE GIR 30).
• Try to place thermal mass inside the insulation. This dampens down daily temperature fluctuations and can provide radiant surfaces that are cooler in summer and warm in winter.
• As insulation standards go up, so does the impact of both internal and solar gains; so ensure that the proportion, orientation and transparency of openings is examined thoroughly at outline design stage.
• The higher the occupancy of a building, the greater the importance of ventilation heat loss, relative to fabric heat loss, as a contribution to annual heat load.
• The greater the variation in the use of the building, the greater the importance of the response time of the heating/cooling system. Air-based systems offer faster response; radiant underfloor systems are slower.
• Ensure envelope details have continuous lines of insulation, vapour control and waterproofing. Attention to detail will highlight cold bridges as well as points of air leakage.
• Specify thermographic/air leakage tests to ensure completeness of the envelope.
• Design with the climate rather than against it. Undertake a simple site microclimate analysis at an early stage and record wind direction, solar gain, shading etc.

FCBa monitors temperatures in its own offices and has found this very helpful in understanding more about comfort and how to improve working conditions. There have been several occasions when personal perceptions of feeling chilly on a summer morning seem at odds with a recorded temperature of say 25 degrees C.

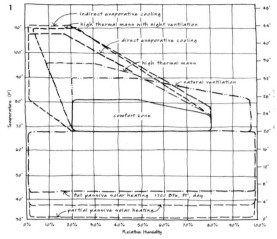

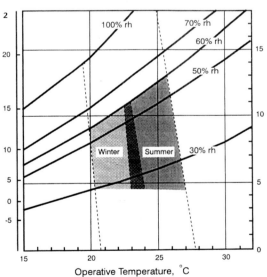

1 Bioclimatic chart with design strategies for extending the comfort zone (source: Brown and Dekay 2001).

2 Winter and summer comfort zones, relating relative humidity to 'operative' temperature (source: Liddament 1996).

Further information

• Victor Olgyay, Design with Climate: (New York 1963, 1992)

• GZ Brown and Mark Dekay, Sun Wind and Light (New York 2001)

• Martin Liddament, A Guide to Energy Efficient Ventilation (Oscar Faber, London 1996)

Andy Couling

The best insulation is a vacuum and, next to that, still air. Penguins somehow manage to maintain a temperature difference of 90 degrees celsius across a 25mm thick layer of down feathers, the equivalent of half a metre thickness of fibreglass.

In assessing the impact of particular building materials on the environment, all stages in their life cycle should be considered: production, transportation, use, re-use and disposal. While for most materials the impact in use can be negligible relative to the other stages, with insulation materials this is not the case.

As long as energy production remains reliant on fossil fuel consumption, the energy used in buildings is responsible for a huge proportion of our carbon dioxide production. Over the life of a building, the energy used in manufacturing, transporting and disposing of the insulation materials used in its construction can represent a negligible proportion of the total energy consumed by the building in use. The performance of the insulation is therefore of much greater significance than the impact of its production.

In the past, the use of CFCs as blowing agents for the majority of foamed closed cell insulants meant that they had a disproportionately large effect on global warming, as a result of the damage they caused to the ozone layer when released either in production or disposal. Some years ago they were replaced by HCFCs and these in turn are now being replaced with new blowing agents. These are generally HFCs which, although they have no effect on the ozone layer, are still significant greenhouse gases and thus continue to affect global warming. To overcome this some manufacturers are now beginning to switch to hydrocarbons like pentane or to carbon dioxide.

Types of Insulation

Insulation materials can generally be categorised into three groups:
• Cellular plastics: these are generally foamed petrochemical-based products and include rigid polyurethane, phenolic foam and expanded or extruded polystyrene.
• Mineral fibres: typically made by spinning molten rock or glass and adding binders to create the required degree of rigidity to the quilts or boards.
• Plant or animal fibres: these include cellulose, sheepswool, hemp and a number of others. They are made by processing plant or animal products to produce fibres and boards.

Choice of Insulation

The performance of insulation materials varies by about a factor of two across their range. In other words the best insulants are about twice as effective as the worst. The petrochemical foams perform best but it is these which have the greatest environmental impact in their production and disposal.

When specifying insulation materials these two factors, energy in use and global warming potential, make it important to prioritise the factors affecting the selection of insulants.
• Ensure that U-values are optimised.
• Specify high-performance materials or increase the thickness of less efficient ones.
• Ensure that the performance of the insulation will be maintained over the life of the building.
• Avoid specifying inappropriate materials in locations where they are liable to become waterlogged, compacted or otherwise degraded. This tends to mean specifying synthetic materials in more vulnerable locations.
• Ensure that the materials specified

UK government indicative standards for fabric insulation – U-Values W/m2K			
	2002	2006	2010
Roof (insulated between/over joists): all sectors	0.20	0.16	0.16
Roof (integral insulation in roof structure): dwellings	0.25	0.20	0.16
Roof (integral insulation in roof structure): non-domestic	0.35	0.25	0.16
External walls	0.35	0.30	0.25
Ground floors	0.30	0.25	0.22
Average of all windows, doors and rooflights	2.2	2.0	1.8

Source: DETR Consultative Document: Proposals for amending energy efficiency provisions (June 2000)

have zero ozone depletion potential. This simply means avoiding foams that are not certified as Zero ODP.
• Ensure that the embodied energy and toxicity in production and disposal are minimised.
• Specify the least harmful materials provided the criteria above can be met.

It is perfectly possible to design buildings that are well enough insulated to do away with conventional heating systems (eg at the superinsulated houses in Milton Keynes 1985, the ventilation system was able to deliver the space heating requirement). This can bring a major benefit to the life cycle cost of a building and therefore can be a persuasive argument with commercial or institutional buildings.

Further information

• XC02 Conisbee, Insulation for Sustainability – a Guide (sponsored by the rigid foam insulation industry but nevertheless very comprehensive and fair). See www.xco2.com.

• Jane Anderson, David Shiers with Mike Sinclair, The Green Guide to Specification, third edition (Oxford 2002).

• Tom Woolley, Sam Kimmins, Paul Harrison and Rob Harrison, The Green Building Handbook (London 1997).

U-values were calculated for the following:
• Pitched roof with insulated slope and sloping ceiling (U-value: 0.2): 1 plaster-board 12.5mm, 2 insulation/rafters variable, 3 air layer (ventilated) 50mm, 4 sarking felt 1mm, 5 air layer (ventilated) 25mm, 6 tiles (clay) 15mm.
• Masonry partial fill cavity wall (U-value: 0.3): 1 plaster (lightweight) 13mm, 2 concrete block (dense) 100mm, 3 insulation variable, 4 cavity (slightly ventilated) 15mm, 5 brick outer leaf 105mm.

Comparative costs per square metre based on thickness needed to achieve a roof U-value of 0.2. Prices at 2005 levels include additional costs of transporting material from abroad where applicable.
1: £10, 2: £10-20, 3: £20-30, 4: £30-40, 5: £40+

Sources: Insulation for Sustainability: a Guide (XC02/Bing); Green Building Handbook (Spon 1997); The Green Guide to Specification (BRE 2002); The Green Guide to Housing Specification (BRE 2000); other information from manufacturers.

Element	Common or Trade Name	K-Value W/mK	Embodied CO_2 GJ/m^3	Environmental Rating According to BRE Guides		Thickness (mm) to Achieve Roof U-Value of 0.2 w/m^2 °C	Thickness (mm) to Achieve Cavity Wall U-Value of 0.3 w/m^2 °C	Comparative Cost Low 1 to 5 High	Notes
				General Guide 2002	Housing Guide 2000				
Organic Synthetic - Petrochemical									
Expanded Polystyrene (EPS)	Jablite	0.032*	High	A	A	160	75*	2	Formed into boards, Zero Ozone Depletion Potential. Available under different trade names, so environmental performance may vary.
Extruded Polystyrene (XPS)	Styrofoam	0.028*	High (4.05)**	C	C	140	50*	2	Should be specified in its Zero Ozone Depletion Potential (ZODP) form, performs well when intrinsic strength required.
Rigid Urethane Foam (PUR/PIR)	Celotex	0.022 – 028*	Very High	A	B	125 with 0.025 K-value	50* incl Foil Facing	3	Should be specified in its Zero Ozone Depletion Potential (ZODP) form, proper respiratory equipment required when installing.
Phenolic Foam	Celotex	0.020*	High	-	-	100	50* incl Foil Facing	2	Should be specified in its Zero Ozone Depletion Potential (ZODP) form, has excellent fire resistance.
Multi-layered foil and cellular plastic sandwich	'Triso-Super 9'	Not available R-value 5 $m^2/K/W$	Not known	-	-	25	Not suitable for use in cavity walls	2	Supplied by 'Actis UK'. Consists of 14 alternating layers of foams, wadding and reflective films with a total thickness of 25mm. Only certified for use in roofs. Some concern over performance in use. All components can be recycled. Certified by BM TRADA.
Mineral / Glass									
Low Density Mineral Wool	Rockwool	0.035	Medium (0.83 for $60kg/m^3$)	A	A	175	75	2	$45kg/m^3$ density. Can contain recycled material from iron ore blast furnaces. Irritant when installing. Embodied energy figure is for product RW3 provided by Rockwool.
High Density Mineral Wool	Rockwool	0.040*	Medium	B	B	200	130	4	$200kg/m^3$ density. Can contain recycled material from iron ore blast furnaces. Irritant when installing.
Low Density Glass Wool	Glass Fibre	0.032	Medium	A	A	160	75 ave	1	Contains up to 50% recycled glass from manufacturing waste and post consumer glass (cullett) so uses less energy to produce. Available as batts, slabs or pellets, potential irritant when installing.
High Density Glass Wool	Glass Fibre	0.040	Medium	B	B	200	130	2	As Above
Foamed Glass	Foamglas	0.040* - 0.050	High (2.7)**	B	B	225 ave	150 ave	5	Available in board form, raw material is usually new glass, but a rougher product can also be made from recycled glass in the form of blocks or granules. High compressive strength type can be used as thermal break in wall constructions.
Mica	Vermiculite	0.047- 0.058	Medium	-	-	250 ave	160 ave	1	Useful as an aggregate additive to concrete or as loose insulation.
Organic Natural									
Cork	Cork board	0.04*	Low	B	B	200	130	5	Formed into boards, good ability to withstand loads.
Wood fibre batts	WoodFlex 040	0.040	Low	-	-	200	130	3	Available from www.constructionresources.com, absorbs up to 17% of moisture, suitable for all timber construction, durable, reusable.
Wood fibre boards	Gutex Thermosafe	0.040	Low	-	-	200 ave	160 ave	4	Available from www.constructionresources.com. Made from waste timber by-product.
Cellulose Fibres	Warmcell	0.038* - 0.040	Low (0.48)**	A	A	190 ave	Not suitable for masonry cavity wall use	1	Made from recycled paper, good acoustic properties, information available from www.fillcrete.com, not suitable for moist environments.
Recycled cellulose batts	Homatherm	0.040	Low	-	-	200	130	3	Available from www.constructionresources.com, contains 80% recycled material, no toxins or toxic emissions during manufacture, durable, reusable, flexible in all directions, avoids need for treated timber. Being hydroscopic, this material is said to reduce the need for timber preservation when used in timber frame construction.
Cellulose/ viscose fibre batts	Vital 040	0.034	Low	-	-	200	115	3	Ideally suited to timber frame construction, able to absorb moisture, by-products recycled into process, good acoustic damper.
British sheeps wool	Thermafleece	0.039	Very Low (0.13)**	-	-	190	Not suitable for masonry cavity wall use	2	Available from www.secondnatureuk.com, suitable for use in moist environments. Fully renewable and recyclable.

Timber based
Cellulose based
Animal derived

Passive solar design

Peter Clegg

Passive solar collection involves designing the building to maximise useful solar gain in winter through all its south-facing surfaces (1). The most obvious way of achieving this benefit is through orienting windows towards the south and adding shading or overhangs to prevent summertime overheating. The approach is most applicable to dwellings which still have a significant requirement for heating rather than, say, offices, where cooling tends to be the dominant design driver.

There are other options and FCBa experimented with a number of them in the 1980s. The Cleveland Reach housing project used trombe walls (a layer of glazing over the outside of a dense concrete block wall) to turn solid walls into solar collectors (2, 5). A selectively surfaced copper foil glued to the wall was used to enhance absorption and reduce emission. The wall soaked up heat well during winter sunny days but probably lost more heat at night because it was effectively uninsulated; it also tended to overheat in summer.

The refurbishment of an agricultural building at Woodbridge Farm incorporated a roof space collector. An insulated attic was glazed with twin-wall polycarbonate, with a system of fans and controllers that distributed warm air when available (and required) into the thermally heavyweight house below. Monitored performance showed about 25 per cent of the heating requirement of the house was met by solar energy, although the windows were more useful than the roof space.

Several experiments were conducted with conservatories, both double- and single-glazed, which provided space for plants as well as people at certain times of the year and acted as buffer zones to those spaces where the temperatures were more controlled.

Conservatories can provide great places for plants although they generally need huge amounts of ventilation during the summer; the intense heat from small south-facing spaces can cause plants to overheat and shrivel rapidly without constant care or an automatic watering system. In view of the higher summertime temperatures facing us through global warming, the problem is likely to get much worse unless very effective (preferably external) solar shading is provided; 95 per cent shading was used when evaluating the effect of climatic change on dwelling construction for Bill Dunster/Arup Research supported by FCBa and RIBA (download from www.feildenclegg.com/research). Conservatories can be very special places but only very rarely can they be shown to be energy-saving. In fact experience has shown that relatively well sealed double-glazed conservatories tend to be net energy consumers (because occupants try to heat them in winter). Single-glazed, relatively draughty conservatories tend to perform better overall – they tend to be used when the weather is right and cannot realistically be heated when not.

Nonetheless, in the 1980s sunspaces became a passive solar icon, along with large amounts of unprotected south-facing glazing and rooflights. The problem with this approach to energy-saving is that increased levels of insulation reduce the winter heating season in the UK to just two or three months a year – the time when useful sunshine is in short supply.

Winter sunlight is vital to us psychologically however and the basic principles of passive solar design are still worth adhering to in buildings where overheating and glare are less of a problem. These are:
• design for penetration of winter sunlight, particularly on south and east elevations.
• where this results in large areas of glazing, ensure protection from summer sunlight by shading and overhangs and also provide plenty of summer ventilation.
• maximise exposed internal thermal mass particularly on floors.
• ensure that localised control in the heating system can accommodate useful solar gains.

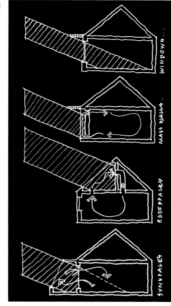

1 Passive solar options
2 Cleveland Reach, Bath 1983
3 Bloomfield Crescent, Bath, third-floor conservatory 1983
4 Woodbridge Farm, Ubley, Somerset, passive solar roofspace collector 1986
5 Cleveland Reach, Bath, trombe wall 1983

Cooling systems and sources

Bill Gething

Even an energy-efficient air conditioning system in the UK can add 40-50kg/m²/yr in terms of a building's carbon dioxide emissions, or up to 175 in the case of a local 'split system' packaged air conditioner. So how can we keep cool indoors without the cost and complexity of an air conditioning system, particularly with the prospect of increasing summertime temperatures?

Potential sources of cooling are summer night-time air (which can be used to cool building structures overnight) and nearby bodies of water or groundwater (which maintain temperatures below ambient conditions). There are a variety of ways in which these sources can be utilised, ranging from fully passive systems through to more technically sophisticated mechanical ventilation and heat pump systems (1).

Night-time passive cooling
• Make sure that the system is independent of wind direction by careful design of vent openings.
• Make sure that the openings seal properly and the controls work.
• Make sure that the controls do not over-cool the space and produce uncomfortably conditions first thing in the morning.
• Remember that cross ventilation will generally over-ride stack ventilation in the UK climate.

Night-time mechanical ventilation
• Adding mechanical systems means adding fan power; so use large ducts and/or low flow rates.
• Fans give improved control and the ability to add cooling if necessary.

Groundwater source cooling
• Groundwater temperatures are commonly at a constant 10-12 degrees celsius at two metres or so below

ground level. But water temperatures can vary, as can its quantity or quality. Unusually high temperatures of around 15 degrees celsius were found in practice for the borehole at the Rare headquarters and this has significantly reduced the performance of the cooling system.
• Systems either use water extraction (which requires Environment Agency permission and approved disposal of

heated water) or a heat exchange system, either within boreholes or pipes buried approximately one metre in the earth. The former often requires deep and expensive drilling, the latter a very large area for heat rejection.
• In areas where the water table is rising (eg London), extraction can be actively encouraged.
• The quality of extracted water varies

significantly. Particularly hard water is limited in what it can be used for and can cause difficulties from scaling. Check nearby boreholes but note that quality can vary even over a short distance.
• The effectiveness and control of a groundwater cooling system can be improved dramatically by connecting the source to a heat pump (as at Falmouth Digital Media Centre),

although this is then dependent on the coefficient performance of the heat pump in order to produce a low-energy design solution. Heat pumps can be used for heating as well as cooling.
• Account for higher summertime temperatures and provide additional capacity in the system or the building design to incorporate a potential back-up solution without undue disruption.

1

'Natural' cooling systems and sources

	Examples	Cooling capacity W/m²	Advantages	Disadvantages
Night-time passive cooling				
Passive: cross ventilation	BRE – offices and leisure barn	20-30	No energy costs	Need to design to take account of wind direction
	BRE – lecture room			Motors and controls expensive
				Maintenance access needs proper provision
				Take care with security through vent openings
Passive: stack ventilation	Portland Square, University of Plymouth	20-30	No energy costs	As above (but wind can enhance stack effect)
	Wiltshire Music Centre			NB: Cross-ventilation usually dominates stack
	BRE – offices and lecture room			ventilation
	Bedales, Olivier Theatre			
	EMV Housing, Madrid			
Night-time mechanical ventilation				
Mechanical: through building	Yorkshire Sculpture Park visitor centre	20-30	Can be independent of wind direction	Fan energy, noise
			Smaller ventilation openings	
Mechanical: through underfloor storage/earth tubes	Earth Centre Galleries, Exemplar schools	30-40	Remote storage gives improved temperature control	Cost of additional structure at substructural space(s)
Mechanical: through floor voids eg Termodeck	Oxstalls campus, University of Gloucs Martial Rose Library, King Alfred's College, Winchester	40-50	Upgradable with adiabatic cooling (Martial Rose) and air conditioning (Oxstalls) Can work with displacement ventilation (Oxstalls)	Cost of Termodeck licence Complexity of ductwork and controls
Groundwater source cooling				
Pipes in slab/ceiling/chilled beams	BRE Offices	30-40	Low energy costs	Potential condensation problems on cooled structure
Pipework and fan coil units	Rare hq	40-50	Improved and localised control	Costs of controls, pump and fan
Heat pump assisted cooling	Digital Media Centre, Falmouth	50-60	More accurate control Can be used for heating as well as cooling	Additional cost and maintenance of heat pump Dependence on electrical energy to drive heat pump
Chilled ceilings		70	Low maintenance, quiet, draught-free Suitable for use with natural sources eg boreholes Can fit in shallow ceiling, eg restricted headroom	Controls needed to avoid condensation risk
Chilled beams	London Centre for Nanotechnology	100-160	As chilled ceilings, but high performance	As chilled ceilings

Solar water heating

HEAT & POWER
Cooling systems and sources
Solar water heating

Peter Clegg

The viability of solar water heating depends on the availability of solar radiation and the cost of fossil fuel-based energy. Currently China is by far the world's largest manufacturer and user of solar water heating, with more than 40 million square metres installed and an annual production of eight million square metres in 2002, dominated by evacuated tube collectors. In Europe, with 1.1 million square metres of installed capacity, flat plate collectors are the most common.

Flat plate collectors consist of a glazed and insulated box, typically roof-mounted, enclosing a metal absorber plate with a selective surface (high solar absorption, low thermal emission). Tubing in contact with the absorber plate contains a transfer fluid that moves heat to a storage tank (1). Sometimes this circuit operates by gravity but more often it is pumped; some systems use a photovoltaic-powered pump which is activated only when collection is possible. The National Trust has had considerable experience of installations and prefers to use pumped 'drain-down' systems, which avoid the problem of the transfer fluid freezing at night. All other systems need to use anti-freeze additives in the transfer fluid to prevent freezing.

Evacuated tube collectors (2) comprise a sealed glass tube with a metal absorber plate inside with a heat pipe in the centre, which contains a temperature sensitive medium such as methanol. The sun heats up and vaporises the pipe fluid and rapidly transfers it to a heat exchanger at the top of the tube. Evacuated tube collectors have higher efficiencies (3), particularly at higher temperature differences between the collector and the outside air (ie in colder climates). Some evacuated tube collectors such as the Solamax can be

mounted horizontally or vertically and the absorber plates can be tilted to an optimal orientation. Otherwise collectors for domestic water heating in the UK should be mounted at about 30 degrees to the horizontal and within 30 degrees of due south. The drop-off in efficiency is similar to that of a photovoltaic collector.

Flat plate collectors can be flush-mounted within a roof, although it is often easier to install them outside the waterproofing and reduce the roof penetration to two pipes and a cable. Evacuated tube collectors need to be mounted above the roof. As evacuated tubes are more efficient than flat plates, the overall absorber area required for the same performance is a little bit less, although (because of gaps between the collectors) the difference is negligible. Generally an area of 2.0 to 2.5 square metres provides for around 50 per cent of domestic requirements. Further savings may be achievable by being able to turn off hot water boilers altogether through the June-September period. Currently however, without grant, aid pay back is between 20 and 30 years.

Further information
• Volker Quaschning, 'Solar Thermal Water Heating', Renewable Energy World (April 2004) (www.volker-quaschning.de).
• www.Thermomax-group.com

1 Manufacturer's schematic of the drain-down solar water heating system (source: Southern Solar)
2, 3 Thermomax solar water heaters
4 Efficiency graph of evacuated vs flat plate collectors (source: Quaschning)

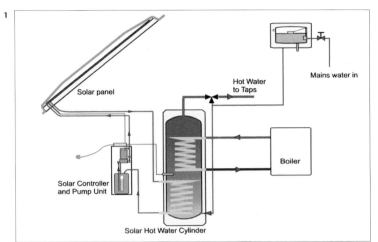

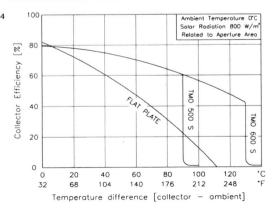

Photovoltaics

Bill Gething

The sun provides the only energy input to the earth and it is therefore the only truly sustainable source of energy. Photovoltaic cells convert sunlight directly into electricity whereas other renewable resources such as wind, hydro or biomass effectively represent current solar energy transformed by intermediate processes.

In contrast, fossil fuels are a form of solar energy stored for 300 million years and converted first into vegetation by photosynthesis and then by pressure, heat and time into coal, peat, oil, gas and other hydrocarbon variants. Releasing this stored carbon is the primary cause of global warming.

Current world energy demand could be met by covering three per cent of the Sahara with photovoltaic (PV) cells.

Types of cell

PV cells commonly use silicon semiconductor technology to generate electricity from both direct and diffuse solar radiation. There are three principal types which vary in appearance and efficiency. Cells generate at low voltage and are typically connected together in series to form modules, which produce direct current (DC) at a higher, more useful voltage.

These efficiencies compare favourably with the national grid (25-30 per cent efficient at the point of use). Theoretical maximum efficiencies are around 30 per cent, although concentrator systems such as the Improved Triple Junction (ITJ) solar cells recently developed by

2-4 Monocrystalline, thin-film silicone and polycrystalline pv panels (Solar Century).

California-based Spectrolab for use in space are reported to achieve efficiencies of more than 36 per cent.

The cells themselves are opaque and are typically sandwiched between a protective layer of (highly transmissive) low-iron glass and a backing material which can be opaque (eg Tedlar) or transparent (eg glass). Cells in a glass/glass module can be spaced apart to allow light to filter through the module. Bendable thin-film modules are also available which use a flexible transparent plastic covering material.

With PV, overshadowing should be avoided. Even a small shadow falling across a crystalline array can have a very significant effect on total output.

PV cells generate heat, which needs

to be removed – efficiency drops by about 0.5 per cent for each degree celsius rise in temperature. There are examples where the waste heat from PVs has been recovered for use elsewhere in the building. The following is a useful rule of thumb: no gap, 10 per cent less efficient; 50mm gap, five per cent less efficient; 150mm-plus gap, no reduction in efficiency.

Orientation and Output

The UK receives a similar amount of solar radiation to most of northern Europe where there are numerous PV installations. The south of England receives only 20 per cent more radiation than the north of Scotland (5).

The amount of electricity generated

by a PV array (collection of modules) depends on its orientation (optimum is due south) and tilt from the horizontal (optimum is the latitude of the site minus 20 degrees for maximum total annual generation). However, as can be seen from the diagram, an array will produce over 90 per cent of maximum for quite a wide range of orientations and tilts (9).

As a rough guide, one square metre of a monocrystalline array in the southern UK will produce approximately 100 kWh/y. A more accurate calculation for the approximate annual energy production of a system (E) is E=SxAxDxKxL, where S is maximum total annual solar radiation for the site (eg 1045kWh/m²/y for London); A is the basic efficiency of the module (eg 15 per cent for monocrystalline modules); D is a direction factor from the orientation and tilt diagram for the site (eg 95 per cent for an array facing due south at a tilt of 50 degrees); K is a correction factor to take account of losses due to temperature, dust, cell mismatches etc, taken at about 0.9; and L is a loss factor covering losses in the associated electrical systems (typically 0.8).

Prices are dropping but PV is still relatively expensive and almost all UK installations have been subsidised by grants.

By incorporating PV cells in a building, part of their relatively high cost can be offset against the building materials and components they replace. Figure 6 sets out some comparative costs for 2002 (PV are generally dropping prices).

While conventional financial payback periods as compared with grid-supplied electricity are extended (considerably more than 30 years – see below), the time taken to generate the energy embodied in the modules is only something of the order of six years and reducing. Alternative uses for the electricity generated also make the economics look healthier, for example using it to power electric cars.

PV-generated electricity is currently more expensive than grid-supplied electricity. The situation is likely to change during the life of a building and it makes sense where possible to allow for retrofitting modules in the design.

Given the current financial climate it is normal therefore for systems to be sized so that as much as possible of the energy generated is used in the building rather than being exported to the grid. PVs generate different amounts of electricity through the day and through the year so it follows that building types that match this pattern of generation as closely as possible are best suited.

1

Efficiencies of different PV types		
	Cell	Module
Monocrystalline	13-17%	12-15%
Polycrystalline	12-15%	11-14%
Thin film/amorphous	5%	4.5-4.9%

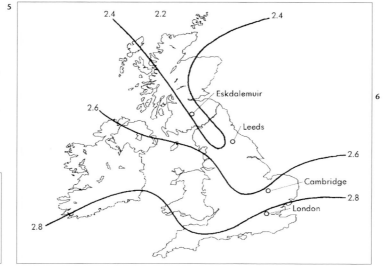

6

Comparative costs of PV systems (2002 prices)			
Standard construction	£/m²		PV system
Wall systems			
Cavity wall (brick/block)	50-60		
Rainscreen overcladding (steel)	190	600	Rainscreen system
Stone cladding	300		
Double-glazed cladding	350	780	Glass/glass module curtain walling
Granite-faced concrete cladding	640		
Polished stone cladding	850-1500		
Roof systems			
Concrete/clay tiles	32	500	PV tile system
Aluminium pitched roof	44	500	Modules on pitched roof of large office

Source: Randall Thomas (ed), Photovoltaics and Architecture – a design guide (London 2001)

7
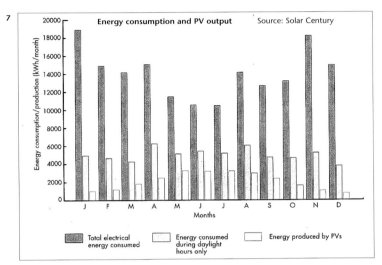
Energy consumption and PV output   Source: Solar Century

Total electrical energy consumed | Energy consumed during daylight hours only | Energy produced by PVs

Figure 7 shows typical domestic electrical use compared with the pattern of PV generation. Domestic buildings are not particularly well suited to PV, given the variation in their demand for energy, which tends to be high when PV generation is low or zero. Schools similarly have relatively low electrical demands and may be under-used at times of the year when generation is at its maximum.

Grid connection

It is essential to contact the local Distribution Network Operator (DNO) to obtain permission to connect into a building's grid supplied alternating current systems and to identify the DNO's conditions for connection. This is a requirement regardless of whether or not any surplus electricity will be exported to the grid. At the time of writing, there is no standard procedure across the country; a list of contacts for each DNO however is available (www.pv-uk.org.uk).

If surplus is to be exported, you need to agree whether or how much the DNO will pay. To date, unfortunately,

the rates typically paid for surplus electricity have been considerably less than the rate charged for grid-supplied electricity but the situation is changing as the renewables obligation starts to impact on supply authorities.

System design

For larger institutions which are eligible to receive Renewable Obligation Certificates (ROCs), the value of the ROCs can significantly impact on the payback period; for the National Trust headquarters it is only 11 years.

A typical system (8) consists of the following components:
• an array or set of arrays of PV modules connected together and generating DC current. This is terminated on:
• a DC switch panel which is connected to a Power Conditioning Unit (PCU) consisting of:
• an inverter to convert DC to AC that ensures that the AC-generated matches the grid's voltage, phase, power factor and frequency characteristics;
• a maximum power point tracker to

keep the installation operating close to its maximum power under varying radiation and temperature conditions);
• protection devices on the DC and AC side including automatic disconnect and restart if the grid supply is lost;
• the building's AC distribution board which is connected to:
• an AC mains isolator and via:
• a two-way meter or two separate meters to:
• the grid.

In a domestic installation, the PCU might be wall-mounted alongside the consumer unit. In larger installations, as a rough rule of thumb, the plant room should be increased in area by three to five per cent of the array area.

AC modules are also available which have integral inverters.

The following issues should be borne in mind:
• while touching the front surface of a module presents no danger, it is not possible to 'switch off' a PV cell except by covering it;
• DC wiring (from the modules to the inverter) is not common in the UK and contractors may be unfamiliar with it;
• voltages can be higher than the usual 240V single-phase AC (higher voltages are sometimes used to minimise the voltage drop associated with DC and the consequent need to use large cables);
• detailed design of wiring routes should allow for simple installation and easy maintenance, particularly if the PV modules form part of the weathertight skin of a building. Particularly care is needed when using glass/glass modules.

Further information

• www.pv-uk.org.uk – British Photovoltaic Association website with lists of projects, manufacturers and installers.

Diagrams and tables from: Randall Thomas (ed), Photovoltaics and architecture: a design guide (London 2001); www.solarcentury.com.

8
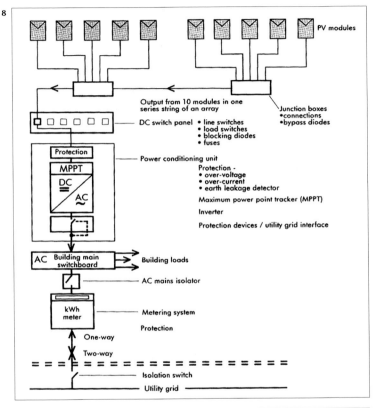

Output from 10 modules in one series string of an array
PV modules
Junction boxes •connections •bypass diodes
DC switch panel • line switches • load switches • blocking diodes • fuses
Protection   MPPT   DC   AC
Power conditioning unit
Protection – • over-voltage • over-current • earth leakage detector
Maximum power point tracker (MPPT)
Inverter
Protection devices / utility grid interface
AC Building main switchboard   Building loads
AC mains isolator
kWh meter   Metering system   Protection
One-way
Two-way
Isolation switch
Utility grid

9
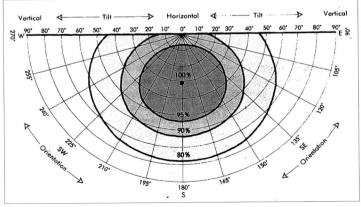

Combined heat and power

Bill Gething

Combined Heat and Power, also known as 'cogeneration' or 'total energy', is the simultaneous generation of usable electricity and heat in a single process. Suitable installations are those where there is a simultaneous and balanced requirement for electricity and thermal energy (direct heat, hot water, steam, process heating and/or cooling) – eg the leisure, hotel, health, housing, office, education and university sectors.

CHP is inherently more fuel-efficient than conventional electricity generation – 75 per cent compared even with the 50 per cent of a modern combined cycle gas turbine. This is for two main reasons: a significant proportion of the heat produced as a by-product of the electricity generation process is used; and energy is produced close to the point of use and so transmission and distribution losses are reduced (1).

A design advice report on the student residences for the Oxstalls Campus produced by ESD set out the suitability of a CHP solution, given the excellent match between a baseline demand for hot water throughout the year and electrical demand (2).

CHP systems consist of a number of components: the prime mover (heat engine), generator, heat recovery and electrical interconnection. The prime mover typically identifies the system and figure 3 summarises the relative merits of the different types.

Most new CHP schemes in the UK use natural gas but a number use alternative renewable fuels, some of which (eg bio-fuels) qualify for government grant support. Examples include the 120 kWe gasifier plant at Bill Dunster Architects' BedZED at Sutton, which uses local tree waste that would otherwise go to landfill. Initial problems with this energy technology are understood to have been overcome.

CHP has traditionally been associated with large applications (see Defra's April 2004 report on the government's strategy for CHP). Interest is growing however in smaller schemes, including replacing domestic boilers with micro-CHP units. ESD's report, The potential market for micro CHP in the UK (2002), concluded that approximately 1.3 million households were potentially suitable for 1-3 kWe capacity units, with a niche market of 1.7 million 'low demand' houses (less than 12 MWh/yr annual gas consumption). There were a further 780,000 oil-fired heating systems which were a target if oil-fired micro CHP units were developed.

At present however there are very few micro-CHP units on the market. One example is the 1.2 kWe /8 kWt Stirling-engined WhisperGen domestic unit, marketed by Powergen, which replaces a floor-standing boiler but also generates electricity.

A difficulty in establishing a market for micro-CHPS in the past was the uncertainty regarding the relative cost of the fuel to power the plant compared with the value of electricity produced. Coupled with the highly competitive nature of the electricity market, this has meant that larger consumers have been able to obtain very low prices which reversed the economics on which they based their decision to install a CHP plant. There are a worrying high number of examples where CHP plants have been removed – in some cases without even being used – for this reason.

Further information
• Defra, The Government's Strategy for Combined Heat and Power to 2010 (London 2004)
• Tim Crozier-Cole and Gareth Jones, The potential market for micro CHP in the UK (London 2002)

Comparative generation (Source: CHP Technologies, US Environmental Protection Agency)

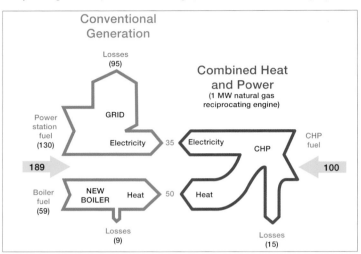

Suitability of CHP for Oxstalls campus residences (Source: ESD, design advice report 2001)

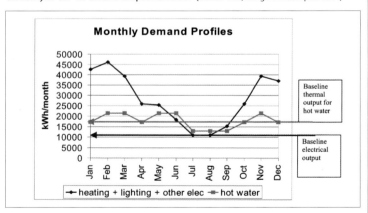

Take-up of different types of CHP in the UK

Size	kW of electrical power	Total schemes	% of schemes	% QPO
Micro	<5 kWe	0	0%	0%
Mini	5-500 kWe	1237	80%	3%
Small scale	500 kWe-5MWe	175	11%	7%
Medium scale	5-50MWe	98	6%	27%
Large scale	>50MWe	29	2%	63%

Biomass

Bill Gething

Biomass (any fuel derived from plant or animal matter) offers huge potential to reduce carbon dioxide emissions. Whereas burning a fossil fuel releases carbon dioxide that has been locked away for millennia, biomass is in balance, absorbing carbon dioxide as it grows (directly, in the case of vegetative biomass, or indirectly, in the case of animal-derived material) and releasing this back into the atmosphere when it is burnt. Some carbon is released during processing and transport but overall this is an order of magnitude less than fossil fuels (for example, wood chips release less than 13 per cent of the carbon dioxide released by natural gas in producing the same amount of energy).

Wood-based materials include:
• forestry, including thinnings and prunings, both rural and urban;
• short-rotation coppice – fast-growing timbers grown specifically as a fuel crop such as willow, coppice or poplar;
• wood waste such as sawdust, joinery waste, paper sludge and used pallets.

Vegetative crops and by-products include:
• perennial grasses such as miscanthus (elephant grass) or reed grass grown specifically as a fuel;
• vegetable oils such as rape and soya, either harvested for fuel or recovered after a primary use (eg biodiesel recovered from used cooking oil);
• bio-ethanol and bio-oil;
• agricultural by-products such as straw.

Animal by-products include:
• animal dung and human sewage;
• animal fats.

It is not generally appreciated that bio-energy (energy generated using biomass as a fuel) provides more than five times as much energy in the UK as large-scale hydroelectricity. In 1997 bio-energy accounted for 81 per cent of all UK renewable energy generation.

Examples include the Elean power station near Ely, which generates around 36 MWe (MW of electricity) by burning more than 200,000 tonnes of straw per year (still only two per cent of the UK's surplus straw) and the 12.7 MWe chicken litter fuelled power station at Eye.

For buildings, most of the bio-fuels listed are more suitable for use in large-scale or specialist installations. For example, even a small straw burner with an output of 45kW would need to be fed with two or three bales per day. Storage and handling space and equipment size are significant and need to be designed in at an early stage.

In contrast, wood-based materials such as logs, wood chips and wood pellets lend themselves to single-building and even domestic use. Chips and pellets in particular are suitable for automated control in purpose-designed modulating burners that operate at up to 95 per cent efficiency (compared with 10-20 per cent for an open fire and 30-65 per cent for a wood-burning stove). Wood chips need less processing than wood pellets; they require low investment in plant; and in some cases they can be produced as an integral part of harvesting. They do not have the free-flowing characteristics of wood pellets and tend to be used for larger installations (above 50kW). Fuel supply companies will supply chips of the required size and density for a particular installation. The heat output is highly dependent on the moisture content of the chips, which can vary from 50 per cent (wet) to ten per cent (dry).

As an example, the 350 kW lead boiler proposed for the SciTec facility at Oundle school is estimated to use eight cubic metres of wood chips per day during the heating season. This is about 320 tonnes of wet wood chips, which

could be provided from some 16 hectares of short rotation coppice. These would be delivered loose in 100 cubic metre loads (two weeks' supply) or in 30 cubic metre roll-on/off units linked to automated cradles, with automated fuel transfer to the burners (with about four days' supply per unit).

Energy crops are still in their infancy in the UK, particularly miscanthus, where particular care should be taken to ensure that the boiler technology is suited to the fuel. Short rotation coppice (SRC) crops are better developed but the dominant fuel for UK biomass heating is forestry woodchip – chipped roundwood, chipped slabwood and (to a lesser extent) chipped forestry brash. Energy output figures for a given area of land are difficult to pin down but, as a rough guide, one hectare of short rotation willow coppice can provide 32-38 MWh of heating energy per year and miscanthus 20-40 MWh. It should be noted that SRC is a large-scale agricultural crop requiring professional management, large-scale contract harvesting, seasoning and processing in order to produce a relatively tightly controlled fuel at around 30-40 per cent moisture content.

Wood pellets are suited to a broad range of installation sizes, including domestic, and are available in bulk or (at twice the price) in bags. They have been used extensively in parts of Europe since the mid-1980s, particularly in Sweden, where take-up has been rapid following the introduction of taxes on mineral fuels. Pellets are made by first milling the biomass material into sawdust and drying it, if necessary, at the same time. The material is then compressed and extruded at 90 degrees celsius to melt the natural lignin which binds the pellets. The finished pellets are consistent, clean, can be lit by

electronic ignition and are self-feeding from a hopper. Burners are very efficient (up to 92 per cent) and a hopper fill will last two to three days. Ash is typically less than two per cent of the volume of fuel burnt, so pans need to be emptied only every three months. Given wood pellets' relatively high energy intensity (3,036kWh/m³ compared with 795 for wood chips), fuel storage requirements are manageable, particularly for a low-energy house.

While straightforward combustion is generally the most economical way to produce heat from biomass, techniques using gasification and pyrolysis are under development. Gasification involves heating the biomass with a restricted air supply to convert it to a combustible gas. The gas has a low calorific value and is therefore normally used immediately to generate electricity, using either a slightly modified internal combustion engine or a gas turbine rather than transporting or storing it.

Pyrolysis involves heating the biomass in the absence of oxygen (as with traditional charcoal production) to produce a liquid fuel and a solid char plus a combustible gas. The resulting oil has a calorific value about half that of diesel fuel; it can be stored and transported and can be used for stationary engines and turbines. On the other hand the oil tends to contain a lot of water, can be corrosive and difficult to pump, may decompose at high temperature and can deteriorate if exposed to air.

In looking at the carbon dioxide emissions from FCBa as a business, it was sobering to note that emissions from car transport were very significant – higher, in fact, than those from building energy use. Bio-diesel can offer an (almost) zero carbon alternative to conventional mineral diesel without engine modification and at marginal extra cost.

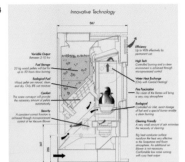

	Energy use (kWh/yr)	Pellet fuel (m³)
Typical house	26,880	10.60
2002 house	14,520	5.75
Low-energy house	6,600	2.61

1 Storage requirements for pellet fuel (source: Low-carbon heating with wood pellet fuel, XCO2 Conisbee, 2003)

2 Miscanthus bales being fed into a chipper unit (Biomass Industrial Crops)

3 Wamsler Inga pellet stove

4 Principles of heating from biomass

5, 6 Roll-on/roll-off wood chip supply containers (Econergy)

Further information

• www.biodiesel.co.uk (The British Association for Bio Fuels and Oils)

• www.xco2.co.uk/plus.htm (detailed report on wood pellet heating by XCO2)

• www.sac.ac.uk/envsci/External/WillowPower (Scottish Agricultural College website on energy from willow)

• www.bical.net (Biomass Industrial Crops – for information on miscanthus)

• www.binder-gmbh.at (Austrian manufacturer of biomass boiler systems)

Wind power

Bill Gething

Generating electricity from wind, particularly on a large scale, is one of the most cost effective methods of electrical production, even when compared to conventional fossil fuels. According to the British Wind Energy Association, the cost for a new installation is 3-4p per kWh, compared with 2.5-4.5p for clean coal and 4-7p for nuclear.

The technology is also very effective in terms of embodied energy, with each turbine generating as much energy as it takes to manufacture in 3-5 months. Turbines are reliable, typically requiring servicing every two years and last 20-25 years (there is also an increasing market for refurbished turbines as the first wind farms upgrade).

The most common design of wind turbine is with three blades mounted on a horizontal axis which is itself free to rotate to face the wind. The blades drive a generator either directly or via a gearbox to produce DC current which can either be stored in batteries or converted to AC using an invertor to feed into the grid. Other designs include vertical axis types and building integrated 'concentrator' solutions like those developed by Bill Dunster for the SkyZED project and Altechnica's ridge integrated Aeolian roof wind energy systems.

The UK has a disproportionately high wind resource compared with the rest of Europe; higher even than Denmark which generates 15 per cent of its electrical needs using wind (compared with about 1 per cent in the UK). This should increase to make up a very substantial part of the 10 per cent renewables target by 2010, a level at which our current regime for providing backup capacity can cope with the fluctuations of wind generation thanks to the accuracy of forecasting. Increasing this to about 20 per cent is possible but this would need extra storage or spinning

reserve which would increase costs.

Wind speed is critical as the power available is proportional to the cube of the wind speed. Turbines are typically designed to reach their optimum power output in winds of about 15m/sec and to shut off in gale force winds (above about 25m/sec) to avoid damage. Turbines can operate with wind speeds as low as 4m/sec.

Wind speed increases with height as the effect of ground roughness reduces. The power available at 24 metres above the ground is about 150 per cent of that at 10 metres. A turbine site should also be free of obstructions within 60 metres and, if there any trees in the area, the turbine should be mounted at least 10 metres above them.

Ideally the actual wind resource for an intended location should be monitored for at least a year before installing a turbine. However, a rough guide to the available resource at a height of 10 metres in open countryside is shown on the map (right; note that turbine losses would reduce the figures by about a third) and there is a database on the BWEA website to give the approximate average wind speed for a particular set of coordinates for different heights.

The BWEA suggests that a large turbine requires a minimum average wind speed of about 7m/s to guarantee a reasonable return. However, different economics apply to installations which use the electricity generated on site. For example, the Renewable Energy Systems headquarters in Langley (by architect Studio E with Max Fordham & Partners) is located in an area that has one of the lowest wind speeds in the country but the installation of a (second-hand) 225kW turbine was judged viable and this now generates more electricity than is needed on site. As a rough guide to the total amount of

energy generated over a year by a turbine, a wind farm operator might expect 2,600,000kWh per MW of rated capacity of a turbine, whereas the equivalent figure for the RES site might be 1,000,000kWh/year.

The power available from a turbine of any design is directly proportional to its swept area and turbines are available in a range of sizes to suit a variety of locations and applications, from small units of around 30 watts and under 600mm diameter used to charge caravan or boat batteries up to 4.5MW and 120 metres in diameter for offshore wind farm applications. Generally the larger the turbine, the more economic it is, but increasing size increases their impact and the potential for public resistance.

Wind turbines require planning permission so early consultation is advised, and the impact on the local ecology and on key view points should be assessed. For turbines over 50kW, demonstration of 'very special circumstances' will be required for any site in Greenbelt or Metropolitan Open Land. The UK also has some of the strictest policies on avoiding interference with civil and military radar and aviation which will need to be taken into account for larger structures. The London Renewables Toolkit published by the GLA and Wind Power in the UK published by the Sustainable Development Commission provide useful guidance on the process.

At the domestic scale, there are moves to allow small turbines (up to 1.5m diameter) under permitted development as for satellite dishes. They can be mounted directly onto buildings provided simple measures are incorporated to isolate vibration. These devices typically cost less than £1,000. However, this is a very new market, as

yet with no agreed standards. Great care should be taken to check quality of build, robustness and realistic output predictions before buying.

Modern turbines are remarkably quiet thanks to improvements in gearbox design. The only discernible noise is from the swish of the blades as they pass the tower – and this would be drowned by a passing car. Minimum distances from occupied buildings need to be assessed according to the particular site's circumstances and background noise levels – particularly at night. Small turbines can even be located in dense urban areas; temporary planning permission was obtained for a small turbine on the roof of the RIBA headquarters in central London after monitoring noise levels.

Wind turbines are generally eligible for Government sponsored credits awarded for generation of electricity from renewables. Even small turbines may generate sufficient electricity to qualify and turbine companies are developing products that aim to be 'plug and play' via a simple 13amp plug. However their performance in practice is yet to be proved.

Further information

• Sustainable Urban Design, an Environmental Approach, ed Randall Thomas (Spon).

• British Wind Energy Association www.bwea.com

• Danish Wind Industry Association www.windpower.org

• Grants: www.clear-skies.org

• London Renewables Toolkit www.london.gov.uk

• Sustainable Development Commission Wind Power in the UK www.sd-commission.org.uk

• European Wind Energy Association www.ewea.org

1

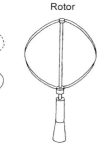

| Savonius Rotor | Darrieus Rotor | H-type Darrieus Rotor | Large Turbine |

2

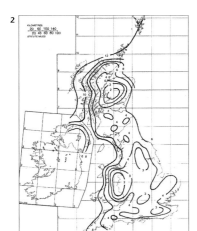

3

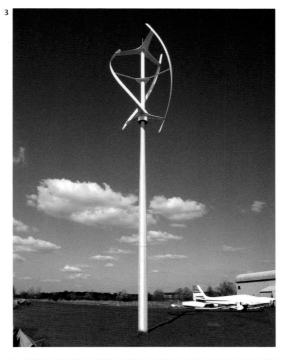

1 Vertical axis turbines (source: Sustainable Urban Design).

2 UK wind power potential (source: Sustainable Urban Design).

Right Quiet Revolution, Swift and Vestas V90 wind turbines.

Comparative outputs for different sized turbines

Rated output	Diam	Approx output	Turbine
0.6kW	2.55m	900-2,300 kWh/yr	Proven WT600
1.0	1.75	1,400-3,300	Windsave
2.5	3.5	3,300-7,400	Proven WT2500
6.0	5.5	9,000-19,400	Proven WT6000
15.0	9.0	23,000-48,500	Proven WT1500

Typical annual domestic electrical consumption

1,500kWh	2-bedroom, 4-person flat
2,500kWh	4-bedroom, 7-person house

Sources: Proven, Windsave, Building Regulations

205

Principles of daylighting

Peter Clegg

Louis Kahn said, 'without daylight architecture does not exist'. Buildings can leap into life with 100,000 lux on a bright sunny day and become subdued and restrained under a diffuse and overcast sky. Daylight penetrating the building enlivens it and makes the connection with the outdoor climate, the time of day and the season of the year. But we need to be able to apply controls and filters to achieve either visual excitement or visual comfort. Our buildings should allow us to manipulate daylight. Spaces designed to raise the spirits often play on the variation in intensity of light and dark, but many functional spaces require a more even and glare free environment. A difference in light levels between a south-facing window sill in direct sunlight and the back of a six metre deep room can be a factor of 30, and the architectural challenge in minimising electrical lighting is to achieve a more uniform and diffuse lighting level throughout the space.

Electric lighting accounts for 15 per cent of our total electrical consumption. The energy cost of lighting a typical workspace is between 5 and 10 kWh/m²/year at a carbon cost of 50-100Kg of CO_2/m²/year. In schools and offices this can amount to more than

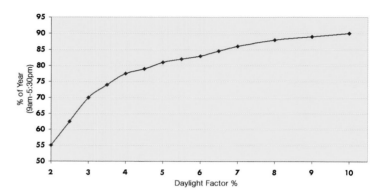

1 Percentage of the working year in London when artificial light is not required for a given daylight factor (source: Max Fordham llp).

Direct sunlight	100,000+ lux
Average diffuse sky illuminance: London, 12am, June	35,000 lux
Average diffuse sky illuminance: London, 12am, December	10,000 lux
5% daylight factor based on the above	500 lux
2% daylight factor based on the above	200 lux
Recommended illuminances for: corridors/wcs	150 lux
vdu usage/classrooms	300 lux
standard general office	500 lux
high precision task work	1,000 lux
Recommended maximum levels for highly sensitive materials	50 lux

2 Typical and recommended illuminance levels.

Ten key points

• Where high levels of uniform diffuse light are needed, north-facing windows provide the easiest solution. South-facing windows are easier to protect from unwanted solar heat gain and glare than east and west elevations. Thus it is easier to daylight a linear building facing north-south than one facing east-west.
• Light from two sides (or a roof and one side) provides more uniform and natural distribution of light.
• A square metre of rooflight admits about three times as much daylight as a square metre of glazing in a wall – but generally also admits more solar gain.
• Generally there will be good daylighting on a working surface if it can 'see' the sky. Optimising daylight therefore tends to require high-level glazing.
• The extent of daylight penetration depends on the height of the window wall. For effective daylighting, a reasonable height-to-depth ratio for a room would be 1:2 (maximum 1:3).
• The ideal percentage of glazing to achieve a reasonable trade-off between daylighting and heat loss should be between 35 and 55 per cent. Below 20 per cent will result in excessive artificial lighting; above 60 per cent could result in excessive heat loss, unless very high performance glazing is used.
• Glare often occurs at the window-to-wall surface. It can be reduced by deep reveals or light shelves which bounce the light up, or by solar control blinds.
• External light shelves will enhance overall light distribution, mainly in direct sunlight on southerly elevations. Their effect in diffuse sunlight is negligible.
• The object of a good daylighting scheme should be to reduce the incidence of 'blinds down, lights on'; but with VDU usage, fine tuning of glare control means that internal blinds are necessary anyway. Internal blinds need to be 'designed in' – make sure they don't impede natural vents and allow windows to be operated.
• Reflectivity of internal surfaces is essential to diffuse natural light deep into the plan and reduce glare.

50 per cent of the total carbon dioxide emissions. Good daylighting has the ability to halve that environmental cost.

For an office, a three per cent daylight factor may result in reducing the need for artificial light by 70 per cent (1). At the National Trust offices the aim was to achieve a five per cent daylight factor to all working areas, so that artificial lighting is necessary for less than 20 per cent of working hours.

We need to understand illuminance: tune our eyes and walk around with a light meter. Variation in lux levels can result in liveliness as well as glare.

Daylight modelling

Internal light level modelling (eg radiance) can look at the three-dimensional illumination of the room. We modelled the National Trust building using Ecotect. Physical models under an artificial sky can dramatically illustrate changes in light level with orientation.

Further information
• Lighting for Buildings BS8206-2 (1992).
• Energy Research Group, University College Dublin, Daylighting in Buildings (Dublin 1994).
• DfES Building Bulletin 90, Lighting Design for Schools (1997).
• Paul Littlefair, Daylighting and Solar Control in the Building Regulations (BRE Garston 1999).

Light

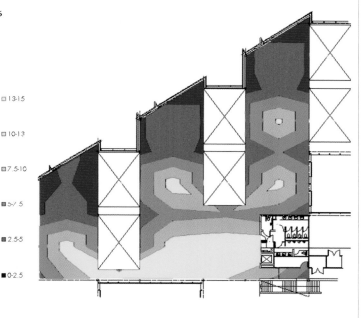

□ 13-15

□ 10-13

□ 7.5-10

■ 5-7.5

■ 2.5-5

■ 0-2.5

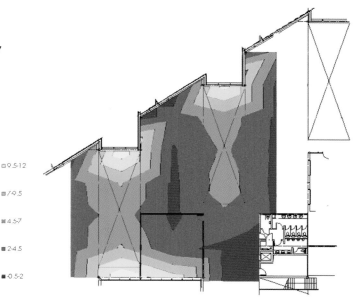

□ 9.5-12

■ 7-9.5

■ 4.5-7

■ 2-4.5

■ -0.5-2

3 Physical model of the National Trust central office in the artificial sky at the Bartlett, UCL.
4 Interior photograph of model at equinox: 5pm March 21st.
5 Ecotect model of the National Trust central office.
6-7 Ground- and first-floor daylight factors produced from artificial sky tests (Max Fordham).

Harry Montresor
Montresor Partnership

Transparency plays a key role in low energy architecture. The balance between light transmission and heat insulation of the building skin is a key design decision.

Glass is a peculiar super-cooled liquid of calcium and sodium silicates. It has been around for 2,000 years but it is only recently that a number of processes have been developed that allow us to vary its transmission and insulation properties. These include:

Tinting and coating
• Tinted body colours (with a range of percentage light transmissions):

grey	25%
blue	30%
bronze	33%
green	61%
clear	84%
super clear (low iron)	91%

• Ceramic coating or 'fritting' to partly or fully opacify glass (see University of Plymouth, Portland Square).
• Pyroltic coating used to create hard transparent reflective and refractive coatings for solar control and low-E glass.
• Sputtering which involves depositing a very thin layer of metal on the surface of the glass, producing 'soft' low-E coatings which need to be protected by incorporation into double glazed units.

Laminated glass
Lamination involves bonding two or more panes of glass with an integral interlayer to obtain a composite glazing material. Options include:
• Polyvinyl butyral (PVB) to create laminated glass for greater strength.
• Prismatic interlayers. A micro-edged prismatic acrylic interlayer can produce an integral venetian blind, eg Serraglaze (www.Redbus.Serraglaze.com).
• Fabric interlayers of woven glass fibre

or silk can produce translucency.
• Photovoltaic interlayers using monocrystalline cells or thin film poly-crystalline wafers can produce glazing with a variable proportion of transmission. (see Photovoltaics, Earth Centre)

Sealed units
Even greater flexibility can be achieved using sealed units of multiple layers of glass incorporating heat insulating cavities. The optimum cavity width is 15mm; greater widths induce convection currents. Standard U-values for 6:15:6 units are:

Air filled cavity	2.7w/m²K
Air filled cavity + standard low-E coating	1.6w/sm²K
Argon-filled cavity + standard low-E coating	1.3w/m²K
Krypton-filled cavity + standard low-E coating	1.1w/m²K
Argon-filled cavities + two low-E coatings	0.6w/m²K

These figures are for a 'mid-pane' U-value. Edge seals cause thermal bridges (though plastic is better than metal) and normally result in a 5-10% increase in U-value. Krypton is still prohibitively expensive as are the new vacuum-filled cavities which are predicted to give U-values down to 0.3w/m²K.

Interstitial layers
The space between the two layers of glazing allows scope for further light and heat modifying properties to be added such as:
• Interstitial louvres, polished aluminium louvre blades to redirect sunlight eg OkaSolar (www.okalux.de).
• Interstitial capillary tubes made from glass, acrylic or polycarbonate and used to reflect or redirect solar radiation eg Okalux (see above).

Typical thermal resistance and light transmittance characteristics of various glazing configurations (source: FCBa/Montresor Partnership)

Product	Description	Approx cost 1-5 scale	Thickness mm	Max size m	Typical U-value	Typical transmittance Total solar %	Total visible %	Comments
Clear single glazing	Clear float glass	1	6	2.7 x 6	5.4	83	87 (transparent)	Maximum size dimensions are theoretical – in practice, live loads and self weight would reduce these dimensions or increase thickness. Maximum sizes can increase with special production runs
Clear double-glazed units	Two panes of clear float glass with a hermetically sealed air filled cavity	2	6.16.6	2.7 x 6	2.8	73	73 (transparent)	Maximum size dimensions are theoretical – in practice, live loads and self weight would reduce these dimensions or increase thickness.
Clear low-E coated double-glazed units	Air filled cavity	3	6.16.6	2.7 x 6	1.4	53	73 (transparent)	Maximum size dimensions are theoretical – in practice, live loads and selfweight would reduce these dimensions or increase the thicknesses. Gas-filled units restrict the use of some glazing systems since they require UV-sensitive (polysulphide) edge seals.
	Argon filled cavity		6.16.6	2.7 x 6	1.1	53	73 (transparent)	
	Krypton filled cavity		6.16.6	2.7 x 6	1.1	53	73 (transparent)	
Combination coated double-glazed units	Two panes of clear float glass with a combination Low E and Solar Control coating to the cavity surface of one and an Argon filled cavity	4	6.16.6	2.7 x 5	1.2	32	61 (transparent)	The soft nature of combination coatings requires their use in multiple pane units only. Many combination coatings have a neutral colour in transmission but a slight green or blue bias in reflection.
Clear low-E coated triple-glazed units	Three panes of clear float glass (two with Low E coatings) with Argon filled cavities	4	6.16.6.16.6	2.7 x 6	0.6	52	68 (transparent)	Maximum size dimensions are theoretical – in practice, live loads and self weight would reduce these dimensions.
Light re-directing interlayers	Light refracting and reflecting (by TIR) micro-replicated plastic mosaic interlayers laminated and sealed to clear glass panes	5	1 (interlayers)	0.3x0.3 mosaics	5.3	75	85 (transparent)	These interlayers, unlike other prismatic products, are almost completely transparent and may be used in combination with other glass, coating and cavity configurations.
Profiled glass	Cast glass channel section planks	1	6 thick 40 flange	0.5 wide x7 long	5.6	78	85 (translucent)	Can be low-E coated and site assembled into rudimentary double glazing.
Glass blocks	Hollow cast glass blocks	2	100	0.3 x 0.3	2.9	57	75 (translucent)	Available with different surface textures (including prismatic for light redirection)
Interstitial acrylic capillary tube slabs	Thermally insulating and heat and light reflecting capillary tube slabs mounted within glazed unit cavities	4	16	2 x 3.5	2.2	40	67 (translucent)	Capillary tube slabs can be obtained in thicknesses between 8 and 40mm with correspondingly different properties. The slabs also provide a significant reduction in UV transmission.
Interstitial fixed reflective louvre blades	Light and heat reflecting louvres mounted within glazed unit cavities	5	6.23.6	2 x 3.5	2.7	Dependent on configuration 10-50	Dependent on configuration 2-60	Different profile and shape blades are available and their angle may be configured in relation to performance requirements.
	As above with low E coating and gas filled cavities		6.23.6	2 x 3.5	1.7 (argon) 1.4 (krypton)	Dependant on configuration 10 - 50	Dependant on configuration 2-60	
Translucent grp panels	Glass fibre filled GRP faced translucent panels	4	70	1.5 x 6	1.25	20	19 (translucent)	Appearance of panels determined by orientation and relatively small scale of the internal supporting grid (typically 300mm x 600mm).
	As above but aerogel filled				0.28	12	11 (translucent)	
Extruded polycarbonate multiple wall sheeting	2-wall 4-wall 6-wall	3	10 20 25	2.1 x 6 1.2 x 7 1.2 x 7	3.2 2.0 1.5		79 (translucent) 77 (translucent) 66 (translucent)	Difficult to completely seal the cavities.
Pneumatic EFTE Foil cushions	Multiple translucent skin pressurised ETFE film cushions	4				Variable	Variable	Constant air supply required to maintain pressure within the cushions.

Shading and solar controls

Peter Clegg

• Interstitial aerogels – these are highly porous filigree microscopic cavity structures of 2-5% silicate and 95-98% air. Still in development, 20mm thick aerogel in a sealed unit has a theoretical U-value of 0.7w/sqmK.
• Interstitial films – low-E coated polymer films suspended between two layers of glass can give properties similar to triple glazing but with reduced weight, eg heat mirror (www.south-wall.com).

And remember… the glazing can be filled with all kinds of natural and artificial objects, broken glass, light bulbs, bamboo etc to filter light, though increased conductivity is bound to increase U-values. Details of transmittances, costs and properties of various glazing materials are given in the adjacent table.

Further information
• www.serraglaze.redbus.co.uk (interlayers)
• www.reglit.com (profiled glass)
• www.okalux.com (interstitial systems)
• www.kalwall.com (translucent grp panels)
• www.makroform.com (multiple wall sheets)
This section was compiled with help from Harry Montresor, cladding consultant on many FCBa projects.

Direct sunlight that enhances and enlivens our buildings can cause unwanted heat gain and glare. Controlled and filtered light can produce usable solar heat gain in winter and can also reduce the need for artificial lighting.

The first thing to decide is whether shading is needed to control solar heat gain or glare. External shading is essential to stop sunlight getting in through the glass and can also help with glare control and light diffusion. Fine tuning of glare is best done by inter-pane or internal blinds. Double-skin solutions are rarely cost-effective but they do provide a good solution to the protection of blinds, so long as the heat can be vented away from them.

To design for solar shading it is necessary to understand where the sun is coming from throughout the day and throughout the year (1).

Further information
• Paul Littlefair, Solar Shading and Buildings (BRE 1999)

Ten key points

• Horizontal louvres are best for south elevations, vertical 'blinkers' work well for east and north west elevations. Movable shading is generally needed for east and west elevations.
• Avoid external moving parts if possible and check maintenance regimes carefully.
• Diffusing sunlight with fritted glass, tinted glass, diffusing laminations or external screens cuts down on solar gain and glare but can impact on view.
• Help in directing incoming sunlight can be provided by translucent insulation material such as Okasolar or Serraglaze (which has darkened louvres built into the glass) and prismatic glass.
• Electrochromic and photochromic glass can switch from opaque to transparent; both are still expensive but worth keeping an eye on.
• Think about cleaning blinds and shading systems as well as the glass; it is often better to space shading off the building to allow for this, and also to make sure that windows can open.
• Perforated materials or a fine stainless steel fabric mesh can preserve the view, as do thin but widely spaced louvres.
• Test mock-ups with three-dimensional modelling in artificial skies and think about junctions and details – it is amazing how light can get in.
• Remember that a lot of shading can be done within the glass itself. 35 per cent of the total solar transmission can be cut out while still maintaining 65 per cent of visible light; but in order to reduce summertime solar gain significantly, 80-90 per cent shading is often necessary.
• Finally, try trees. Deciduous ones provide summertime shading but let the winter sun in (see Yorkshire Sculpture Park Visitor Centre). But they can take some time to grow and don't last for ever.

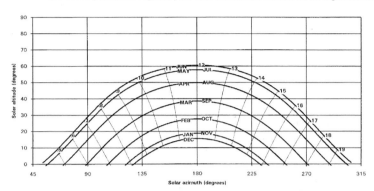

Calculating the sun's position through the year: solar altitude and azimuth for 52 degrees north

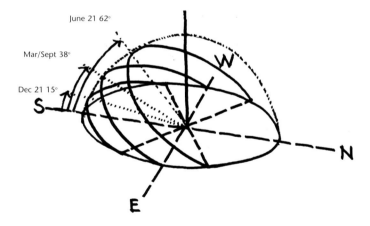

Sunpath for 52 degrees north

June 21 62°

Mar/Sept 38°

Dec 21 15°

Earth Centre restaurant

Oriention: E/S/W
Green oak battens: slatted timber screen walling extends over glazing.

Painshill Park visitor centre

Oriention: S
Kiln-dried oak panels: gardenesque sun/rain shading to walkway and glazing; caused more light reduction than anticipated.

Greenpeace UK headquarters

Oriention: S
Painted steel, suspended: combination of external suspended steel lightshelves with internal fabric lightshelves.

Oxstalls campus, University of Gloucestershire

Oriention: S
Standard Merlin aerofoil sections: horizontally mounted and south-facing, acting as lightshelves in conjunction with mesh access walkways.

BRE New Environmental Offices

Oriention: S
Colt 10mm fritted glass louvres, BMS control/individual override: used with vertical stacks and horizontal walkways; all summer sun is excluded; minimal sightlines.

Kingswood school

Oriention: S
Motorised Levolux perforated white aluminium louvres: used for high-level south-facing glazing; perforations provide approx 5 per cent diffused light when closed.

Oxstalls sports science building

Oriention: S
Motorised Merlin aerofoil section cedar furs Suspended louvres to shade the fully glazed restaurant facade.

Open University east elevation

Oriention: E
Perforated grey-painted steel on suspension cables: used with horizontal walkways and internal fin-shaped columns.

Oxstalls Learning Resource Centre

Oriention: N
Perforated steel suspended from eaves: 'blinkers' to prevent glare from the north west (evening summer use).

Francis Close Hall University of Gloucestershire

Oriention: W
Proprietary aluminium aerofoil sections: Teleflex-type operation system not designed for student use… louvres no longer move!

Open University west elevation

Oriention: W
Proprietary perforated pvc blinds, motorised activators: pvc blinds on cables spanning between walkways; solar sensor closes blinds but wind sensor tends to close them again; does not tolerate wind speeds over 5m/sec!

John Cabot City Technology College

Oriention: S/W
Proprietary pvc blinds, motorised activators; yellow (more transparent) and blue (less so) fabric blinds enliven elevations.

Rare hq

Oriention: S
Cedar slats, Merlin system: cedar slats in aluminium framing; operated by manual handle from inside (not very sophisticated!).

Rare HQ

Oriention: S/E/W
Aluminium slats, Merlin system: similar to above but aluminium; tended to rattle but manufacturer has improved guiding system.

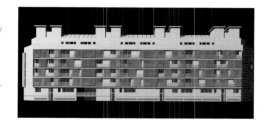

EMV Housing Madrid

Oriention: E/W/S
Timber slats in aluminium frame: multi-layered 2.5m square sliding shutters to entire elevation; vertical slat on east and west elevations.

Portland Square, University of Plymouth

Oriention: E/S/W
Fritted glass 30/60 per cent opacity: fully-fritted panes at spandrels; 60 per cent frit reduces solar gain on south and west.

CPTMC Building, University of Bath

Oriention: S/E
Stainless steel 50 per cent mesh suspended on front of glass: mesh has to be tensioned horizontally and vertically; has surprisingly little visual impact.

London Centre for Nanotechnology

Oriention: E
Perforated aluminium: fritted pattern developed with artist using moiré patterns found in studying sub-atomic particles.

Kingswood school

Oriention: S
Typical projecting eaves: extended horizontal zinc-clad gutters and eaves provide 'eyelids' to windows.

Oxstalls campus

Oriention: E
Typical projection in plan: projecting stair tower shades glazed atrium entrance after 10am in mid-summer.

Artificial lighting

Sara Grohmann

Artificial lighting is one of the main components of the service costs and energy consumption of a building. In naturally ventilated offices lighting can account for over 40 per cent of the overall electricity cost. Good lighting design can reduce these running costs and the risk of high internal heat gains, which may in turn affect the need for air conditioning.

To achieve an energy-efficient artificial lighting system two elements are fundamental:
• to install efficient light fittings; and
• to maximise the use of daylight when appropriate.

A good balance between artificial and natural light can also critically affect the safety, health and welfare of the occupants.

An interesting study on 39 households carried out by BRE as part of an Energy Efficiency Best Practice Programme shows the average hours of lighting in different rooms in a house. The greatest savings associated with energy-efficient lighting can be achieved in the rooms that are lit for the longest period (fig 1).

The Cibse Code for Interior Lighting sets out recommended maintained illuminance levels for various activities and building types. For office environments where computers are used the recommended level of light varies between 300 and 500 lux.

The effectiveness of a light installation in terms of a balance between the required luminance level and the minimum power consumption is related to four key factors:
• the efficacy of the lamp (defined as the luminous flux, plus power consumed by any control gear), measured in lumens/watt;
• the Light Output Ratio (LOR), ie the efficiency of a luminaire in delivering light on the working plane;
• the efficiency of the control gear – low loss and high frequency ballasts can improve substantially the efficiency of a lighting system; and
• the arrangement of the luminaries within the space.

A summary of the characteristics of currently available lamps is given in Figure 2. New lamps are coming onto the market regularly and technology such as LEDs may prove extremely energy-efficient.

Part L of Building Regulation states that in order to serve office environments with reasonably efficient lamp/luminaire combinations, lighting systems should be installed with an initial efficacy average over the whole building of not less than 40 luminaire-lumen/circuit-watt. Circuit-watts is defined by Approved Document L2 as 'the power consumed in lighting circuits by lamps and their associated control gear and power factor correction equipment' (1).

Lighting control systems

In trying to maximise the use of daylight, effective control systems for the light fittings have a crucial role. This can be achieved either with presence or absence detectors and light sensors as well as manual switches. According to BRE, in office spaces the flexible manual control of the lighting system together with time switching, can help to reach energy savings of 30-40 per cent. The ability to boost lighting levels at individual work stations just when it is needed, while keeping lower levels of general lights elsewhere, can be an energy-efficient solution, especially in offices with a high use of computers.

Lighting control systems can vary from simple presence and daylight sensors, which switch lights off and on depending on the use of the space and on the daylight level, to more sophisticated automatic dimming and computerised systems, which can vary levels of light in different spaces in relation to different uses and daylight factors (3). Control systems need to be manually overridden by the individual users, either in zones or at every individual workstation, depending on the sophistication of the system.

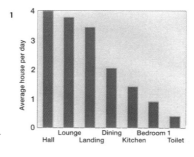

1 Use of artificial lighting in a domestic building (source: Low Energy Domestic Lighting).

2 Characteristics of current lamp types (source: Illustrated Guide to Electrical Building Services).

Further information

• Oxford Brookes University, Energy Effective Interior Lighting 2002, Workshop Manual (Oxford 2002).

• http://europa.eu.int/comm/energy_transport/atlas/htmlu/lightdintro.html (Atlas).

• Cibse, Code for Interior Lighting (London 1994).

• Building Regulations England & Wales, Approved Document L2 (2002).

• BSRIA, Illustrated guide to electrical building services (London 2001).

• BRE, Energy Efficient Lighting: Part L of the Building Regulations Explained (BRE Garston 2001).

• BRE, Low Energy Domestic Lighting, Summary Guide (BRE Garston 2002).

2

Standard incandescent	Lamp type	Incandescent	Comments
	Efficacy (lm/W)	10 - 13	• Low costs.
	Average life (hours)	1000	• Excellent colour rendering.
	Colour temp. (K)	2800	• No requirement for control gear.
	Colour rendering (R₂)	100	• Short lamp life. • Low efficacy.
Tungsten halogen	Lamp type	Incandescent	Comments
	Efficacy (lm/W)	15 - 22	• Around 60% more efficient than standard incandescent lamps.
	Average life (hours)	1500 - 3000	• No control gear is required.
	Colour temp. (K)	2700 - 3100	• Produce a significant amount of heat.
	Colour rendering (R₂)	100	
Standard tubular fluorescent	Lamp type	Discharge	Comments
	Efficacy (lm/W)	60 - 100	• Good efficacy.
	Average life (hours)	8000 - 16 000	• Broad range of colour rendering characteristics.
	Colour temp. (K)	2700 - 6500	• Long lamp life.
	Colour rendering (R₂)	54 - 98	• Requires electronic control gear.
Compact fluorescent	Lamp type	Discharge	Comments
	Efficacy (lm/W)	50 - 85	• Long lamp life.
	Average life (hours)	8000 - 10 000	• Good efficacy.
	Colour temp. (K)	2700 - 5400	• Good colour rendering.
	Colour rendering (R₂)	80 - 98	• Initial cost is high.
High pressure mercury	Lamp type	Discharge	Comments
	Efficacy (lm/W)	40 - 55	• Generally cheaper than sodium lamps.
	Average life (hours)	9000 - 24 000	• Long lamp life.
	Colour temp. (K)	3000 - 4000	• Control gear required.
	Colour rendering (R₂)	40 - 65	• Long start up and restrike time*.
Low pressure sodium	Lamp type	Discharge	Comments
	Efficacy (lm/W)	100 - 200	• Long lamp life and high efficacy.
	Average life (hours)	10 000 - 15 000	• Very poor colour rendering.
	Colour temp. (K)		• Often used for external lighting.
			• Control gear required.
	Colour rendering (R₂)	20 - 25	• Long start up and restrike time*.
High pressure sodium	Lamp type	Discharge	Comments
	Efficacy (lm/W)	50 - 90	• Good efficacy and lamp life.
	Average life (hours)	8000 - 10 000	• Better colour rendering than low pressure sodium lamps.
	Colour temp. (K)	2000 - 3000	• Control gear required.
	Colour rendering (R₂)	60 - 85	• Long start up and restrike time*.
Metal halide	Lamp type	Discharge	Comments
	Efficacy (lm/W)	75 - 90	• Good efficacy.
	Average life (hours)	8000 - 10 000	• Good colour rendering.
	Colour temp. (K)	3000 - 6000	• Long lamp life.
	Colour rendering (R₂)	80 - 90	• Control gear required. • Long start up and restrike time*.

* Modern control gear can enable instantaneous on/off switching of the lamp (hot restrike control gear).

Principles of
natural ventilation

Peter Clegg

Traditional English architecture has always been based on sound principles of natural ventilation, from the flexibility of the Georgian sash window, allowing flexibility in high- and low-level openings, to the complex use of ventilating chimneys in late Victorian buildings. The principal reasons for employing natural ventilation are to:
• provide oxygen;
• reduce odours and pollution;
• reduce internal temperatures using cool air from outside and the cooling effect of air movement;
• purge the building at night to reduce summertime overheating.

Wind and stack effect ventilation
In the UK, wind-driven ventilation will generally dominate stack-driven ventilation and it is important to understand where the wind comes from in relation to the site, obstructions etc. Generally, the prevailing winds in the UK come from the south west, although advanced natural ventilation systems must be able to cope with all directions. Figures 1 and 2 show wind 'roses' indicating the prevalence of wind direction throughout the year. Local data is generally available from airports. The table (right) shows the Beaufort scale of wind speed related to the delivery air speed of mechanical systems (for half the time in the UK hourly wind speeds are 3.5-5.5 m/sec).

Allowing air into buildings also brings the potential of noise, insects and air pollution. The first can be reduced by attenuation (see Wiltshire Music Centre) and the second by filtration (even insect screens as used at the Rare headquarters can reduce air speeds by about half and therefore imply larger openings). Sources of external air pollution need to be considered when designing natural ventilation air paths: always take in air from a clean source.

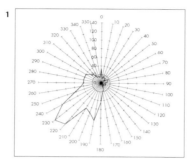

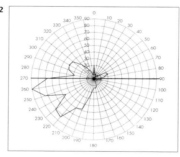

1, 2 Wind direction at Kew

Single-sided natural ventilation with carefully controlled high- and low-level openings can be used to ventilate spaces up to six metres deep or where the room depth is up to about 2.5 times the height. Rules of thumb suggest openings should be approximately five per cent of the floor area.

Cross ventilation can increase room depths to approximately 12 metres, providing that there are relatively clear ventilation air paths at high level. Beware the installation of partitions or large impediments to cross ventilation such as banks of filing cabinets.

Stack ventilation requires careful design of both low-level intakes and high-level exhaust openings so that wind direction does not cause reverse flow. High-level exhausts, in particular, should be protected or be omni-directional or, alternatively, use rotating air scoops which tend to be expensive and require maintenance. All openings, particularly high-level ones, require careful attention to the detailing of seals and control systems. Driving rain

and driven snow can come from anywhere and the system has to be failsafe.

As a starting point for natural ventilation design for high-occupancy buildings, plan for high- and low-level openings each equivalent to around 3-4 per cent of the floor area. Dampers, insect mesh and framing can reduce this to an effective area of less than two per cent.

When to go mechanical
Small high-efficiency fans with electronic draughtproof shutters are extremely reliable for short bursts of ventilation (wcs, showers etc). They can also incorporate smart control systems and heat recovery. The long-term efficiency of passive stack ventilation systems still needs to be proven and, if the brief calls for a high degree of control over air quality, ventilation rates and heat removal, mechanical ventilation with heat recovery may be a more logical approach. In exposed situations, mechanical systems may also prove advantageous. The challenge is to integrate both options without paying for too much duct work.

3

Wind speed and effects (adapted from Thomas 1999)

Beaufort scale	Description	Specification	Speed (mph)	(m/s)
0	Calm	Smoke rises vertically	Less than 1	Less than 1
1	Very light	Direction of wind shown by smoke drift but not by wind vanes		
		Acceptable flow rates for low level outlets	1-3	1-1.4
2	Light breeze	Wind felt on face, leaves rustle, ordinary wind vane moved by wind	4-7	1.5-1.9
3	Gentle breeze	Leaves and small twigs in constant motion, wind extends flags	8-12	2-3.4
4	Moderate breeze	Wind raises dust and loose paper, small branches move	13-18	3.5-4.9
5	Fresh breeze	Small trees in leaf start to sway; crested wavelets on inland waters		
		Acceptable flow rates for ceiling level outlets	19-24	5-6.4
6	Strong breeze	Large branches in motion, umbrellas used with difficulty	25-31	6.5-8.4
7	Near gale	Whole trees in motion, inconvenient to walk against wind	32-38	8.5-10.4
8	Gale	Twigs break from trees; difficult to walk	39-46	10.5-12.9
9	Strong gale	Slight structural damage occurs; chimney pots and slates removed	47-54	13-14.9
10	Storm	Trees uprooted, considerable structural damage occurs	55-63	15-17.4
11	Violent storm	Widespread damage	64-73	17.5-20.4
12	Hurricane	Widespread damage	>74	>20.5

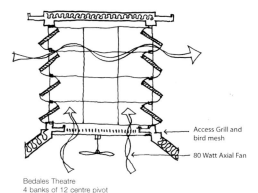

Bedales Theatre
4 banks of 12 centre pivot
Metal window frames
Opened according to wind conditions

Access Grill and
bird mesh

80 Watt Axial Fan

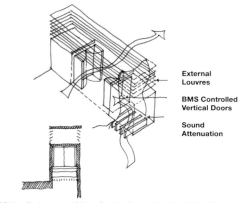

External
Louvres

BMS Controlled
Vertical Doors

Sound
Attenuation

BRE New Environmental Office : Seminar Room Natural Ventilation Outlet

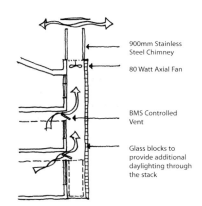

900mm Stainless
Steel Chimney

80 Watt Axial Fan

BMS Controlled
Vent

Glass blocks to
provide additional
daylighting through
the stack

BRE New Environmental Office

Rare Headquarters

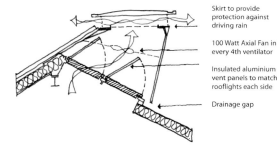

Skirt to provide
protection against
driving rain

100 Watt Axial Fan in
every 4th ventilator

Insulated aluminium
vent panels to match
rooflights each side

Drainage gap

National Trust Central Office

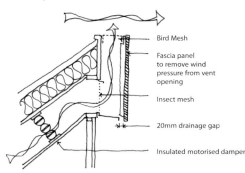

Bird Mesh

Fascia panel
to remove wind
pressure from vent
opening

Insect mesh

20mm drainage gap

Insulated motorised damper

Further information
• Cibse Applications Manual (revised version) AM10, Natural Ventilation in Non-Domestic Buildings (Cibse London 2005).
• Martin Liddament, A Guide to Energy Efficient Ventilation (Air Infiltration and Ventilation Centre, University of Warwick 1996).
• Randall Thomas (ed), Environmental Design: An Introduction for Architects and Engineers (second edition, London 1999).

Bill Gething

Adequate ventilation is essential for the health, safety and comfort of a building's occupants. However, to avoid discomfort and energy waste, it is important that this is controlled rather than the result of uncontrolled leakage through the building fabric – particularly so for air conditioned or low-energy naturally ventilated buildings.

Whereas airtightness standards have been mandatory in a number of countries for some years, the concept is new to UK construction. While voluntary energy performance schemes, such as the Medallion 2000 standard for houses, have included airtightness requirements, mandatory standards were not introduced into the Building Regulations until April 2002 (and then covering only non-domestic buildings over 1000 square metres). In contrast, in Sweden airtightness is so ingrained in the construction industry that tests are no longer compulsory.

Air leakage is commonly described in three ways:
• Air permeability (as used for the Building Regulations): the average volume of air (m³/hour) passing through one square metre of the building envelope (which includes all enclosing walls, including party walls, ceilings/roofs and floors) when the building is subject to a pressure difference (usually 50Pa) between inside and outside.
• Air leakage index: the commonly used standard before the introduction of mandatory standards into the Building Regulations (see Air Tightness Specifications, BSRIA Publication 10/98). Most historic test data uses this index, which is calculated in the same way as air permeability but does not include the area of the ground floor in the envelope area. So a given building leaking a given amount of air at a given pressure difference will have a lower air

permeability index than air leakage index. The difference will be most marked for low buildings with large footprints and correspondingly less for tall buildings with small footprints.
• Air change rate: expressed in air changes per hour, based on the volume of the building. Again an historic standard, this measure has traditionally been used by engineers to define ventilation rates for different uses.

Useful targets are shown in figure 2. To put these in context, it is worth noting that, traditionally, UK buildings perform badly. Even recently built houses vary considerably; the worst in the sample of 60 new houses tested by BRE was about 300 per cent worse than even the 'normal' air permeability standard proposed by BSRIA. It should also be noted that performance tends to deteriorate as new buildings dry out.

Specifying and detailing a building to achieve a high standard of airtightness requires the same level of rigour as that required to ensure it is watertight and with no gaps in its insulation. It is useful to identify these three layers (water, insulation and airtightness) when working up each detail, making sure they are continuous (in three dimensions!). The airtight layer is usually at, or close to, the inside surface of the external walls, restricting the passage of moist internal air into the fabric to avoid potential problems with condensation.

Air leakage paths are not necessarily obvious. There is an excellent checklist of typical air leakage paths in BSRIA Technical Note 19/2001 (available as a free download) but there are some general principles that are worth bearing in mind:
• Some materials that might appear solid are air permeable. Builders' work ducts formed in blockwork are notoriously leaky – for example unfinished

blockwork leaks between 0.1 and 60m³/(h/m²).

• In situ wet finishes such as plaster and screed are generally good at forming an airtight seal.

• Beware of hidden voids and joints even if they are apparently remote from the external surface of the building. Hollow-core concrete planks for example provide an air path from the middle of a building to the outside wall unless the ends and the joints between the planks are sealed.

• Allow for movement and shrinkage as the building dries out; will the seal be maintained?

• Design seals properly – for example, use mastics appropriate to the degree and frequency of movement and follow manufacturers' recommendations on joint design and detailing.

• Take particular care at the junction between subcontract packages.

Testing is essential and there are a growing number of UK contractors offering the service. A house can typically be tested in an hour or two using an electrically driven fan fitted into a doorway to pressurise or de-pressurise the building, with results available immediately. The Association for Environment Conscious Building has a test kit that can be hired by members.

Buildings are best tested as a whole rather than in sections. Larger buildings require more powerful equipment, such as the vehicle-powered fans used by BSRIA.

If the building fails, problems can be identified while the building is pressurised by using a smoke bomb and watching where smoke emerges or by walking round the depressurised building with a smoke puffer to identify where air is getting into it. It is extremely instructive to do this – a huge amount can be learnt about

potential failure paths by attending such a test. Thermography (infra-red photography) can also be useful in identifying where air is leaking (in addition to its normal use for spotting missing or weak points in insulation), although losses cannot be quantified.

As airtightness is an issue that cuts across many specification sections, we recommend using a dedicated specification section in the preliminaries.

Similarly, as airtightness depends significantly on quality of workmanship and work sequences, we recommend that the contractor is made responsible for rectifying failures identified when the building is tested. Under traditional forms of contract (eg JCT 98) the contractor is required to take on design responsibility, which will need to be formalised by the appropriate Contractor's Designed Portion Supplement. This should include a requirement to employ a specialist to carry out the test but also for the specialist to comment on design drawings, to visit site as work proceeds and advise the contractor of watch points that may affect airtightness. Formal reports on these visits should be issued to both contractor and contract administrator.

Further information
• Cibse Technical Memoranda TM23 (2000) – Testing buildings for air-leakage (London 2000)
• BSRIA Technical Note 19/01 – Air-tightness testing (London 2001)
• BSRIA Specification 10/98 – Air-tightness specifications (London 1998)
• BSRIA Technical Note 19/99 – Envelope integrity demonstration study (London 1999)
• BS EN 13829:2001 – Thermal performance of buildings: determining air permeability of buildings, fan pressurisation method (London 2001)
• BS EN 13187:1999: Thermal performance of buildings: qualitative detection of thermal irregularities in building envelopes, infra-red method (London 1999)

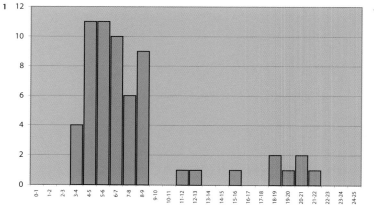

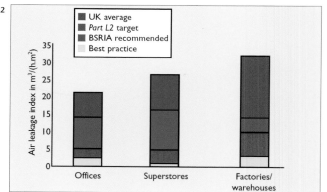

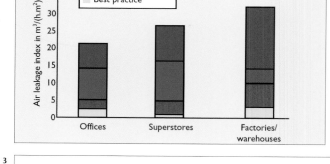

1

Maximum air leakage and permeability targets (m²/(h.m²) at 50 pascals)

	Leakage BSRIA		Permeability BSRIA	Best Practice Programme (GIL 72)		
	Normal	Best practice	Normal	Good practice	Best practice	Advanced
Dwellings	10.0	5.0	7.0	4.0	3.0	1.0
Offices:						
– naturally ventilated	10.0	5.0	7.0			
– mixed mode	7.5		5.0			
– air conditioned/low energy	5.0	2.4	3.5			
Factories/warehouses	10.0	3.0	7.0			
Superstores	5.0	0.9	3.0			
Museums and archival stores	2.0	1.4	1.4			
Cold stores	0.5	0.3	0.4			

1 Air leakage rates (m³/h per m²) for sample of dwellings built between 1987 and 1994.
2 Comparative air tightness standards for commercial buildings.
3 Maximum air leakage and permeability targets (from BRE Information Paper IP 1/00).
4 Typical equipment for testing a dwelling.
5 Vehicle-powered equipment for testing large buildings.

Mechanical ventilation

Ian Taylor

The more we demand of our buildings in terms of control over air quality, ventilation rate and heat removal, the more sensible it is to consider mechanical ventilation.

Advantages of mechanical ventilation
• Better control of ventilation rates in high occupancy areas.
• Better control of minimal ventilation rates (winter and summer).
• Better control of air quality – mechanical ventilation can filter incoming air.
• Better acoustic control – it is easier to provide attenuation within a mechanical ventilation system.
• Can be used to control air quality in spaces in deep-plan buildings with remote access to external walls or roof.
• Can be used to control air quality in spaces where high humidity or high levels of internal pollution are generated (eg showers and kitchens).
• Can be enhanced to provide heating and cooling as well as humidity control and can add a level of 'future proofing' to the building against future changes in use and climate.
• Exhausting heat from appliances at source.

Disadvantages can include
• Maintenance requirements are often higher than with natural ventilation.
• Capital cost and complexity of controls and maintenance.
• Poor air quality can result if ducts are not cleaned regularly.
• Potential lack of user control and local adjustment to suit individual preferences.
• A sense of remoteness from the external environment – the psychological benefits of opening windows should not be underestimated.
• Need to integrate ductwork into the design of the building.

Domestic buildings
In the UK domestic sector, until recently mechanical ventilation has been limited to simple bathroom and kitchen extract fans. However, increasing regulatory pressure to reduce energy use means that whole-house mechanical ventilation systems with heat recovery (MVHR) are likely to be used increasingly as the heat lost through ventilation becomes increasingly significant in highly insulated homes. FCBa has explored the use of such systems over some 20 years.

The critical issue is the balance between the amount of heat recovered and the energy used by the system's fans. The advantages become clearer for buildings with high occupancy levels such as theatres and auditoria.

At Cleveland Reach, Two Mile Ash and the Solar Courtyard houses at Milton Keynes, FCBa used MVHR to extract air from kitchen cooker hoods, wc's and bathrooms and input air into all other habitable rooms. Extract and intake fans blow air through a cross-plate heat exchanger with measured efficiencies in excess of 75 per cent (systems are now available with 90 per cent efficiency). The system can be boosted through the cooker hood, where all the kit is located. In an airtight house such as those at Two Mile Ash, with duct-work built into stud partitioning and floors, the system worked extremely well and it was possible therefore to omit central heating in favour of a 1.5kW heater battery located in the incoming air stream. At the Solar Courtyard houses, the construction was not sufficiently airtight to enable the system to work optimally.

Mechanical heat reclaim ventilation systems are appropriate for use in houses in multiple occupations (eg Aston University Student Housing and Queen Mary phase 3) and on localised systems

dealing with deep plan spaces (such as the central area of the Greenpeace building). This is particularly the case in accommodation with internal en suite bathrooms such as student residences, where extract/supply air ductwork can be grouped and connected to efficient units serving a large number of rooms. This usually adds a small cost premium, which unfortunately modest student housing budgets cannot rise to.

Offices and Institutional buildings
Termodeck systems, which pass air slowly through the floor slabs of the building (see Martial Rose Library and Oxstalls campus) can provide improved comfort and control in areas of high internal gain, maximising the benefits of night-time structural cooling with relatively low fan speeds and electrical consumption. The various systems for heat recovery are shown in the chart below.

Mixed mode systems
There are occasions when hybrid

solutions provide the best answer. FCBa's studies for the National Trust headquarters showed that lack of control of a natural ventilation system in winter would probably justify a mechanical ventilation system with heat recovery, although the payback could be in excess of 15 years.

Even buildings that can operate with natural ventilation for most of the year can sometimes benefit from being sealed and mechanically ventilated, in winter and even in hot summer-time conditions – increasingly so given our expectations of a warming climate. Most buildings require variable ventilation rates. Consider extracting from local source of humidity/pollution (eg grouping kitchens, wc's and photocopier areas in offices), using mechanical extract but natural ventilation supply. Alternatively, as at the Rare headquarters, use mechanical supply (with the option of fine-tuning a localised system with heating and cooling) and natural ventilation extract. But take care that heating and

cooling loads are balanced with the ventilation requirement.

The position of supply and extract grilles is influenced by the supply air temperature and speed as well as the air movement required in the space. As a general rule, it is more energy efficient to supply air near people and extract from spaces at high level, utilising the natural buoyancy of warmer air. But where cooling loads are very high, take care to minimise discomfort from air streams, which will need to be at a correspondingly low temperature.

The extra cost of mechanical systems can be offset more easily if they provide some, if not all, of the heating or cooling of the building, acting in conjunction with the building's thermal mass and purging the building at night.

Further information
• Best Practice Programme GIL072, Energy Efficiency Standards – for new and existing dwellings (Housing Energy Efficiency Best Practice Programme 2003 – download from www.housingenergy.org.uk).

Heat recovery system	Advantages	Disadvantages	FCBa examples
Partial air recirculation	Controllable Can recover sensible and latent heat components Efficient	Supply/extract ducts must be adjacent Risk of cross-contamination	Exemplar Schools
Plate heat exchanger	Simple, static device Low risk of cross-contamination between air streams	Supply/extract ducts must be adjacent Efficiency typically less than 50% Bulky	Solar Courtyard housing Aston student housing Oxstalls campus
Thermal wheel	Controllable Can recover sensible and latent heat components Efficiency 65-80%	Supply/extract ducts must be adjacent Risk of cross-contamination between air streams Difficult to clean Bulky	Martial Rose Library
Run-around coils	Controllable No risk of cross-contamination between air streams Supply and extract ducts need not be adjacent	Efficiency typically less than 65% Frost protection required	
Heat pipes	Simple, static device Low risk of cross-contamination between air streams Efficiency up to 75% Compact	Supply/extract ducts must be adjacent Relatively high costs	

Adapted from GPG303 The Designer's Guide to Energy Efficient Buildings for Industry (Brecsu, Garston 2000).

Bill Gething

A successful natural ventilation system will be based on clear principles, carefully selected products and a well organised process for its design, specification, construction, commissioning and maintenance. Designers and clients need to agree how the natural ventilation system will be controlled and managed. They also need to understand in some detail how occupants will be affected by, and interact with, the system. It is worth setting this down at an early stage as a simple description using non-technical language and diagrams.

Ten key points

• How will manual and automatic controls be integrated? The need for local over-ride by occupants must be carefully considered.
• What control and feedback devices will be provided for occupants and management?
• Take account of the pattern of usage of the building. A system that requires in-depth understanding will not be suitable if there is likely to be a high turnover of occupants – eg students.
• How many different types of ventilation device will be required to cope with all seasonal and occupational requirements?
• What restrictions are there in terms of noise, security and vandalism?
• Will protection be needed against high winds and rain penetration? If so, how will these be detected and how fast will the ventilators need to close?
• Is screening required against insects, birds and small animals?
• Will there be safe and convenient access for maintenance?
• Will the vents be genuinely airtight and insulated when closed?
• Be wary of cost: reliable actuators don't come cheap.

Products

Prototype automated naturally ventilated buildings tended to use components derived from different contexts or put together in non-standard combinations. While more tailored products are becoming available, an automated system will often bring together opening devices, builders' work, actuators and control systems from different 'worlds' that need to interface with each other and perform in a non-standard way.

The window/vent and its actuator should be supplied by the same company and delivered pre-assembled – one person needs to be in control.

Ventilators

• Do they have good levels of thermal integrity?
• Will they seal well when closed, even after years of use?
• Will they clash with other devices, eg fixed or movable blinds?
• Are they vulnerable to high winds? Anemometers are often used to close (or limit the travel of) openings when windspeeds are high.

Actuators and linkages

• What actuators and linkages will be used, and how will they be integrated and fixed?
• Is protection against dust and moisture required?
• Can they operate reliably with little maintenance, often for many cycles per day?
• Will they be sufficiently quiet in operation?

Controls

• Can the actuators communicate simply with local and/or centralised BMS controls?
• Has provision been made for all control devices, cabling and tubing?

• Have the user interfaces been properly considered and effectively designed?
• How will feedback of operational status be provided, both to individuals and to the central control system?

Process

A natural ventilation system may involve many different design disciplines, component suppliers and subcontractors. How is design responsibility allocated? Who specifies what? How do the various components and systems interface with each other?

Ten key points

• Agree the ventilation strategy with the client and keep it under review.
• Take early advice from suppliers.
• Clarify design responsibility: for strategies, components and integration.
• Include design intent and make responsibilities clear in the specification.
• If performance specifications are used for any elements, note that a change of component may affect other elements outside the scope of the specification.
• Clarify construction responsibility for key areas: subcontract package boundaries, coordination and programming; recording progress and build quality; rectifying faults.
• Clarify commissioning responsibility: static completion, mechanical testing, control systems.
• Plan for handover, operation, and maintenance.
• Make sure occupants are able to understand the system, both at first and in the future when occupants change, through system descriptions, staff training and leaflets for individuals.
• Plan for fine tuning during the first year of occupancy. Clearly define the roles of occupier, designer, contractor, controls and commissioning specialists.

Further information
• This section draws heavily on Specification of Automatic Ventilation Opening Devices, an umpublished Partners in Technology research project on which FCBa collaborated with Brian Ford Associates and Fulcrum Consultants: Bill Bordass (ed), 2000.
• Probe studies: http://www.usablebuildings.co.uk/
• Natural Ventilation for Offices (BRECSU, Garston 1999).

ACTUATOR TYPES

Linear push-pull piston
A motor propels a push rod forward; most commonly pneumatic but electro-hydraulic versions are also available.

Suitable for: high-level windows, sash windows, rooflights.

Advantages include mechanical simplicity, robustness, fire resistance of pneumatic units, and generation of large forces. Disadvantages include large projecting cylinders and mechanical damage to windows, linkages and fixings which are not robust enough. Travel is typically 200-500 mm, but longer distances are possible with large cylinders. Linkage options: single opening only.

Chain drive push-pull
Projecting chain drive push-pull actuators. An electric motor drives a chain over a sprocket wheel, providing linear motion to push out a window.

Suitable for: top- and bottom-hung, horizontal pivot, casement window.

With some exceptions, these units are modest in size and mechanical strength and have a limited travel of typically 150-200 mm. A useful feature is that the motion tends to be at right angles to the axis of the actuator body, which can therefore be tucked away in the plane of a window frame, or even concealed within it. Their compact size and unobtrusive appearance makes them best suited to smaller windows such as inward- and outward-opening fanlights.

Linkage options: single opening only.

Rack-and-pinion
A rotary electric motor drives a geared shaft which engages with one or more racks, providing linear motion with less bulky projections than linear actuators.

Suitable for: top-hung vents, sash windows, rooflights.

Capable of operating a large number of openings in series. They are also useful for windows which require paired actuators (on each side of a large window for example). With a common pinion the two racks move together. This avoids the potential for a large window to become twisted or even broken by the failure of one of a pair of independent actuators. Typical travel distances are 500 mm but 1000mm or more is possible.

Linkage options: large single openings, multiple openings in series; to maintain airtightness, ensure that individual adjustment of each linkage is allowed for.

Linear sleeved cable or rod
Often referred to as Teleflex drives, these are driven by a rack-and-pinion, worm gear or chain drive electric motor and allow linear motion to be transferred, for example to sliding sashes.

Suitable for: louvres, rooflights.

Individual components and fixings are often not as robust as other actuator types. Size and weight of individual vents should therefore be limited. Linkage options: multiple openings in series.

Rotary
These are most commonly supplied with dampers and louvres, often rotating one of the shafts directly, with mechanical linkages to the other louvres. Sometimes they also operate shafts connected to cranks and lever arms to provide linear motion.

Suitable for: dampers, louvres.

There are two main types: one with a bi-directional motor used for opening and closing; and one which motors in one direction only and uses a spring to return, which can be useful for fail-safe operations. Linkage options: single- or multiple-damper or louvre assemblies.

Lead screw
These actuators form the majority of linear actuators and are sub-divisible into high- and low-power applications. For general applications from 200N to 2000N; a low friction nut is driven along the lead screw to provide motive force.

Suitable for: louvres, rooflights.

The motor can be mounted in line with the lead screw or perpendicular to it. In-line mounted motors use a planetary gearbox to transmit the drive to the lead screw. This keeps the profile of the actuator slim but limits the available torque and therefore force of the actuator. Linkage options: multiple openings in series.

Lever arm actuator
Traditional type of vent opening gear often found in older (Victorian) buildings. Robust but visually intrusive.

Suitable for: top-hung vents, centre pivot vents.

Linkage options: multiple openings in series.

Gas struts with cables
A linear variant on the spring return motor is where an automatic catch releases the window and a gas-filled strut opens it, or holds it open. The window is closed by pulling on a cord, either manually or by means of a small electric winch.

Suitable for: high-level rooflights.

Typically used for smoke ventilation. Even in this application, make sure that windows can be closed easily as this will be necessary regularly when testing the alarm systems. Linkage options: single opening only.

Further information

• Available from manufacturers, including Automated Control Services, Belimo, Climate Control, Geze, Morse Controls, Rotary, SE Controls, Vent Gear, Windowmaster.

DAMPER TYPES

Standard blade dampers
Typically used for ventilation systems to control ductwork volume flow rates in connection with ductwork balancing. Low pressure loss when in the open position. Intermediate positions control volume flow rates. Maximum operating temperature: +100°C (special models: +200°C).

Construction: flanged steel casing for installation in rectangular or circular ductwork. Standard dimensions: height and width 100-2400mm, in 100mm increments. All dampers have a position indicator and manual adjustment device.

Comments: Not generally suitable for use in natural ventilation systems, as air leakage in the closed position is significant. See also comment on Sealed blade dampers below.

Sealed blade dampers
Typically used to close a ductwork branch as, in the closed position, air leakage is low. System pressure: up to 5000 Pa. Low pressure loss when in the open position. Intermediate positions control volume flow rates. Operating temperature range: -40°C to +200 °C (+300°C for short duration).

Construction: also available as a heat-tight damper for rectangular and circular ducts which can also tolerate mechanical stress and corrosion. Standard dimensions: circular 100Ø to 1000Ø, rectangular: 100-2000mm, in 100mm increments. Casing and blades: usually painted hot-dipped galvanised or acid-proof steel. Gaskets fitted to blade edges and between blade ends and frame.

Comments: The motor operating the blades protrudes from the side of the casing. This is ideal for ductwork installations but causes difficulties when building into structural openings. In this case a separate frame enclosing both damper casing and motor is required (including provision for access to the motor for replacement and maintenance). Even then, beware of cold bridging through the blades and casings, potentially leading to condensation etc. It is preferable to use an insulated damper unit, purpose designed for use in external walls – see below.

Insulated and sealed dampers
Purpose-designed natural ventilation unit for building in to external walls. Acoustically attenuated versions available. 24 or 240v actuators, modulating (24v only) or simple open/closed options.

Construction: Thermally broken frame with draught-sealed insulated internal motorised louvres, integrated insect screen, motor and external weatherproof louvres. Internal louvres: pvc; external louvres: aluminium. Standard dimensions: height: 235-525mm, width: 750-1500mm.

Comments: Designed to combine the ease of building in, and weather/thermal resistance of, a window with the ease of electrical operation and control of a conventional damper. Motor is integrated into external frame with provision for wiring and access for maintenance.

Circular blade dampers
Motor-operated shut-off damper typically used with circular spiral ducts to open/close a ductwork branch. Seals well in closed position; low pressure loss when in the open position. Intermediate positions control volume flow rates.

Construction: hot-dipped galvanised or acid-proof steel. Standard dimensions: 100Ø-315Ømm in 50mm increments.

Comments: The damper casing can be thermally insulated. Also available with manual adjustment. See Sealed blade dampers above. Not commonly used for natural ventilation systems.

Iris dampers
Typically used for air volume flow rate adjustment and as a measurement device for circular ducts.

Construction: Hot-dipped galvanised or stainless steel cone-shaped casing and blades with gasket seals. Standard dimensions: 80Ø-1000Ø.

Comments: See Sealed blade dampers above. Not commonly used for natural ventilation systems.

Building materials: the environmental issues

Peter Clegg

Building construction is inherently damaging to the environment as it involves the extraction, processing and transportation of large quantities of high-energy materials. We rarely know the source or the detailed composition of many composite materials and, as designers, we often have little control over the manufacturing process. So we can either get very depressed about this and worry our way through the minutiae of decision-making, or we can wash our hands of the materials and components industries while assuming they are someone else's problem.

The reality is that we operate in between these extremes, trying to keep abreast of the scarce and often contradictory information that is available, making value judgements about the key environmental issues and asking manufacturers the questions that will encourage them to take their own environmental agendas seriously.

The best sources of environmental information on materials are the BRE's Green Guide to Specification, which includes the rating of materials by Eco-points (which also forms the basis for ENVEST software), and the Green Building Handbook (ed Tom Woolley et al, Green Building Digest). The Green Guide to Specification attempts to provide a full life-cycle cost analysis of common methods of construction and is most useful as an instant checklist. The origin and weighting of the data used in the software is not transparent, which makes it rather difficult to interpret; it is also rather limited because the software makes gross generalisations in terms of building shape and specifications. Hence FCB finds it really useful only for quick comparisons. The Green Building Handbook provides more detailed information on a variety of materials and components.

The two give slightly different methods of analysis but tend to focus on the following issues:
• ozone depletion potential (now being minimised by successful legislation);
• toxicity to plant and animal life during manufacture, use and disposal of materials;
• pollution of air or water during manufacture, use or disposal;
• resource depletion (biological or man-made materials);
• recyclability and the recycled content of materials;
• embodied energy and carbon dioxide emissions, and therefore contribution to global warming.

The Green Guide to Specification provides some surprising data on the embodied environmental impact of constituent elements of a building over a 60 year lifetime. For example the pie chart (3) shows the environmental impact contribution of each element of a typical office building, and indicates that floor finishes have by far the greatest impact, largely because of the frequency of carpet replacement. If one excludes this (because the fit-out may be beyond the architectural brief), the upper floor construction then makes the biggest contribution, largely because of the mass of reinforced concrete construction.

Biological and technological materials

There is a philosophy that holds that green buildings come from materials that are grown, rather than mined and manufactured. In this sense timber is the ultimate sustainable material, with other vegetable products such as hemp, straw and bamboo, with animal products such as wool following close behind. A new generation of bio-composite materials, such as clayboard (see www.constructionresources.co.uk), is under constant development.

Harvested materials are extremely low in energy compared with heavyweight manufactured materials such as clay or concrete products, which in turn are cheap in terms of embodied energy per unit mass when compared with metals. But metals are much easier to recycle and, as the recycling industries improve both throughput and output, embodied energy becomes less significant. Figure 4 gives the embodied energy per metre cubed for various building materials.[1] Data is taken from various sources and can be quite variable. The recycled content of materials can significantly impact on their embodied energy. High-energy materials need to be used in a way that makes them recyclable.

In Cradle to Cradle, McDonough and Braungart discuss the dangers of mixing the 'biological' and 'technological' nutrients that form the staple of our building industry. We need to think about the separation of materials for recycling purposes and avoid the natural tendencies towards landfill or 'down-cycling' of high-energy materials.

Notes

1 Some sources give figures for embodied energy per kilogram, which can make the table look very different, eg lead has a very high embodied energy per kilo largely due to its mass.

Further information

• Jane Anderson and David Shiers with Mike Sinclair, The Green Guide to Specification, third edition (Oxford 2002)

• Tom Woolley, Sam Kimmins, Paul Harrison and Rob Harrison, The Green Building Handbook (London 1997)

• Bjorn Berge, The Ecology of Building Materials (London 2001)

• William McDonough and Michael Braungart, Cradle to Cradle: Remaking the way we make things (San Francisco 2002)

Ten key points

• Think carefully before using pvc. The industry puts up a good case for its defence but there are so many references to it on the OSPAR list (2) that it is worth trying very hard to avoid it. Figure 1 provides a list of alternatives.
• Ensure that all timber is from certifiable, sustainable, managed sources.
• Seek locally-sourced materials to reduce transportation costs, especially for high mass materials.
• Concrete is responsible for almost ten per cent of all man-made carbon dioxide production – so don't over-specify the cement content of concrete mixes and use cement substitutes if possible.
• Avoid wood preservatives; they are designed to kill things.
• Optimise the mass in the use of high density materials, providing it is not detrimental to environmental performance. Buckminster Fuller's idea that lightweight buildings were inherently good does have some sense to it, bearing in mind that energy in use is more significant than embodied energy.
• Check that there are recycling pathways for high maintenance, short-life products such as floor finishes, which are often the most environmentally damaging (eg consider leasing carpets instead of buying).
• Avoid solvents – they generally contain toxic, volatile compounds. Use water-based paints and stains.
• Use lime mortar to allow brickwork to be recycled.
• Design for minimum wastage – factory-produced components and prefabrication can often help to promote this.

1 — Alternative materials to pvc

Roofing membranes	Polyolefin or EPDM	Most pvc membrane manufacturers are moving towards products that produce less toxins during manufacture but this doesn't necessarily help with disposal. Mechanically-fixed solutions provide improved recyclability over fully-adhered solutions.
Insulation: cavity closures	Polyethylene profiles available as alternative	
Windows	Aluminium/wood combinations	The National Housing Federation has found pvc-u window frames more expensive in terms of initial capital and life cycle costs. Polyeolethane windows are now available.
Flooring materials	Wood, linoleum, cork, rubber	Some cork contains pvc covering. Rubber flooring with chlorine-based ingredients should be avoided. EPDM-type rubber is recommended by the Danish EPA. Polyolefin (PP and PE) are now offered as alternatives.
Electrical equipment	LSOH (low-smoke zero halogen)	'Halogen free' cables cannot contain pvc or other organochlorines.
Electrical trunking/fittings	Polyethylene and steel	
Underground drainage	Vitrified clay, HDPE, ductile iron	Clay has a higher resistance to chemicals and a longer life than pvc.
Interior wall finishes	Ceramic tiles with epoxy grouting	Most kitchen specifiers prefer Whiterock or sheet vinyl systems for catering areas. This is a very difficult one to argue. Epoxy grout is not a brilliant alternative.
Paint finishes	Water-based vinyl-free emulsions	Large ranges of natural organic paints now available.
Above-ground drainage	High density polyetholene and ABS	Sometimes difficult to source for 400mm pipework.
Guttering and downpipes	Zinc, cast iron, galvanised steel, aluminium	All will have longer life, but metal guttering requires maintenance.

See also: Greenpeace Alternatives Database (http://archive.greenpeace.org/toxics/pvcdatabase/)

2 — OSPAR list of chemicals for priority action

Chemical name	Uses
Polychlorinated dibenzodioxins (PCDDs)	By-product of industrial processes which use chlorine, including iron and steel production, and the production and burning of pvc plastic.
Polychlorinated dibenzofurans (PCDFs)	Nothing – also accidental by-products; very similar to PCDDs.
Polychlorinated biphenyls (PCBs)	Transformer fluids – banned in the UK but present in older electrical equipment.
Polyaromatic Hydrocarbons (PAHs)	Products of incomplete combustion of fossil fuels.
Pentachlorophenol (PCP)	Timber treatment; use now restricted in the UK but may be present in imported/old timber; releases dioxins when burnt.
Short-chained chlorinated paraffins (SCCP)	Metal-cutting oils, paints, mastics and sealants, fire retardants; used as secondary plasticisers in pvc cables and vinyl flooring.
Hexachlorocyclohexane isomers (inc Lindane)	Lindane is banned in many countries; still used in the UK as a pesticide.
Mercury and organic mercury compounds	Mercury used in many industrial processes. Chlorine production, iron and steel works, cement kilns and waste incinerators emit mercury.
Cadmium	Stabiliser for pvc-u windows, used in batteries, as a pigment in paints (restricted).
Lead and organic lead compounds	Use in sheet form as roofing/flashing has decreased dramatically; lead used as UV-stabiliser for pvc.
Organic tin compounds	Pvc stabilisers and ingredient in some wood preservatives; Swedenvironment says organotins are also used in plastic-coated metal.
Nonylphenol/ethoxylates (NP/NPE's) etc	Used as additive in some paints and epoxies.
Musk xylene	Artificial fragrance used in detergents, soaps, cleaning agents and perfumes.
Brominated flame retardants: PBDE's, PBB's	Flame-retardant additives; the main applications are in flexible polyurethane foam for furniture and upholstry and in ABS plastics, used for example as casings for electronic equipment.
Phthalates	Used mostly as softeners for pvc (vinyl) in cable sheathing and floor coverings.
1,2,3- and 1,2,4-1,2,3-trichlorobenzene	Industrial raw materials, intermediates and solvents.
Octylphenol	Very similar to and used in the same applications as NP/NPEs (see 12 above).
Hexamethyldisiloxane	One of a poorly researched group of chemicals which may be termed the organosilicons: silicon oils and greases.
Tetrabromobisphenol-a (TBBA)	Fire retardant used in electronic equipment.
Dicofol, Endosulfan, Methoxychlor	Pesticides.
Hexachlorocyclopentadiene	Pesticide.
2,4,6-tris (1,1-dimethylethyl) phenol	Pesticide.
1 (1,1-dimethylethyl)-4-methylbenzene	Pesticide.

Source: Oslo and Paris Commissions, set up in 1998 to combat marine pollution in the North Atlantic from on- and off-shore sources.

3

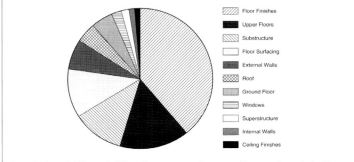

Contribution of different building elements to environmental impact of a typical office
Source: The BRE Green Guide to Specification (Garston 2000)

Legend: Floor Finishes; Upper Floors; Substructure; Floor Surfacing; External Walls; Roof; Ground Floor; Windows; Superstructure; Internal Walls; Ceiling Finishes

4

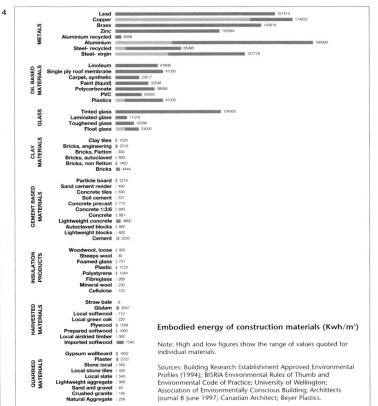

Embodied energy of construction materials (Kwh/m³)

Note: High and low figures show the range of values quoted for individual materials.

Sources: Building Research Establishment Approved Environmental Profiles (1994); BISRIA Environmental Rules of Thumb and Environmental Code of Practice; University of Wellington; Association of Environmentally Conscious Building; Architects Journal 8 June 1997; Canadian Architect; Beyer Plastics.

Cement and concrete

Toby Lewis

According to cement manufacturer Lafarge, concrete is 'second only to water as the most consumed substance on earth, with almost one ton of it being used for each human every year' (www.ubcsd.org).

Concrete is the ultimate plastic construction material, able to make both single structural elements and continuous structural forms or surfaces. It is limited, as much as anything, by the formwork used to cast it – think of the work of Le Corbusier, Felix Candela or Pier Luigi Nervi. Nonetheless there are several drawbacks to be considered.

Each tonne of cement produces about one tonne of carbon dioxide in its manufacture, making an annual global total of 1.6 billion tonnes. This is about eight per cent of all man-made carbon dioxide production. About half the carbon dioxide produced is from the fossil fuel burnt to provide heat for the process and half is from the chemical reaction that turns limestone into cement. The latter is unavoidable and alternative fuels are currently uneconomical.

Thus each cubic metre of concrete, which contains about 300kg of cement, will have an embodied carbon dioxide burden of 300kg.

One method of improvement that can halve the embodied carbon dioxide of concrete is to use a fine inert filler such as ground granular blast furnace slag (ggbfs) or pulverised fuel ash (pfa). These are both waste industrial products, abundantly available, which would otherwise go to landfill. They can also improve the colour of the concrete. Just as the sand in the mix fills the gaps between stones, so the fine inert powder fills the gap between sand grains and replaces some of the cement. This can even save money (cement costs more than filler) and is common in civil engineering work where volumes of

concrete can be very large. Unfortunately most concrete mixes are performance-specified by strength (eg a C35 mix is required to have 35N/mm² compressive strength at 28 days) and so the engineer does not control the cement content or the use of any cement replacement. Nonetheless the use of some cement replacement is becoming increasingly common as it is more economical.

Dirty fuel

Hazardous waste incinerators must comply with the 94/67/EC limits, which require pollution abatement technology that is not needed by cement kilns or other industrial combustion processes. Cement kilns are intensive fuel users and there is a continual drive to burn the cheapest fuel. Although fossil fuels tend to be used by the cement industry, both low-grade fuels, such as shales and coal washings, and waste fuels, such as waste oil, solvents and tyres, are increasingly employed. In recent years the cement industry has burnt bone meal and animal fat from the 4.4 million cows slaughtered as a result of the UK's BSE crisis. These are all regarded as dirty fuels which may lead to the release of SOx, NOx and particulates, among others. The cement industry however claims that its emissions are mainly determined by the raw materials of cement production and not by the type of fuel. For example, the high NOx emissions are inherent to the process because of the high temperatures of combustion. Emission of sulphur dioxide, ammonia and ammonium compounds are mainly due to raw material content. Other emissions such as dioxins are not affected by the type of alternative fuels. Most of these inherent emissions can be reduced, at some cost, by processes such as filtration and

washing of flue gasses, as emissions are increasingly controlled by government legislation, with Europe and the US some way ahead of the third world.

Recycled aggregate

Gravel extraction and aggregate production from quarries have significant environmental impacts: in traffic generated, on natural groundwater resources, on nature conservation and in visual impact on the landscape. The government has acknowledged (ODPM, Mineral Planning Guidance Note 6) that the current primary aggregate supply cannot be sustained and it looks to coastal super-quarries and secondary and recycled materials to increase their contribution. Production costs for recycled materials are generally the same as for primary aggregates and so, as well as the environmental benefit, the delivered cost of recycled material can be lower if the distance between waste arising, recycling centre and point of use are minimised. The use of recycled aggregate depends primarily on finding a source of suitable quality, quantity and proximity. For example, at the BRE Environmental Office the existing building, due for demolition, was crushed to form aggregate for the new building while old precast railway sleepers were used by Bennetts Associates for the Wessex Water Operations Centre (2000). It is also essential to allow enough time for the concrete supplier to test the recycled material and set aside bins for its storage. A directory of 250 UK suppliers of recycled aggregate is on www.aggregain.org.uk.

Thermal mass

One of concrete's advantages in building design is its high thermal mass. This can provide free cooling, particularly in summer, making use of day-to-night

changes in outdoor temperature. The mass of the building absorbs surplus heat during the day and can be cooled by ventilation at night, enabling it to repeat the cycle the next day. The efficiency of this heat exchange can be increased by ducting the air supply of the building through elements of the fabric such as hollow-core floor planks.

Beauty

If a building is beautiful, it may be kept longer and so there is a better use of the embodied resources. In our climate expressed concrete has created some horrors – stained dark with dirt and streaked with bleached stripes from acid rain – and as a result it is more often used now as the hidden structure behind another cladding material. Nonetheless there are steps that can be taken to improve the appearance of concrete. The first is colour, as in FCB's Persistence Works. The second is the quality of the surface. This depends principally on the quality of the formwork and the craft techniques used to remedy defects such as blow holes and grout runs. David Bennett has shown how the smooth 'as stuck' surface can be repaired without resorting to 'stoning', which can produce a ragged sanded look. The third is to reduce dirt staining. This can be achieved by designing in ledges that throw water off evenly or, more effectively, by avoiding any ledges at all that may collect dirt. For example in Persistence Works windows were positioned flush with the wall face, removing any window cill.

Finish

Lotexan, manufactured by Keim, is a surface treatment that binds with minerals in the concrete. It prevents the surface from absorbing rainwater and thus inhibits dirt from sticking; there-

fore it also means that the concrete retains the pale colour of the dry surface, even in dull wet weather. The treatment must be applied in very dry weather and is almost undetectable until water is splashed on, when the difference becomes startlingly apparent.

Alternatives to cement as a binder

- Rammed earth (aggregate with clay as binder). Almost no embodied carbon dioxide, apart from transport fuel, but less strong. Suitable only where it can be protected from continuous moisture and used without reinforcement.
- Limecrete (aggregate with lime as binder). While the production of lime generates half the carbon dioxide of cement, experience has shown the need for twice as much lime in the mix for an equivalent strength, thus removing the carbon dioxide advantage. On the other hand lime absorbs significantly more carbon dioxide, as part of its curing, than Portland cement. Limecrete has proved suitable only for use without reinforcement (see next section).
- Eco-cement: like Portland cement but with magnesite substituted for limestone in the mix with chalk and clay. This mix can be kilned at lower temperatures and, according to its Tasmanian inventor John Harrison, releases no carbon dioxide. Like lime it absorbs carbon dioxide on curing. But, again like lime, the higher carbonation reduces its alkalinity and may make it only suitable for use in concrete without reinforcement. As yet untried on a large scale in the UK.

Advances in concrete technology

- Superflowing concrete mixtures – no compaction required.
- Glass aggregate – the surplus of low-quality recycled glass, unsuitable for glass making, can be used as aggregate.

- High-strength cements and concretes. Silica particle cement (DSP) uses microsilica, a by-product of the manufacture of silicon metals and its alloys, which is made up of very small spheres (each 0.1um) of reactive silica. Very high compressive strengths are obtained, ranging between 200N/mm² and 800N/mm². Developed by Bouygues, Lafarge and Rhodia, the material is marketed as Ductal (www.ductal.com). A more recent development is high strength Macro Defect Free (MDF) cement polymer paste, which is extruded or injection moulded. If MDF cement is reinforced by fibres such as glass, carbon or Kevlar, a composite material can be produced which has a fracture toughness exceeding that of aluminium.
- Fibre reinforcement – self-reinforcing mixes that reduce or eliminate laborious in-situ steelwork.

Above/below At Persistence Works, Sheffield, attractive light-coloured concrete was important and the addition of ggbfs produced a paler, warmer colour without the cost of Portland cement. Mixes of 40-80 per cent ggbfs cement replacement were tested; above 60 per cent there was no further lightening. There were concerns that less cement would mean less heat of hydration and a possible freezing risk in winter working.

Further information

- www.mander-sd.co.uk (Tim Mander of Mander Structural Design was the structural engineer for Persistence Works (scheme design) and Wessex Water, and advocates the cement replacements in standard mixes).
- 'Using re-cycled aggregates: Wessex Water', Structural Engineer (19 June 2001) pp16-18.
- David Bennett, Concrete Architecture: Tone, Texture, Form (Basel 2001). By the same author: Innovations in Concrete (London 2000); Redefining Concrete's Architectural Direction, Concrete Quarterly, 202 (2002) (www.concretequarterly.com); 'Cementing relationships', New Civil Engineer (30 May 2002).
- www.burohappold.co.uk. Steve Fisher of Buro Happold was structural engineer for Persistence Works (construction).
- Friedbert Kind-Barkauskas, Bruno Kauhsen, Stefan Polonyi and Jörg Brandt, Concrete Construction Manual (Basel 2002).

Lime

Geoff Rich

Used as a binder in mortars, plasters, renders and some paints, lime has provided an effective, flexible and durable building material in the UK since the Romans introduced it in the first century AD. It has been the binder of choice for 2000 years for bedding masonry units and floors and it has provided waterproof and breathable surface finishes for interior and exterior walls across all building types.

In the late nineteenth century, Portland cement (OPC) gradually replaced lime, principally because of its rapid drying properties and increased compressive strengths. While lime continues to be an essential ingredient in the repair of traditional solid construction, its potential as a more sustainable alternative to cement for use in new build is now being explored.

The lime cycle
The lime cycle diagram overleaf demonstrates the innate efficiency of lime as a building material:
- carbon dioxide and water is driven off;
- water is added to burnt limestone to produce calcium hydroxide;
- aggregate is mixed into the soft putty for the production of mortars;
- mortar is applied and exposed to the air, where it begins to reabsorb some of carbon dioxide emitted during burning.

The performance of lime-based products varies according to the natural properties of the burnt limestone. Where the original stone is pure calcium carbonate, a soft 'fat' putty is produced, which can be used where a soft mortar is required. Pure lime is generally considered more suitable for work on traditional building structures.

When argillaceous or siliceous limestone (with naturally occurring clay particles) is burnt, the result is known as hydraulic lime. In part the properties of natural hydraulic lime (NHL) resemble those of cement: it is a strong material, capable of setting under water and suitable for use in new construction. Compared to cement, hydraulic lime mortars have a far lower compressive strength but greater flexibility.

Mortar, render, limecrete and cob
Lime can be used as a flexible, breathable binder in the following applications:
- mixed with sand to form mortars for bedding masonry or blockwork, pointing, rendering, plastering, historic building repairs;
- mixed with aggregate/glass for floor screed and limecrete floors;
- mixed with water/pigment for limewash for internal and external application.

Other additions
Addition of pozzolanic materials such as crushed brick, pulverised fly ash or granulated blast furnace slag will increase the chemical set of hydraulic lime. The amounts required vary and trial mixes should be carried out prior to any application.

Lime versus cement
There is a range of issues which could affect the choice of lime on grounds of its sustainable characteristics.
- Lime is produced at a temperature of 900-1100 degrees celsius while cement is produced at 1200-1500 degrees celsius. Less energy is therefore consumed and less carbon dioxide emitted during its manufacture.
- The bulk density of lime is half that of cement, leading to overall energy savings of 30-50 per cent.
- Lime mortars re-absorb some carbon dioxide emitted during manufacture

(as part of the lime cycle).
• Global cement production is believed to be responsible for ten per cent of all worldwide carbon dioxide production.
• The lower strength of lime mortars increases the potential for recycling of bricks and masonry after demolition, thus attenuating the embodied energy of the whole building. A reduction in the number of bricks manufactured (currently an estimated 3000 million bricks are fired every year in the UK) would reduce carbon dioxide emissions.
• Lime is generally more expensive and more labour intensive than cement.
• While conservation applications invariably involve careful testing and planning to produce the right mix, there remains an unnecessary air of mystery around the subject. This is beginning to improve through some bold moves, including certain cement companies who deliver ready-mixed lime mortars to site in a silo (see below).

Merits of lime mortars and renders
• Being softer than cement, lime mortars reduce incidence of cracking due to differential movement and may limit the need for expansion joints in new buildings.
• Where hairline cracks occur in cement-based renders, moisture penetration is commonly encouraged by capillary action. In contrast lime will absorb water and continue carbonating, thereby 'healing' the crack.
• The porous and 'softer' properties of lime, which allow the transfer of moisture, generally work well with softer building materials such as straw bale and rammed earth.
• Lime-based mortars and renders do not normally have the dull grey appearance of OPC and can be easily coloured using natural pigments and aggregates.
• Lime mortars have a 'natural'

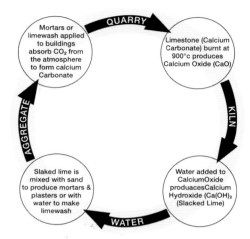

chemical compatibility with some limestones.
Other applications include limecrete floors, which can provide a lightweight alternative to concrete, especially when mixed with lightweight expanded clay aggregate (LECA). Lime can also be used in screeds.

Typical mixes
Vitruvius is credited with establishing the general mix of lime to sand mortars at 1:3. Nonetheless – whether working on historic or new buildings – it is vital to undertake trial mixes and consult closely with the manufacturer, as appropriate mixes vary according to the nature of the substrate, the desired finish, exposure of the building, length of building programme and seasonal/weather conditions.

Further information
• Foresight Lime Research Team, Hydraulic Lime Mortar for Stone, Brick and Block Masonry (Shaftesbury 2003)
• www.limetechnology.co.uk (technical data)
• BS EN 459-3:2001
• www.castlecement.co.uk
• www.lime.org.uk
• John and Nicola Ashurst, English Heritage Technical Handbook volume 3, Mortars Plasters Renders (London 1998).
• S Holmes and M Wingate, Building with Lime: A Practical Introduction (London 1977).
• JAH Oates, Lime and limestone: chemistry and technology, production and uses (Chichester 1998)

Timber and timber treatment

Andy Couling

Trees have a symbiotic relationship with people. They feed us with oxygen and absorb our carbon dioxide. A tree produces enough oxygen to keep a family of four breathing for a year. But five trees with a hundred-year lifetime are needed to absorb the carbon dioxide that a family car generates over a year.
Timber has been used for construction since prehistory and it remains one of the most flexible, durable and beautiful materials available. As well as being recyclable, waste efficient, biodegradable and non-toxic, it has the potential to regenerate itself and to provide an infinite supply.

Embodied energy
Converting trees into a usable building material takes far less energy, and therefore generates far less carbon dioxide, than virtually any other alternative, including aluminium, steel and concrete. But whereas sawn softwood is quoted as having an embodied energy of as little as 0.5 Gj/tonne, glue-laminated timber (glulam or GLT) and laminated veneered lumber (LVL) are quoted as having figures between 4.6 and 11 Gj/tonne. In exercises that we undertook for the structural frame of the National Trust Central Office, this meant that the embodied energy argument for engineered timber became a lot less significant. A similar exercise for the single-storey building for Neal's Yard however showed that the change in embodied energy from a steel to a glulam timber frame represented between two and five years of operative heating energy for the building.
The inherently low embodied energy of sawn timber means that transportation energy becomes a significant factor. Locally grown timber therefore has a lower embodied energy than imported timber. The Timber Research

and Development Assocation (Trada) estimates that a lightweight concrete block wall takes 1.7 times as much energy to construct as a standard timber stud wall, although if the timber is transported across the Atlantic the difference becomes negligible.

UK-sourced timber
The UK timber industry is largely geared to the production of high-grade hardwoods for furniture or low-grade softwoods for packaging and pallets. There is however some production suitable for structural or construction use.
Oak and sweet chestnut are both durable hardwoods which are strong and suitable for external use and require no treatment. They do however contain tannins, which can lead to initial staining of adjacent finishes. Douglas fir and European (not Japanese) larch are both moderately durable softwoods. Their durability can be further improved by treatment, although they do not absorb chemical treatments readily. Good detailing has a major effect on durability – so avoid moisture traps and ventilate well.
Britain currently imports around 80 per cent of the timber it uses. Some 89 per cent of imported timber is derived from coniferous forests located mainly in Scandinavia, Canada and Russia; three per cent is derived from deciduous forests in Europe and North America; and the remainder, about eight per cent, is imported from tropical regions.
UK timber production is set to increase dramatically over the next two decades. There is a government-backed initiative to double the UK forest cover to 15 per cent (the average continental European forest cover is 25 per cent), in addition to reaping the benefits of post-war planting.

Timber certification

There are a number of different certification schemes operating in the timber industry worldwide, with differing levels of credibility and scales of activity. The FSC (Forest Stewardship Council) scheme, one of the largest and most respected, is supported by WWF, Friends of the Earth and Greenpeace.

Though limited, the availability of certified timber has grown significantly in the last few years and this is likely to continue. It is already possible to obtain commercial quantities of most commonly used softwoods and a wide (if somewhat obscure) range of tropical hardwoods from FSC-certified sources. It is also possible to obtain certified boards such as chipboard and oriented strand board (OSB) at no extra cost.

The same timber type may be available from certified and non-certified sources; these may be geographically very close together, but harvested to completely different standards of forest husbandry, human rights etc. We believe it is important to ensure that only certified timber is used.

A number of the large Scandinavian producers are certified under the PEFC (Pan European Forest Certification) scheme. This scheme is strongly supported by the forestry industry but less so by environmental groups. Theoretically it also ensures that the certified timber is produced sustainably but non-governmental organisations such as Greenpeace Nordic and the Finnish Nature League have concerns over practices carried out in a number of PEFC-certified forests.

In June 2004 the UK government set up CPET (Central Point of Expertise on Timber) to assess various certification schemes and inform government procurement policy. Initially it identified FSC and CSA (Canadian Standards Association) as the only schemes which satisfied both legality and sustainability criteria; the certification schemes by MTCC (Malaysian Timber Certification Council), PEFC (Programme for the Endorsement of Forestry Certification Schemes) and SFI (Sustainable Forestry Initiative) met only the legality criteria. But the position is subject to ongoing review and specifiers should check the latest position with CPET.

Given the current uncertainties over the availability of FSC-certified timbers, FCBa deals with the issue pragmatically. The practice is very clear about excluding all tropical hardwoods unless they are documented to be from FSC-certified sources. This involves policing all plywoods, which can often contain such species. Temperate hardwoods are expensive and therefore usually only used where particularly specified. FCBa will sometimes use non-FSC supplies if it is known where the trees are sourced, as general European forestry laws provide a degree of protection against destructive practices. The practice will accept European softwoods which are not FSC-certified if the contractors can demonstrate that they have tried and failed to obtain certified supplies.

Tropical hardwoods

In 1950, 30 per cent of the earth's land was covered by forest, half of which was tropical forest. By 1975 the area of tropical forest had declined to 12 per cent and today it is less than six per cent. In contrast timber forests overall remain at a steady 20 per cent, thanks to reforestation. Tropical forests however still comprise half the planet's wood and house 70-90 per cent of the earth's organisms. Greenpeace estimated that in 1995 tropical deforestation from all causes contributed around 80 per cent of all global warming (30 per cent of all

1 The Earth Centre, Doncaster. The solar canopy is supported on a tree structure which consists of untreated larch roundwood poles, jointed with fabricated plate connectors made from galvanised steel.

2, 3 Woodland Enterprise Centre, East Sussex. The building uses small-section coppiced sweet chestnut in the form of 27x70mm laths, finger-jointed into 15m lengths to form a gridshell. The roof was constructed at ground level in six metre bays and craned into position onto the supporting larch pole structure. The finger-jointed chestnut is also used for the external wall cladding. The chestnut was harvested in the local area, where there is an abundance of coppiced woodland, traditionally used for fencing but for which there is no longer a demand. The larch was also from Sussex woodland.

4, 5 Olivier Theatre, Bedales School, Hampshire. The green oak frame combines traditional jointing techniques with stainless steel elements, which allow the structure to produce the clear spans needed for its function. The roof cladding is treated larch planks and the wall cladding is untreated Douglas fir.

Further information

- www.trada.co.uk (timber species database)
- www.tropicalforesttrust.com
- www.goodwoodguide.com (Friends of the Earth guide)
- www.forestry.gov.uk/ukwa (UK woodland assurance scheme)
- www.woodforgood.com
- www.fern.org (European forests campaign)
- www.panda.org (WWF)
- www.forestforum.org.uk (UK tropical forest forum)
- www.greenpeace.org.uk (ancient forest campaign)
- www.forestsforever.org.uk
- www.pasa.nhs.uk/sustainabledevelopment/environment/timber.stm (for CPET)

carbon dioxide emissions).

With the advent of reliable FSC certification, however, it is once again possible to specify timbers from tropical climates which are forested sustainably. For the housing project at Century Court in Cheltenham the external cladding is red louro, supplied by Ecotimber (www.ecotimber.co.uk). It was selected from stock imported into Rotterdam before delivery to site.

Trada has a searchable database for members which gives the properties of well-known timbers. FSC-certified supplies however often consist of species which are not widely known in the UK and the lack of data causes some difficulty in ensuring correct specification. The Ecotimber website contains technical information for the timbers it supplies.

Preservative treatment

Durability is an important issue, as multiple replacement of materials over the life of a building can add significantly to the environmental cost. This can be minimised either by selecting species that are naturally durable or by treating with preservative any timber that is liable to decay. Careful detailing to minimise the risk of decay is essential.

The level of natural durability varies from species to species and is a consequence of the oils contained within the timber. Trada produces information on the durability of all available species.

Timber can decay by three mechanisms: fungal attack, insect attack and degradation by exposure to daylight (UV attack). Timber which is not vulnerable to any of these need not be treated with preservative. It is therefore not necessary to treat timber used internally in the UK if there is no risk of it getting damp. BS5589 prioritises untreated timber by recommending risk assessment in accordance with the table (right).

Once the need to treat the timber has been established, the next step is to decide what form it should take. A number of different timber preservative treatments are available. All are toxic to varying degrees. The two main methods of off-site treatment are dipping and vacuum impregnating. The most common form of treatment is CCA (copper-chrome-arsenic), which is used on most carcassing timbers. It imparts a green tint to the timber after treatment. But in recognition of its hazardous properties, with effect from June 2004 its use was restricted and it was banned from use in domestic buildings. Less toxic alternatives, based on copper with an organic biocide, are becoming available, for example Tanalith E by Arch Timber Protection, which FCBa now specifies in place of CCA. Solvent-borne preservatives are often used for joinery and clear-finished timbers, since they help preserve the natural colour and finish.

One of the best environmental options is boron. Introduced in the nineteenth century, boron salts were generally replaced with more toxic chemicals in the twentieth but they are now available again. The material is available in paste, spray or pellet form from a number of suppliers. The Green Building Store (www.greenbuilding-store.co.uk) sells water-based and glycol-based products made by Sovereign Chemicals.

Currently nearly half of the world's production of borates comes from a huge open-cast mine in California operated by Borax (www.borax.com). Borates however cannot solve all timber treatment problems. Although relatively stable, they are water-soluble and will eventually leach out of timbers that are exposed to wet conditions.

Hazard categories from BS5589

Hazard category	Risk of fungal decay	Examples
1	Where conditions of use involve negligible risk	Joinery inside dwellings, e.g. stairs and architraves
2	Where there is low risk	Timber in normal pitched roofs; joists in ground floors
3	Where experience has shown there is a high risk	Cladding and external joinery
4	Where there is a continually hazardous environment and unacceptable risk	Fence posts; sleepers; freshwater lockgates
M	As for category 4, but in the marine environment	Marine piling, piers and jetties

Julian Gitsham

As the use of prefabrication techniques in the building industry has increased, the technology has been refined. Prefabrication started out at the level of bricks and plywood sheets, grew to encompass components such as doors and windows, and now includes wall panels and volumetric components.

Volumetric systems are three-dimensional units that are manufactured and fully fitted out in a factory off-site, usually including all service requirements and internal finishes. The units are then transported to site and placed in position. They may be load-bearing or non-loadbearing and usually arrive to site sealed and protected. Increasingly, volumetric units are being developed with the external cladding and even balconies added in the factory, limiting on-site activities to substructure and sealing between the units.

Panelised systems consist of flat panels produced in a factory and fixed together on site to produce a three-dimensional structure. Usually a fair amount of the internal finishing and services installation is carried out on site, although systems are being developed with internal and external finishes and services in the panels.

Items that are most likely to be made off site include:
• bathroom and toilet pods – fully fitted-out and tested and sealed for delivery, with final connections outside the pod (eg at Beaufort Court, Aston, and University of Bath student housing).
• kitchen pods – combined kitchen and bathroom units, keeping the serviced elements in one place.
• prefabricated risers – either installed in the factory, with the final connections made on site between pods above or below; or horizontal runs only, installed with prefabricated risers plugged in on site. If the pods are

made abroad with different standards, then the risers and the pods could be manufactured together to reduce any problems with interfaces. Ask for packages of spare parts to be included with the pods.
• plant rooms and horizontal service sections.
• window assemblies and pod flashings.
• external cladding systems (eg at Maidenbower School, Crawley and Oxstalls campus).
• housing, student housing and hotels, which lend themselves to manufacture off-site due to the degree of repetition.

The Beaufort Court housing project uses a prefabricated steel loadbearing construction system, incorporating large-scale cold-rolled panels and three-dimensional modular construction. The light gauge steel panel approach provides flexibility in design and also minimises transportation costs and the difficulties of site access with inner-city sites such as this. The reduction of the structural weight also helps reduce the extent of foundations.

Cold-rolled panels incorporated into the structural system provide additional design flexibility, permitting large window openings and extensive balconies, infilled with a prefabricated rainscreen system. A fully fitted three-dimensional modular loadbearing construction is used for bathrooms and lift shafts. Modular construction is limited to these highly finished and serviced areas to reduce off-site transportation, but provides high quality finishes with limited waste and future defects.

Environmental benefits
A key factor to bear in mind in deciding whether to use a system of off-site manufacture is the substantial environmental benefit it can offer.
• The controlled environment of the

factory can guarantee a much greater thermal performance.
• Good airtightness can be achieved and tested in the factory.
• There is potential to reduce waste and minimise pollution by carrying out the work under controlled conditions.
• If a steel frame is used, this can be recycled at the end of the building life.
• Improved working conditions – a controlled factory environment can be cleaner, safer and provide better working conditions.
• Integrated services allow installations to be minimised, thus reducing use of materials and overall cost, for example through shorter pipe runs.
• Reduction in on-site wastage in all materials. The building can be designed to use standard sizes (eg exact sizes of plasterboard without cutting). In the factory, steels or other components are cut initially to the correct length.
• Noise and disruption for neighbours is reduced.
• The use of light gauge steel panels reduces transportation and eases site access and storage issues.

Environmental disadvantages
• One of the problems resulting from prefabrication is potential de-skilling of the local labour force as work moves from site to factory.
• Transportation energy could increase as a result of increased movement of both raw and manufactured goods from source, to factory, to site. Investigations need to be made on a case-by-case basis.

Economic advantages
Economic advantages of off-site manufacture include:
• A much reduced construction period on site, resulting in lower preliminaries.
• Potential for lower costs and time

saved post-construction due to significantly lower defects.
• Improved quality control – factory conditions allow more careful checking of quality, with units sealed for delivery to site (all connections to services/structure should be done outside the unit) and then only opened up for commissioning. For example fully fitted bathroom pods reduce on-site construction time and secure quality of high-value components.
• Greater potential for effective integration of services with the structure.
• The site work is predominantly dry and clean – for example, dry floor construction, drylining to the walls, cladding clipped into place and factory-made bathrooms. The result is high quality of construction and minimum wastage of materials.

Design issues
Issues to be aware of when designing for off-site manufacture include:
• There are inherent steep learning curves.
• Very close co-ordination is required between members of the design team. It can be more difficult to resolve issues on site as all the prefabricated elements must fit together and tolerances are much more rigorous.
• Make the decision early in the design process to fabricate off-site – the building needs to be designed from the outset to ensure a high degree of repetition of off-site elements. This includes deciding the extent to which pre-fabrication is used. Should the building be fully volumetric or a hybrid, with just kitchen/bathrooms or other highly serviced areas as pods?
• Architectural layouts may be influenced by servicing requirements. Consideration should be given to access to risers without entering the unit.

• Repetition and stacking of elements is important. Essentially the design team has to produce production drawings and so minimising variations is important to enabling the team to meet design programmes.

Early liaison with the manufacturer and m&e subcontractors can benefit the design and help identify the most cost-effective route. Procurement under a partnering contract can help this process as it encourages early and close co-operation between all parties involved.

Prefabricated buildings tend to be of lightweight construction. Due to their lack of mass, lightweight buildings can overheat during the summer months. It is important that this is considered during the design stage and appropriate control of solar gain is included, along with methods of secure ventilation.
• Large numbers of units are required to achieve economic viability.
• Units need to be designed to overcome handling and transportation problems.
• The maximum size of the unit is determined by practical problems of transportation – eg the maximum width for a lorry load without a police escort.

Possible future developments
• Variations in type using a factory production line, eg the Smart car design approach.
• Tenants could order some variations to be automatically included in the production line, although the lead-in times may be prohibitive.
• Overseas manufacture offers lower cost and therefore a higher quality of fitting can be provided, but transportation issues in terms of costs and sustainability need to be considered.
• Design furniture/fittings that are integral to the units and designed to optimise on space.

• For large sites it might be feasible to build the factory on site and use it after completion for a community facility.
• In designing for mass-production, we should be looking to standardise certain elements, eg bathrooms and kitchens, but develop systems that are more easily adaptable for different locations/size and finishing requirements. Often mass production doesn't stack up, as it is currently a small part of the industry. Until the volumes increase, the costs won't come down.
• Manufacturers are now developing demountable systems that can be moved when no longer needed.

Further information
• www.designforhomes.org (with reports and case studies on various projects, including a report from the Steel Construction Institute about the value of modular construction).

Manufacturers include: Ayrshire Steel Framing, Ayrshire KA12 8PH (01294 274171); Britspace Modular Building Systems, East Yorkshire HU15 2TS (01430 440673); Terrapin, Milton Keynes MK1 1JJ (01908 270900); Volumetric, Bedfordshire SG19 2QT (01737 261313); Yorkon, York YO32 9P (01904 610990); Degn Jensen Entreprise, Denmark (+45 98422847); EJ Badekabiner, Aberdeen AB11 5PW (01224 588755); Renaissance, Walsall WS2 8T (01922 636100).

Water conservation

Rachel Sayers

Climate change will tend to exaggerate the problems of global water supply. Where there is currently sufficient water, there is likely to be too much, frequently in the form of flooding from increased rainfall, as the UK witnessed in June-July 2007. Where water is badly needed there will be droughts. Rainfall will be heavier in areas of northern Europe but lower in north Africa and Australia.

Frozen freshwater stocks across the globe are shrinking and turning into salt sea water: permafrost is thawing and snow cover has decreased by 10 per cent over the past 40 years. Since the 1950s the area covered by ice in the Arctic has retreated by 10-15 per cent while Arctic ice has thinned by 40 per cent. Approximately 1.7 billion people (one third of the world's population) currently live in countries that are water-stressed. By 2025 this will increase to five billion, with increasing risk of conflicts and health problems.

Global consumption of fresh water is doubling every 20 years. At present, 10 per cent is used by people, 65 per cent by agriculture and 25 per cent by industry.

The UK situation

2003 and 2005 were among the driest and warmest years on record in the UK, despite extensive flooding at times, and 1998-2002 was the wettest five-year sequence on record. The UK is experiencing increasingly unpredictable weather, which is consistent with most long-term predictions of the effects of global warming. Following very high groundwater levels in 1994-5, resources have declined steeply over the past decade. At the same time the UK population is becoming concentrated in the driest areas (the south east), further increasing pressure on water resources.

Climate change is forcing us to consider localised water management and storage in order to reduce flooding and maintain good supplies in dry periods. More than 40 per cent of the water we use at home is flushed down the toilet or used for watering the garden. Using potable water with its relatively high embodied energy for these purposes makes little economic sense.

Mains water is becoming more expensive as the privatised water industry is forced to invest heavily in infrastructure maintenance and expansion. Water metering for new buildings will highlight our wastefulness. Payback periods for water conservation measures are set to reduce in the future as the cost of major infrastructure increases – especially as development continues to be concentrated in the south east of England. Localised water management – ie rain harvesting and greywater recycling – can be more sustainable and cheaper than major infrastructure projects such as reservoirs and pipelines.

Water-saving appliances

Spray taps on hand basins/sinks can save up to 80 per cent of the water and energy used by standard pillar taps. Use taps with a standard M22 or M24 outlet thread. Electronic sensor taps and timed turn-off push taps prevent wastage and flooding where taps may be left running (ie in public buildings). They also remove the need to touch the taps once hands are washed. Stop cocks should be located in accessible (and known) locations. Flow to taps in handbasins where bowls tend not to be filled (eg offices and schools) should be regulated to 1.8l/min.

There are a number of leak detection products on the market which are designed to detect burst pipes and leaks and to shut off water supply in

order to minimise water loss and damage. The National Trust, which has considerable expertise in this area, recommends the Water Minder LD20 (www.ecoelectronics.co.uk).

A quick shower uses one third of the water of a bath with a typical 70 litre capacity. On the other hand, a power shower run for five minutes can use more water than a bath. Figure 3 gives flow rates for showers. Most people are generally happy with a 6-8 litre/minute rate. Water-saver showers work like tap aerators, giving an apparently greater flow.

With washing machines and dishwashers, the energy labels supplied also contain information on water usage. Appliances are getting much more efficient but a recent survey showed the consumption of 22 washing machines varying from 42 to 67 litres. Those dishwashers that use 16 litres per cycle are about two-and-a-half times as efficient as hand washing.

An efficient wc flush system can reduce overall household water consumption by about 21 per cent compared with a traditional nine-litre flush. The relative advantages and drawbacks of dual-flush valve mechanisms, as against low-volume siphon flushing mechanisms, are keenly contested. The UK is the only country that commonly uses the siphon flush mechanism; the rest of the world uses valve technology. Valve mechanisms are able to offer a dual-flush whereas siphon flushing is only really practical with a single-flush volume. The argument centres around the notion that a siphon mechanism cannot leak, whereas a valve mechanism, even the best quality, will eventually leak. This is hotly disputed by the manufacturers of valve flush mechanisms. Dual-flush siphon mechanisms (recently introduced to the

UK market) appear to offer the best of both worlds (www.thomasdudley.co.uk). These require press and release for full flush, and press and hold for half-flush – which is perhaps a bit counterintuitive for public buildings.

We recommend the following:
• siphon mechanism: 4.5 litre siphon action wc such as the Ifo Cera (from www.greenbuildingstore.co.uk or www.rainharvesting.co.uk).
• valve mechanism: most wc manufacturers offering dual flush mechanisms use valve mechanisms. One that claims super-low flush volumes is the IDO close-coupled wc, which can be set with a volume as low as 4/2.5 litres (www.ecoconstruct.com), although the concealed cistern version requires 6/3 litre flushing.

Controlled flush urinals can waste vast quantities of water. If flushed urinals are specified, ensure that precautions are taken to restrict water use to less than 7.5 litres/bowl/hour when occupied, by using presence detection devices. Consider using waterless urinals, but preferably those which do not require replacement of chemicals or disposable traps, as these can prove both costly and difficult to dispose.

The Green Building Store markets an air-flush urinal system which ventilates the urinals through the waste pipe in order to remove odours. The theory is that it is splashing and lack of cleaning that makes a smell so the liquid in the trap is ventilated directly to the outside. But note that the unit includes a 3W fan in the pipework – similar to a fan in the back of a computer.

Untreated greywater (excluding foul waste from wcs etc) can be used for garden watering if used immediately. Waste water from kitchen sinks and dishwashers is not usually collected as it is too heavily contaminated. Greywater can be treated to make it usable for flushing wcs, although this is rarely practical. Grey and brown water can be reused if it is properly treated, using a septic tank or reed beds.

Further information

- www.environment-agency.gov.uk (for Conserving Water in Buildings, 2001, and other Environment Agency factsheets)
- www.defra.gov.uk/environment/statistics/inl-water (useful background information)
- UN Intergovernmental Panel on Climate Change, Third Assessor Report (Geneva 2001)
- University of Wales, Hyrdoinformatics Conference (Cardiff 2002), www.iwaponline.com
- www.bsria.co.uk (BSRIA Rules of Thumb Guide 14/2003)
- Brian Edwards, Paul Hyett and Matthew Thompson, Rough Guide to Sustainability (London 2001)
- James Bruges, The Little Earth Book (Bristol 2000)

1

Maximum daily water demand (litres)

	Hot water	Total water
Housing (per bedroom):		
– 1 bedroom	115	210
– 2 bedroom	75	130
– 3 bedroom	55	100
Student housing (per bedroom):	70	90/100
Schools (per student):		
– day	15	20
– boarding	114	90
Hotels (per bedroom):		
– budget	115	135/550
– 4/5 star	135	200
Offices (per person):		
– with canteen	14	45
– without canteen	10	40
Sports hall (per person):		
– with swimming pool	20	20
– with all-weather pitch	35	35
Art gallery/bar/library (per person):	2	1
Theatre/cinema (per person):	1	3

From BSRIA, Rules of Thumb Guide 14/2003 (August 2003)

2

● Wash basin	8%
○ Toilet	35%
● Dishwasher	4%
● Washing machine	12%
○ Shower	5%
● Bath	15%
○ Kitchen sink	15%
● Outside use	6%

4

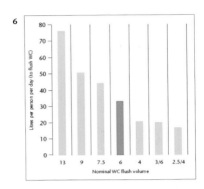

Energy — Washing machine

Manufacturer
Model

More efficient

A
B
C
D
E
F
G

Less efficient

Energy consumption kW cycle (based on standard test results for 60c cotton cycle) Actual energy consumption will depend on how the appliance is used.	1.05
Washing performance A higher G lower	A B C D E F G
Spin drying performance A higher G lower Spin spin (rpm)	A B C D E F G 1400
Capacity (cotton) kg Water consumption	5.0 55
Noise (dBA) re 1 pW) Washing Spinning	52 70

Further information is contained in product brochures

6

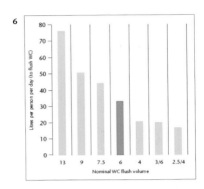

5

7

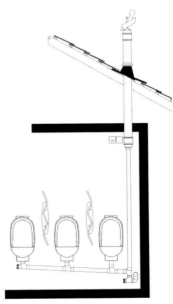

3

Description	Ultra-low water use	7.2k.W electric	9.5kW electric	"Water saver"	"Power shower"
Flow rate	1.5 l/min	3.5 l/min 30°C temp rise	4.6 l/min 30°C temp rise	4-10 l/min	12 + litres/min
Application	Limited non-household application	UK domestic	UK domestic	Mains pressure water or pumped	Mains pressure water or pumped
Comment	Atomising	Usually perceived as poor performance	Better comfort than 7.2kW	Power shower feel Cold feet possible	
Water use for 5 minute shower	7.5 litres	17.5 litres	23 litres	20-50 litres	7.5 litres
As % of 70-litre bath	11%	25%	32%	28-71%	86%

1 Typical water consumption (source: BSRIA Rules of Thumb Guide, www.bsria.co.uk).
2 Typical household water usage in the UK (source: Conserving Water in Buildings, The Environment Agency, London 2001).
3 Shower flow rates (as 2).
4 Appliance labelling (as 2).
5, 7 Air-flush urinal system (source: www.greenbuildingstore.com).
6 Possible savings from low-flush technology (as 2).

Rainwater harvesting

Rachel Sayers

Despite many attempts FCBa has never been able to justify the cost of a rainwater harvesting system. The payback period seems to be in the region of ten to 30 years. We looked in detail at systems for Portland Square, Plymouth and the Central Office for the National Trust but none of these was remotely cost-effective. At Neal's Yard the rainwater will be collected, treated by reverse osmosis and used as a 'pure' source of process water. Table 3 gives an approximate annual yield of rainwater in cubic metres for a range of roof sizes in an average rainfall, assuming 60 per cent of the rain is collected and used. In practice flat roofs will attenuate water run-off and only 50 per cent will be available, compared to 70 per cent on pitched tiled roofs (for a rule of thumb, see www.rainharvesting.co.uk).

One of the main problems in terms of cost effectiveness is the installation and operation of pumps. If, as with the Exemplar Schools project, these can be avoided by collecting rainwater from an upper roof and storing it at high level immediately above toilet cores, then the solution becomes a lot more cost effective. On-site attenuation through swales and soakaways, or storage for use in landscaping, all seem to be much more achievable options.

Information on average rainfall for the UK is available from the Met Office (www.met-office.gov.uk/climate/uk).

Designing for rainwater

The best way to decrease flooding is to increase attenuation.
• A responsive environment is more successful in absorbing rainfall peaks.
• Use grass or sedum on flat roofs.
• Reduce the quantity of drained hard surfaces – use porous paving/roads.
• Use soakaways and swales instead of connecting to storm water drainage.
• Use ponds and wetland features to catch excess water run-off.
• Design for real – 1996 was the driest year since 1960 with UK average annual rainfall of 737.6mm; 2000 was the wettest with 1194.3mm.

Problems with using rainwater

• Space is needed to store water – below ground is best to keep temperatures low. Avoid flat-bottom tanks as they can be difficult to clean.
• When undisturbed for long periods of time, water can become septic and so require chemical treatment to prevent biological activity.
• Current research is concentrating on creating longer retention times without the water becoming septic – otherwise the system is frequently detached and reliance returns to the mains.

Household rainwater systems

• These reduce demand on potable water supplies and decrease pressure on stormwater drains, sewers and water treatment plants, reducing flood risks and recharging ground water.
• Consider rainwater harvesting for garden use and possibly wc flushing.
• Industrial pollution, contamination from bird droppings and other dirt mean that rainwater is rarely used for drinking water.

It is eminently sensible to use rainwater for garden watering and there are a number of simple capturing, filtering and storage devices available. One is the WISY system from Construction Resources, which provides a complete kit, including underground storage, filtration and pumping, on a household basis (www.ecoconstruct.com or www.rainharvesting.co.uk).

Larger systems include the Eco-Vat rainwater travelling tank from Polypipe (www.polypipe.co.uk), while other companies market complete systems eg Acorn Environmental Systems' Rainsava (www.v63.net/acornsystems/pages/rainsava). Recycled bulk orange juice containers make ideal water storage tanks (www.thetankexchange.com).

Further information

• www.elementalsolutions.co.uk
• www. rainharvesting.co.uk
• www.ukrha.org
• www.metoffice.com/climate/uk (Met Office weather data.)
• Sue Roaf (ed), 21AD Water: architectural digest for the 21st century (Oxford Brookes University/Thames Water, Oxford 1998).
• Klaus W Kong, The Rainwater Technology Handbook (Rainharvesting Systems 2001).
• Buro Happold, Review of grey water and recycling and rainwater harvesting opportunities (unpublished report, London Feb 2001).

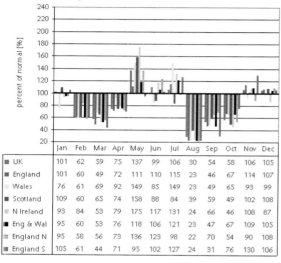

2 rainfall anomaly for 2003:

	Jan	Feb	Mar	Apr	May	Jun	Jul	Aug	Sep	Oct	Nov	Dec
UK	101	62	59	75	137	99	106	30	54	58	106	105
England	101	60	49	72	111	110	115	23	46	67	114	107
Wales	76	61	69	92	149	85	149	23	49	65	93	99
Scotland	109	60	65	74	158	88	84	39	59	49	102	108
N Ireland	93	84	53	79	175	117	131	24	66	46	108	87
Eng & Wal	95	60	53	76	118	106	121	23	47	67	109	105
England N	95	58	56	73	136	123	98	22	70	54	90	108
England S	105	61	44	71	95	102	127	24	31	76	130	106

3

mm rain/year	50	75	100	125	150
600	18	27	36	45	54
800	24	36	48	60	72
1000	30	45	60	75	90
1200	36	54	72	90	108
1400	42	63	84	105	126
1600	48	72	96	120	144

1 Regional rainfall data (source: Met Office).
2 Rainfall for 2003 (source: Met Office).
3 Rainwater yield showing cubic metres of water per annum per square metre of roof, assuming 60 per cent of rainfall is collected (source: Conserving Water in Buildings).

1

Region		UK	England	Wales	Scotland	N Ireland	England & Wales	England N	England S	Scotland N	Scotland E	Scotland W	England E & NE	England NW & Wales N	Midlands	East Anglia	England SW & Wales S	England SE & Central S
Max temp	Actual °C	13.0	14.0	13.0	11.3	12.9	13.9	13.0	14.6	10.9	11.2	11.8	13.2	12.8	14.0	14.9	13.8	14.9
	Anom °C	1.1	1.3	1.0	1.0	0.9	1.2	1.2	1.3	1.1	1.0	1.0	1.3	1.1	1.3	1.4	1.0	1.3
Min temp	Actual °C	6.0	6.6	6.3	4.9	6.0	6.6	5.9	7.0	4.8	4.5	5.4	5.9	6.1	6.4	7.0	7.0	7.2
	Anom °C	1.2	1.2	1.1	1.1	1.0	1.2	1.1	1.3	1.2	1.2	1.1	1.2	1.1	1.2	1.4	1.1	1.4
Mean temp	Actual °C	9.5	10.3	9.7	8.1	9.4	10.2	9.5	10.8	7.8	7.9	8.6	9.5	9.5	10.2	10.9	10.4	11.1
	Anom °C	1.2	1.2	1.0	1.1	1.0	1.2	1.2	1.3	1.1	1.1	1.0	1.2	1.1	1.3	1.4	1.1	1.4
Sunshine	Actual hrs	1304.0	1441.3	1300.7	1096.2	1195.5	1422.0	1332.0	1499.1	1069.9	1124.1	1099.2	1366.1	1301.9	1403.2	1483.3	1423.4	1592.3
	Anom %	97	100	95	93	96	100	100	100	98	94	88	100	98	102	99	96	102
Rainfall	Actual mm	1280.5	1006.0	1627.4	1618.5	1408.3	1091.3	1117.5	947.0	1551.5	1440.6	1909.9	905.1	1464.9	926.7	708.0	1477.4	1004.5
	Anom %	116	122	116	110	128	121	119	123	96	130	114	120	115	120	118	122	131

Rachel Sayers

With all the mains drainage alternatives, the careful design and selection of a system to suit the site and use requirements is paramount. There is no 'green panacea' and the best solution must be individually tailored for the site. The choice of system is as much dependent on the people who will use the system (what will they put down the drains and how much maintenance and management is required) as it is on the physical constraints of the site. When considering alternatives to mains drainage, it is prudent to get a specialist (for example Elemental Solutions) to design and specify the system.

Where mains drainage is available, it is usually both best practice and a legal requirement to connect to it. The exception is stormwater, which ideally should be dealt with on site wherever space and ground conditions allow. Even where mains drainage is provided, there is still an environmental benefit to be gained by reducing water use and minimising the use of environmentally persistent chemicals that might enter the drainage system during construction and operation of the building.

There are various alternatives to mains sewerage (see table) and the careful consideration and choice of system can have ecological benefits. Issues include:
• Water conservation. Proven water efficiency measures reduce the problem of sewage treatment and disposal at source. Reuse of treated effluent is technically feasible but consideration must be given to health risk and the life-cycle impact of such systems. In dry climates reuse for irrigation can have a number of benefits and water is saved when the supply is most stressed.
• The by-product can be useable compost while sludge generation can be avoided.

• Energy (and money) can be saved in infrastructure and sewerage treatment but the mains system benefits from economies of scale in terms of energy use and cost.
• Various systems can be used as a natural way of removing phosphates, nitrates, heavy metals etc.

In England and Wales, the Environment Agency must approve any discharge other than mains drainage. At present there is a presumption that mains drainage should be used where possible and the license is given only in situations where mains drainage is problematic, due to the need to protect watercourses etc. Areas prone to flooding require great care.

Greywater refers to waste from basins, baths, washing machines and showers. Brown (or black) water refers to waste from wc's, kitchen sinks and dishwashers.

Natural treatment systems

Reedbeds are commonly used as a secondary system in lieu of soakaways. Major solids/contaminants are normally removed first by the use of a septic or settlement tank, or sometimes a packaged sewerage treatment plant. Reedbeds are based on the cleansing properties of three elements:
• soil-dwelling microbes;
• physical and chemical properties of the base media (soil, sand or gravel);
• plants.

Soiled water is cleaned and filtered biologically. Wetland plants transfer atmospheric oxygen down through their roots in order to survive in waterlogged conditions. The roots of the reeds supply oxygen to the naturally occurring bacteria in the water which break down any pathogens present. This is an aerobic treatment system, ie not smelly. The most common reed to

be used are Phragmites Australis. The design of complete natural treatment systems is covered in BRE GBG 42.

Composting toilets

The basic principle of a composting toilet is to turn waste into usable compost without adding water to flush it away. The creation of compost requires the correct balance of carbon and nitrogen. Therefore, instead of flushing with water, 'soak' is added. This is normally sawdust, but can include other carbon-based substances like cardboard or straw. Earthworms are sometimes also added to improve the composting process. The container underneath the wc pan must be ventilated and drained.

The principles of a composting toilet include the folowing:
• aeration with warmth if possible;
• ventilation to extract odour;
• drainage to prevent water logging;
• moisture equivalent to a squeezed-out sponge;
• balance of carbon and nitrogen.

Composting wc's have specific space requirements – a void below the wc and up to two metres' headroom – and this can makes them impractical in many situations. The maintenance regime includes adding shavings and raking.

In composting toilet systems the liquid is drained off into a greywater sewage system or infiltrated into the ground or other disposal system. The solids and paper fall into a composting box. The volume of compost is five to15 per cent of the original volume of solid waste added. Solid waste has to be composted for approximately 12-18 months before it can be used. The bio-decomposition is free from odour and flies, as the bio-chamber is ventilated.

Common alternatives to mains drainage

	Uses	Comments
Cesspool	Holding tank only with no treatment – inlet but no outlet	Use only where high water table and ground conditions dictate; needs regular emptying by bulk tanker
Septic tank with soakaway (or 'leachfield')	Brown and greywater disposal systems; common solution where mains drainage not available	Common solution where mains drainage is problematic; space required for soakaway which, unless properly designed, can become clogged after a few years
Septic tank with reedbeds/ponds	Brown and greywater disposal and/or recovery systems; prefabricated units or built in-situ	Reedbeds are an alternative where ground is unsuitable for a soakaway or effluent volumes are too great; landscaping possibilities
Stand-alone reedbed	Mainly greywater disposal and/or recovery systems	As above; solids must be removed before water reaches the reedbed
Composting wc's	Toilet waste only. Rarely used except where water is scarce and there is no mains drainage	High space and maintenance requirement
Packaged sewerage treatment plant	Various different designs/principles available; can be used with reedbed or other secondary treatment	Continuous mechanical agitation of effluent required
'Living machine'	Complete artificial ecosystem used for all stages of waste treatment/recycling	High maintenance and cost, requires many pumps etc; check LCA compared with conventional treatment and other alternatives; could be option for urban situations, eg BedZed in Sutton

Clivus Multrum composting wc

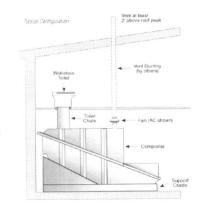

Further information
• www.odpm.gov.uk (BRE GBG 42)
• Nick Grant, Mark Moodie, Chris Weedon, Sewage Solutions: Answering the Call of Nature (Machynlleth, 2001). See also: www.elementalsolutions.co.uk
• www.cresswater.co.uk (reedbeds)
• www.reed-bed.co.uk (disposal systems)
• www.multrum.co.uk (composting wc's)
• www.sustainabledrainage.co.uk (Robert Bray Associates, an environmental design practice specialising in sustainable drainage systems)
• www.cat.org.uk (Centre for Alternative Technology)
• www.conderproducts.com (packaged sewage treatment products)
• www.haycock-associates.co.uk
• www.ciria.org.uk/suds

Using photosynthesis

Marigold Webster

It is sometimes suggested that we can compensate for the carbon emitted by buildings by planting trees. Is this true?

A typical secondary school built in 2005 and complying with DfES Building Bulletin 87, is likely to emit the equivalent of 5kg/m² per year of carbon (about 18.5g of carbon dioxide/m² per year). Assuming an area of 12,000 square metres, the school would emit 60,000kg (60 tonnes) of carbon per year and 6000 tonnes over a 100 year period, equivalent to 22,000 tonnes of carbon dioxide emission. To convert from the carbon to carbon dioxide basis, multiply by the ratio of atomic weights – carbon dioxide 44 and carbon 12, eg nine tonnes of carbon is equivalent to 9 x 44/12 = 33 tonnes of carbon dioxide per square metre per year (Approved Document L2).

As part of the natural carbon cycle, trees absorb carbon dioxide and release oxygen into the atmosphere through the process of photosynthesis. It is possible theoretically to calculate how many trees (ie how much new forest) would be required to offset the amount of carbon dioxide emitted.

One hectare of mature oak woodland is estimated to offset 75 tonnes of carbon, corresponding to 275 tonnes of carbon dioxide over a 100 year period (ECCM Technical Paper 7). One hectare of mixed planting of lowland native woodland containing about 50 per cent oak or other main tree species is estimated to offset between 30 and 60 tonnes of carbon, corresponding to 110 to 220 tonnes of carbon dioxide.

To offset the 22,000 tonnes of carbon dioxide emission from our typical secondary school, 80 hectares of new oak forest would need to be planted and managed for 100 years. This includes only an offset for the energy in use, not for the embodied energy of materials used or for the energy used in the construction or maintenance of the building. 80 hectares is equivalent to 67 times the floor area of the typical secondary school. 336,000 oak saplings would need to be planted for every school (28 oak saplings for every square metre of the school over a 100 year life). Of the 4200 oak saplings planted on each hectare at the beginning of the 100 year life of the forest, 244 might be expected to survive to maturity (ECCM Technical Paper 5).

The capacity to offset carbon dioxide emissions varies over the life of the forest. For example the oak forest described above really starts to accumulate carbon dioxide only after 25 years.

There are also large variations in the capacity to offset carbon dioxide emissions between different vegetation systems. For example one hectare of mixed planting of lowland native woodland containing about 50 per cent oak or other main tree species is estimated to offset between 30 and 60 tonnes of carbon, corresponding to 110 to 220 tonnes of carbon dioxide (Approved Document L2); while a fast-growing species such as Douglas fir planted on a rotation system can provide a greater offset than an oak forest. However, mature woodlands have considerably greater external leaf areas and consequently greater capacity for carbon dioxide offset over time.

There are numerous studies of this subject, and all indicate that the assessment and calculation of carbon dioxide emission is a very complex issue. The figures given above are simplistic.

Although theoretically it may be possible to offset emissions of carbon dioxide by planting trees, this presupposes that every project could have hectares of land allocated for its exclusive 100 year use and have the resources to manage these forests of oak. For clients other than agricultural or rural landowners, this is extremely unlikely to be the case.

In addition there are still many uncertainties regarding the science and long-term prospects of forests as 'carbon sinks'. While offering many environmental and social benefits, planting forests does not address the real problem of reducing the use of fossil fuels.

Further information

• Building Regulations Approved Document L2 Conservation of Fuel and Power 0.21, Conversion between carbon and carbon dioxide indices (HMSO, London 2002)

• DfES Building Bulletin 87 2003, Guidelines for Environmental Design in Schools (London 2003)

• The Edinburgh Centre for Carbon Management, Estimation of Carbon Offset by Trees, ECCM Technical Paper 7 (Edinburgh 2002)

• The Edinburgh Centre for Carbon Management, Counting Carbon for Offset Purposes, ECCM Technical Paper 5 (Edinburgh 2002)

• www.eccm.uk.com (Edinburgh Centre for Carbon Management)

Floresteca: sustainable plantations in Brazil.

Plants

Planting for microclimatic control

Sara Grohmann

It has become increasingly apparent that air temperatures in densely built urban contexts are higher than the temperatures of the surrounding areas. Numerous recent studies have attempted to measure this and assess the effect of urban areas on local climate.

The phenomenon commonly known as the 'urban heat island' (UHI) is probably the most apparent climatic effect of urbanisation. The studies suggest that urban areas are hotter than the surrounding countryside primarily because of the lack of trees and vegetation and the use of materials that absorb and retain the sun's heat.

The UHI effect is most evident in the urban canopy layer, beneath roof level. Here urban vegetation, if correctly selected and located, can have a crucial role in the urban microclimate.

Tree leaves can absorb (normally about 55 per cent), transmit (about 20 per cent) and reflect (about 25 per cent) of solar radiation (Scudo 2002). Trees can also help block rainfall erosion, filter pollutants, reduce ozone in urban areas and reduce noise levels.

A belt of trees, 30 metres wide and 15 metres tall, can reduce highway noise by between six and 10 decibels (Santamouris et al 2001). Deciduous trees can cool urban spaces and buildings during hot periods, and allow for radiation transmission in cold seasons, while evergreens can protect from cold winds and snow.

But most of all trees affect the urban climate through 'evapotranspiration'. This occurs when water, transpired through the pores in the leaves, evaporates, drawing heat and cooling the air in the process. According to the Heat Island Group, 'a single mature, properly watered tree with a crown of 30 feet can evapotranspire up to 40 gallons of water in a day, which is like removing

all the heat produced in four hours by a small electric space heater'. Within ten to 15 years – the time it takes a tree to grow to a useful size – trees placed in strategic locations can reduce heating and cooling costs by an average of 10-20 per cent.

In addition, compared to constructed materials, vegetation has a similar emissivity but a much smaller thermal mass and a significantly smaller capacity of storing and re-emitting heat. Therefore in dense urban contexts, where the emission of long waves from constructed materials contributes to the increase of night temperatures and accentuates the UHI effect, vegetation cover helps to reduce air temperature.

It is difficult to analyse correctly the microclimate of a large urban area and to assess the exact environmental impact of alternative proposals. As a general guide the following should be taken in account when selecting and locating trees in an urban context:
• orientation;
• the dates when individual species loose their leaves and come into leaf;
• the shape and maximum potential height of the plants;
• the solar radiation transmissivity of the canopy in different seasons;
• the crown wind permeability.

In recent years research and consultancy projects carried out at the University of Cambridge by Cambridge Architectural Research and the Martin Centre for Architectural and Urban Studies have developed computer and physical modeling techniques that show strong connections between urban form, microclimatic characteristics and the potential for renewable energies.

Further information
• G Scudo and F Elsa, Thermal Comfort In Urban Spaces, Streets and Courtyards (Milan 2002)
• www.map21ltd.com
• http://eetd.lbl.gov/HeatIsland (Heat Island Group)
• M Santmouris, L Lopes, J Adnot, N Klitsikas, Alvarez and F Sanchez, Managing the Growth of the Demand for Cooling in Urban areas and Mitigating the Heat Island Effect (ECEEE Summer Study Proceedings 2001). The proceedings are on www.eceèe.org.
• TJ Chandler, The Climate of London (London 1965)

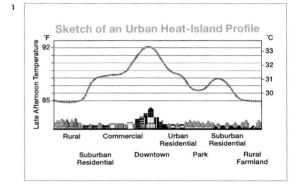

1 Urban heat island (UHI) profile (source: Heat Island Group).

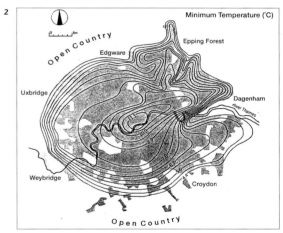

2 The London heat island (source: Met Office).

231

Green roofs and green walls

Marigold Webster

Green roofs have become an icon of the green movement in architecture, but we need to be very clear about their real advantages. These can be summarised, in order of importance, as follows:

• They offer solar and thermal protection to the roofing membrane.
• They provide an improvement to the aesthetics of the membrane.
• With a reasonable depth of soil (and therefore considerable extra cost in structure) they provide a fully landscaped roof.
• They provide improved rainwater attenuation and therefore reduce storm water run-off.
• They provide opportunities for increased biodiversity.
• The earth covering provides extra insulation protection, particularly against over-heating in summer.
• They provide a very marginal improvement in carbon dioxide absorption and can soak up particulate pollutants.

There are considerable advantages in having the roof substrate and its landscape covering under one subcontract, using guaranteed systems such as those from Bauder or Kalzip. On the other hand, the earth roofs installed in the early 1980s at Real World Studios have performed without any problems, on specifications which were developed using fibreglass covering and shallow earth growing medium.

There are two basic types of green roof: intensive systems, which use 300mm or more of soil and can therefore support gardens; and extensive systems, which use an 80-100mm plant substrate and grow sedums, succulents and drought-tolerant plants. The comparative advantages and disadvantages are shown in the chart.

Research at the University of Sheffield

has illustrated the potential of 'semi-extensive' roofs, where the substrate depth is increased using materials such as lightweight Leca granules to a depth of approximately 200mm. Greater depth produces longer flowering seasons for plants and, combined with an irrigation system, can support a greater variety of plant material.

Claims can be made to support the environmental credentials of 'brown roofs', ie using 50mm or so of aggregate as a covering to the membrane. Gravel can support lichens and mosses, and associated insect life, as well as improving attenuation, solar protection and aesthetics.

It has been argued that green roofs can have an advantageous effect on the improvement of air quality, by filtering and binding dust particles and absorbing airborne toxins (see Robert Gavin). Stephen Peck, of Green Roofs for Healthy Cities, calculates that a surface of 150 square metres would be required to balance the human intake of oxygen for one person for one year.

Green walls

To maximise the provision of a natural habitat we can use buildings to support walls of plants. Very few plants damage buildings. Plants such as ivies and Virginia creepers have suckers but many require support from trellises or wires. Beautiful systems for plant supports are available but stainless steel or zinc plates and galvanised wire will suffice. A more elaborate solution might provide linear hanging baskets built into the wall, complete with necessary irrigation. Vertical hydroponic panels have been used on a school at Obernai in Alsace, with prefabricated steel mesh panels and an integral watering system.

Research into the environmental advantages of green walls is needed but

they would definitely include:

• An improvement in the U-value of the wall by enhancing the external surface resistance and protection from wind.
• Improvements in the U-value of absorptive masonry by reducing water penetration (which otherwise increases conductivity.)
• Increased oxygen production and absorption of carbon dioxide and pollutants, particularly in urban environments.
• Provision of habitat for insects and nesting sites for birds.

Clearly the orientation of the wall is a key determinant with regard to the foliage that can be grown. Cold, sunless walls have the advantage of even temperatures and moist soil that can suit hydrangeas and ivies. Warm walls that receive a lot of sunlight can be dry but they are excellent for tender plants such as wisteria, jasmine and many types of clematis.

1 Intensive vs extensive green roofs.
2 Sedum roof, Dartington.
3 Real World Studios, Box.

Further information
• www.erisco-bauder.co.uk (Bauder systems)
• www.kalzip.com (Kalzip green roof systems)
• Robert Gavin, 'Environmental benefits of the wider implementation of Green Roofs on the Urban Landscape', Building for a Future, vol 12 no 3 (winter 2002-2003).
• Stephen Peck and Chris Callaghan, Greenbacks from Green Roofs: Forging a new industry in Canada (Toronto 1999)
• Nigel Dunnett, 'Up on the Roof', The Garden, volume 127 part 5 (May 2002)
• Obernai School, AJ (14 April 2005)

1

Types of green roof

	Intensive	Extensive
Potential to grow	Lawns and shrubs	Sedunis, succulents, drought-tolerant plants
Typical Bauder specifications	3.5mm vapour barrier 150mm insulation 5mm waterproof underlayer 5mm waterproof roof barrier 6mm protection layer 50mm drainage board	3.5mm vapour barrier 150mm insulation 5mm waterproof underlay 5mm waterproof roof barrier 5mm filtration layer 80-100mm 'plant substrate' 1mm fleece 300mm earth
Total thickness	380mm + insulation	min 100mm + insulation
Roof pitch	Up to 22°	Up to 40°
Normal weight of soil etc	200kg/m²	50-60kg/m²
Saturated weight of soil etc	Up to 500kg/m²	Up to 200kg/m²
Av water retention potential	71%	58%
Maintenance	High	Low
Irrigation	As normal garden	Little/no requirement

Source: www.eriscobauder.co.uk

2

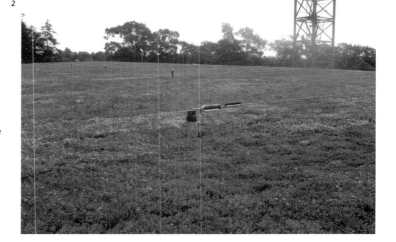

3

Project directory

LIVING

Solar Courtyard Housing, Milton Keynes (1985) p28
FCBa Peter Clegg, Julia Kashdan-Brown, Sarah Hare
Client Haslam Homes
Consultant John Willoughby (m&e engineer)
Ref Architectural Review (Jan 1986), Laboratorio Politecnico di Milano (March 2000)

Upper Lawn, Bath (1998) p30
FCBa Keith Bradley, Rob Gregory
Consultant Whitby Bird (structural engineer), Wraxall Builders (contractor)
Ref Architecture Today (Oct 1998)

Market Lane, Shepherds Bush (2001) p32
FCBa Peter Clegg, Jo Wright, Tim Hall, Magali Marcouire, Gill Smith
Client Peabody Trust
Consultants Ellis & Moore Consulting Engineers (structural engineer), Atelier Ten (m&e), Walker Management (employer's agent, qs), Steven Woodham (landscape architect), Ashe Construction (contractor)
Awards Housing Design Award (1999), Civic Trust Award (2002)
Ref AJ Focus (Oct 2003), Building Design (11 Oct 2002), Guardian (28 June 2002), Independent (20 Dec 2001), London Housing (June 2002), New Architecture in Britain (Merrell 2003)

The Point, Wapping Wharf, Bristol (2001) p34
FCBa Keith Bradley, Andy Theobald, Sara Grohmann, Alan Wainer, Ken Grix
Client Crosby Homes (Special Projects)
Consultants BME Partnership (m&e), Gleeds (qs), Robson Liddle Partnership (structural engineer), Skanska Construction Group (contractor)
Awards Building for Life Award (2002), Housing Design Awards (2002), National Homebuilder Design Awards (2002), RIBA Award (2002)
Ref Architecture Today (April 2002), Strategies for Sustainable Architecture (Paola Sassi 2006)

Beaufort Court, Lillie Road, Fulham (2003) p38
FCBa Keith Bradley, Julian Gitsham, Jillian Jones, Helen Roberts, Richard Marks
Client Peabody Trust
Consultants Max Fordham (m&e), Michael Barclay Partnership (structural engineer), Walker Management (qs), Grant Associates (landscape consultant), Walter Llewellyn & Sons (contractor)
Awards Housing Design Award (2001), CABE Building for Life Award (2004), National Homebuilder Design Award (2004), Housing Corporation (2004): best example of affordable housing, World Habitat Awards (2005): runner-up
Ref Architects' Journal (16 Oct 2003), Architecture in a Climate of Change (Butterworth-Heinemann 2005), New Architecture in Britain (Merrell 2003), Costruire (June 2003), Sustain (March 2004), Green Buildings: Architetture Sostenibil nel Regno Unito (Clean 2005) (includes other FCB projects)

Accordia, Cambridge (2006) p42
FCBa Keith Bradley, Mike Keys, Anne Claxton, Carl Gulland, Chris Mackenzie, Giovanni Meta, Alina White, Hugo Marrack, Louise Blacker, Tara Breen, Olivia Hough, Lily Lau, Alastair Gambles, Jennie Green, Ken Grix
Client Countryside Properties (Accordia)
Consultants Alison Brooks Architects, Maccreanor Lavington (collaborating architects), Grant Associates (landscape consultant), Roberts & Partners (m&e), Richard Jackson (structural engineer), Philip Pank Partnership (qs), Kajima (contractor)
Awards National Homebuilder Awards (2006), Mail on Sunday (2006): best housing project of the year, best house of three or more storeys, Housing Design Awards (2006): overall winner, Civic Trust Award (2007)
Ref Building (27 June 2003), Arq Vol 7 nos 3-4 (2003), Design Reviewed: urban housing (CABE 2004), Building Design (12 May 2006), Architecture Today (June 2006), RIBA Journal (June 2006)

Vallecas social housing, Madrid (2006) p46
FCBa Peter Clegg, Jo Wright, Elena Marco-Burguete, Ken Grix
Client Empresa Municipal de la Vivienda
Consultants Ortiz Leon Arquitectos (associate architect), Emma (environmental engineer), Max Fordham (m&e)
Ref El Mundo (11 Nov 2003), Architects Journal (20 March 2003), Estrategia Eco Valle (EMVS 2005)

Brighton 'One Planet Living' community (2005-) p48
FCBa Keith Bradley, Ian Taylor, Jeremy Gay, Jason Comish, Sam Tyler, Andrew Macintosh, Jillian Jones, Robert Prewett
Client Crest Nicholson–BioRegional Quintain JV
Consultants Fulcrum Consulting (environmental engineer), Cameron Taylor (structural engineer), Nicholas Pearson Associates (landscape consultant), KHK Group (qs)

STUDENT HOUSING

Panns Bank Residences, University of Sunderland (1994) p52
FCBa Richard Feilden, Keith Bradley, Jonathan Hetreed, Jo Wright, Julia Kashdan-Brown, Richard Collis
Client University of Sunderland
Consultants Arup (m&e, structural engineer), Turner & Townsend (qs), Shepherd Construction (contractor)
Awards Brick Award (1994), Housing Design Award (1995): national award, Civic Trust Award (1996)
Ref Architects' Journal (20 July 1994), World Architecture (Oct 2003)

West Downs Student Village, University of Winchester (1996) p54
FCBa Richard Feilden, Keith Bradley, David Stansfield, Marigold Webster, Andy Couling, Tim Hall
Client King Alfred's College of Higher Education
Consultants Halcrow Gilbert Associates (m&e), Buro Happold (structural engineer), Land Use Consultants (landscape architect), Burnley Wilson Fish (qs), Burt & Vick (contractor)
Award Housing Design Award (1997): national award
Ref Building (16 May 1997), World Architecture (Oct 2003)

Lakeside Residences, Aston University, Birmingham (1999) p56
FCBa Richard Feilden, Keith Bradley, Jo Wright, David Stansfield, Simon Shaw, Alan Wainer, Jason Comish, Jayne Barlow
Client Aston University
Consultants Buro Happold (m&e, structural engineer), Teasdale Environmental Design (landscape architect), Faithful & Gould (qs), John Laing (contractor), EC Harris (project manager)
Awards Brick Award (2001): best public building, Civic Trust Award (2002)
Ref Building (5 Nov 1999), Architects' Journal (29 Nov 2001)

Westfield Village, Queen Mary, University of London (2004) p60
FCBa Richard Feilden, Ian Taylor, Helen Roberts, Alex Whitbread, Sam Tyler, Bob Prewitt, Ilona Hay, Simon Shaw, Rachel Calladine, Magali Marcouire, Jonathon Mitchell, Andrew Mackintosh
Client Queen Mary, University of London
Consultants Max Fordham (m&e), Adams Kara Taylor (structural engineer), Laing O'Rourke Construction (contractor)
Ref Building (30 May 2003), Regeneration & Renewal (29 Oct 2004), Building Design (Nov 5 2004), Architectural Review (Oct 2005), Detail (Dec 2005), RIBA Journal (July 2006), New Urban Housing (Hilary French 2006)

LEARNING

John Cabot City Technology College, Bristol (1993) p70
FCBa Richard Feilden, Keith Bradley, Peter Clegg, Linton Ross, Jo Wright, Marigold Webster, Andy Couling, Gill Smith, Julia Kashdan-Brown
Client John Cabot CTC
Consultant Buro Happold (m&e, structural engineer, qs), The Landmark Practice (landscape consultant)
Award RIBA Award (1994)
Ref Architects' Journal (17 March 1993), Building Services Journal (May 1994)

Kingswood Day Preparatory School (1995) (p74)
FCBa Peter Clegg, Andy Theobald, Gill Smith, Hau-Ming Tse
Client Kingswood Day Preparatory School
Consultants Buro Happold (m&e, structural engineer), Cyrill Sweet (qs), The Landmark Practice (landscape consultant), PRC Construction (contractor)
Award RIBA Award (1996)
Ref Building Design (12 Jan 1996)

Exemplar School Design, DfES (2004) p78
FCBa Richard Feilden, Peter Clegg, Simon Doody, Suzannah Lloyd, Simon Gould, Ken Grix
Client Department for Education & Skills
Consultants Buro Happold (m&e, structural engineer), Davis Langdon (qs), Plincke Landscape (landscape consultant)
Ref Building Futures (Oct 2003), Building (20 Feb 2004)

Haverstock School, Camden (2006) p82
FCBa Keith Bradley, Richard Feilden, Marigold Webster, John Southall, Tim Hall, Ron Nkomba, Larissa Johnston, Paul Priest, Sam Tyler, Richard Marks, Carol James, Charlotte Barrows, Eleni Stika, Illona Hay, Jonathan Mitchell, Zoe Fudge, Richard Tucker, Rachel Calladine
Client London Borough of Camden
Consultants Atelier Ten (m&e), Whitbybird (structural engineer), Burnley Wilson Fish (qs), Grant Associates (landscape consultant), Kajima Construction Europe (d&b contractor)

Northampton Academy (2006) p86
FCBa Richard Feilden, Ian Taylor, David Saxby, Toby Lewis, Carol James, Ron Nkomba, Jennie Green, Joerg Majer, Jonathon Mitchell, Trevor Brown
Client The United Learning Trust
Consultants Buro Happold (m&e, structural engineer), CM Parker Browne (qs), Plincke Landscape (landscape consultant), Miller Construction (contractor)
Award RIBA Award (2006), RIBA East Midlands Award (2006), Civic Trust Education Award (2007)
Ref Building Design (6 Feb 2004)

Paddington Academy (2006) p90
FCBa Richard Feilden, David Stansfield, Simon Doody, Akos Juhasz, Olivia Hough, Lily Lau, Matthew Clay, Matt Barrass, Ken Grix
Client United Learning Trust
Consultants Buro Happold (m&e, structural engineer), CM Parker Browne (qs, project manager), Churchman Landscape Architects (landscape consultant), United Learning Trust (project sponsor), MJ Gleeson (contractor)

UNIVERSITY BUILDINGS

The Berrill Building, Open University, Milton Keynes (1997) p94
FCBa Keith Bradley, Peter Clegg, Andy Theobald, Tim Hall, Alan Wainer, Darren Cater
Client Open University
Consultants Buro Happold (m&e, structural engineer), Mace (construction manager)
Ref The Selective Environment, Dean Hawkes, Jane McDonald, Koen Steemers (2001)

Martial Rose Library, King Alfred's College, Winchester (2000) p98
FCBa Richard Feilden, Jo Wright, Richard Collis, Mike Haslam
Client King Alfred's College of Higher Education
Consultants Buro Happold (structural engineer), Burnley Wilson Fish (qs), Plincke Landscape (landscape consultant), Geoffrey Osborne (contractor)
Awards RIBA Award (2000), RIBA Sustainability Awards (2000): shortlisted
Ref Architects' Journal (18 May 2000), An Intelligent Library, Derek Clements-Croome (University of Reading 2001)

Oxstalls Campus, University of Gloucestershire (2002) p100
FCBa Peter Clegg, Bill Gething, David Stansfield, Matt Somerville, Toby Lewis, Ben Slee, Elena Marco Burguete, Ken Grix
Client University of Gloucestershire
Consultants WSP Buildings (m&e), Whitbybird & Partners (structural engineer), Burnley Wilson Fish (qs), Montresor Partnership (facade consultant), Paul Harris Associates (landscape consultant)
Awards Civic Trust Award (2003): national award for sustainability, RIBA Award (2003)
Ref Architectural Review (Feb 2004), Costruire (July 2004), Abitare (November 2004)

Portland Square, Plymouth University (2003) p104
FCBa Peter Clegg, David Stansfield, Andy Couling, Chris Mackenzie, James Feghali, Ken Grix
Client University of Plymouth
Consultants Buro Happold (m&e, structural engineer), Grant Associates (landscape consultant), Davis Langdon & Everest (qs), Montresor Partnership (facade consultant), Bovis Lend Lease (contractor)
Ref Fourth Door Review (2003)

The London Centre for Nanotechnology (2006) p108
FCBa Keith Bradley, Ian Taylor, Tim Hall, Soo-In Oh, Ron Nkomba, Rachel Calladine, Daniel Parker, Ken Grix
Client University College London/Imperial College
Consultants Buro Happold (m&e, structural engineer), Edmond Shipway & Partners (qs)
Ref Fourth Door Review (2003), Building Design (24 February 2006)

WORKING

Greenpeace Headquarters, Islington (1991) p116
FCBa Peter Clegg, Linton Ross, Jo Wright, Andy Theobald, Gill Smith, Andy Couling
Client Greenpeace UK
Consultants Synergy (m&e engineer), Atelier One (structural engineer), BWA Project Services (qs), Bovis Construction (contractor)
Ref Architecture Today (Oct 1990), RIBA Journal (Nov 1991)

New Environmental Office, Building Research Establishment, Garston (1996) p118
FCBa Peter Clegg, Bill Gething, David Noble, Simon Shaw, Craig White
Client Building Research Establishment
Consultants Max Fordham (environmental engineer), Buro Happold (structural engineer), Turner & Townsend (qs), Nicholas Pearson Associates (landscape consultant), Arup R&D (environmental consultant), John Sisk & Sons (contractor)
Awards British Institute of Architectural Technologists (1997): open award for supreme technical excellence, RIBA Award (1998), Design Council Millennium Product (1998), Concrete Society Awards (1998): certificate of excellence
Ref RIBA Journal (April 1997), Green Buildings Pay (Spon 1998), Photovoltaics in Buildings: a design guide (DTI 1999), Building Services Journal (1997), RIBA Journal supplement (1997), Green Vitruvius (UCD 1999), Architecture et Développement Durable (EPF Lausanne 2002), Environmental Design: an introduction for architects and engineers (Randall Thomas/Max Fordham 2002)

Manor Park, Headquarters for Rare, Twycross (2001) p122
FCBa Peter Clegg, Bill Gething, Jo Wright, David Noble, Peter Williams
Client Rare
Consultants Battle McCarthy (m&e, structural engineer), Derek Evans & Partners (qs), Battle McCarthy (landscape consultant), Montresor Partnership (facade consultant), Wates Construction (contractor)
Awards RIBA Award (1999), Civic Trust Award (2001)
Ref RIBA Journal (July 1999), Surface (Jul-Aug 2001)

Neal's Yard Remedies, Dorset (2005) p126
FCBa Peter Clegg, Alex Morris, Ben Slee, Andrew Peters, Ken Grix
Client Neal's Yard Remedies
Consultants Max Fordham (m&e), Alan Conisbee Associates (structural engineer), Davis Langdon & Everest (qs), Melissa Hay (landscape consultant), Blenheim House Construction (contractor)
Ref Building Design supplement (June 2005), Building for a Future (winter 2005-06), Times Online: Back to nature by Lisa Grainger (30 July 2005)

Heelis: New Central Office for the National Trust, Swindon (2005) p128
FCBa Peter Clegg, Jo Wright, Ian Taylor, Anne Claxton, Toby Lewis, Akos Juhasz, Matthew Vaudin, Suzie Lloyd, Simon Gould
Client The National Trust
Consultants Max Fordham (m&e), Adams Kara Taylor (structural engineer), Davis Langdon & Everest (qs), Grant Associates (landscape consultant), Montresor Partnership (facade consultant), Moss Construction (contractor)
Awards Brick Development Association Awards (2005): best commercial building, International FX Interior Design Award (2005): best medium/large office building, RIBA Award (2006), AJ100 Sustainability Award (2006), RIBA Sustainability Award (2006), British Council for Offices Innovation Award (2006), Civic Trust Sustainability Award (2007)
Ref EcoTech/Architecture Today (Nov 03), Building for a Future (winter 2004-05), Daily Telegraph (5 Nov 2002), Times (18 Nov 2002), Building (1 July 2005), FX (Oct 2005), Intra (Sept 2005), Architecture Today (Sept 2005), L'Architettura Naturale (Jan 2006), Architectural Review (July 2005), Financial Times (10 Oct 2005)

GATHERING

The Lantern Building, Ringwood, Hampshire (1992) p138
FCBa Keith Bradley, Jo Wright
Client The Sheiling Community
Consultants John Willoughby (m&e), Whitby Bird & Partners (structural engineer), Richard Sampson (qs), George & Harding (contractor)
Award RIBA Award (1994)

Wildscreen World, Bristol (1996) p140
FCBa Keith Bradley, Richard Feilden
Client Bristol 2000
Consultant Buro Happold (structural and services engineer)

The Earth Centre, South Yorkshire: Arrivals Building, Solar Canopy and Planet Earth Gallery (1999) p142
FCBa Peter Clegg, Keith Bradley, Andy Theobald, Mike Keys, Linton Ross, Andy Couling, Anne Claxton, Tim Hall, Rob Gregory, Ken Grix
Client The Earth Centre
Consultants Planet Earth Gallery and Arrivals Building: Atelier Ten (environmental engineer), Atelier One (structural engineer), Bernard Williams & Associates (qs), Grant Associates (landscape consultant), Bovis Lend Lease (contractor); Solar Canopy: Atelier One (structural engineer), Carpenter Oak & Woodland (timber frame contractor), ECOFYS (environmental engineer), Taylor Woodrow (project manager and contractor), Pilkington Solar International (pv supplier), Active Cladding Systems (cladding contractor)
Award RIBA Award (2002)

Ref Architecture Today (May 1999), Architectural Review (April 2000), Photovoltaics & Architecture (Peter Clegg, Randall Thomas, Max Fordham & Partners, Spon 2001), Building Design (June 2001), Building for a Future (Spring 2002), Ecotech/Architecture Today (June 2002), Wood Design & Building 20 (summer 2002), Duurzaam Bouwen (Sept 2002), Renewable Energy in the Built Environment (Building Centre Trust 2002), Architectural Review (April 2000), Building (18 June 1999), Architecture Today (May 1999), Sustainable Building (summer 2002), Photovoltaics & Architecture (Spon 2001), Independent Review (27 June 2002), The Earth Centre Solar Canopy (PWF Deege, University of Northumbria 2003), Construmat: Construccion Sostenible (May 2004)

Visitor Facilities, Painshill Park, Surrey (2001) p146
FCBa Peter Clegg, Anne Claxton, Toby Lewis, Magali Marcouire, Ken Grix
Client Painshill Park Trust
Atelier Ten (m&e), Structures One (structural engineer), Waterman Associates (qs), Painshill Park Trust (landscape consultant), Formes Alutek (facade/cladding), Nigel Bradon (facade/cladding), Geoffrey Osborne (contractor)
Awards RIBA Award (2003), Civic Trust Award (2003), Elmbridge Borough Council Design Award (2003)
Ref Architect's Journal (5 Sept 2002)

Persistence Works, Sheffield (2001) p148
FCBa Peter Clegg, Julia Kashdan-Brown, Toby Lewis, David Saxby, Magali Marcouire
Client Yorkshire Artspace Society
Consultants Buro Happold (m&e), Environment Agency (environmental consultant), Buro Happold (structural engineer), Citex (qs), Grant Associates (landscape consultant), Montresor Partnership (facade consultant), M J Gleeson (contractor)
Awards RIBA Award (2002), RIBA Yorkshire White Rose Award for Design Excellence (2002), Prime Minister's Better Public Building (2002): finalist
Ref Building (21 June 2002), Architecture Today (March 2003)

Visitor Centre, Yorkshire Sculpture Park (2002) p152
FCBa Peter Clegg, David Stansfield, Toby Lewis, Julia Kashdan-Brown, Nick Brindley, Jason Cornish, Ken Grix
Client Yorkshire Sculpture Park
Consultants RW Gregory (m&e), Michael Heal & Partners (structural engineer), Burnley Wilson Fish (qs), Land Use Consultants (landscape consultant), Formes Alutek (facade/cladding), Montresor Partnership (facade consultant), Galliford Northern (contractor)
Awards Civic Trust Award (2004), RIBA Award (2003), RIBA Yorkshire White Rose Award for Design Excellence (2003), Building on Quality Award (2003): overall winner UK new-build
Ref RIBA Journal (Aug 2002)

Underground Gallery, Yorkshire Sculpture Park (2005) p152
FCBa Peter Clegg, Andy Couling, Ben Elliott, George Samios, Ken Grix
Client Yorkshire Sculpture Park
Consultants WSP (structural engineer), Ernest Griffiths & Son (m&e), Burnley Wilson Fish (project manager, qs), Land Use Consultants (landscape architect), Montresor Partnership (facade consultant)
Awards RIBA Yorkshire White Rose Award (2005): Sport and Leisure Building and Yorkshire Building of the Year (2005), The Gulbenkian Prize (2006): runner up, RIBA Award (2006)
Ref Sunday Times (1 May 2005), Guardian (14 May 2005), Architects' Journal (19 May 2005), Yorkshire Post (10 May 2005), Independent (10 May 2005), RIBAJ (July 2005), Times (12 Nov 2005)

Milestones of Flight, RAF Museum, Hendon (2003) p158
FCBa Richard Feilden, Julian Gitsham, Tim Hall, Alex Whitbread, Helen Roberts, James Risebero, Richard Marks, Soo-In-Oh
Client The Royal Air Force Museum
Consultants Buro Happold (m&e, structural engineer), Turner & Townsend (qs), Edco Design (landscape consultant), Norwest Holst Construction (contractor), Kisa Kawakami (artist)
Awards Museum & Heritage Awards (2004): best exhibition (highly commended), Design & Decoration Award (2004): best commercial project (highly commended), Civic Trust Award (2006)
Ref Times (10 July 2003, 22 August 2003), Building Design (12 Jan 2001), Building (5 Dec 2003), Fly Past (Feb 2004), RIBA Journal (March 2004), Architecture Today (June 2004)

AUDITORIA

Real World Studios, Box, Bath (1989) p162
FCBa Peter Clegg, David Stansfield, Andy Theobald, Julia Kashdan-Brown, Peter Shayler-Webb, Ken Grix
Client Peter Gabriel, Real World Studios
Consultants Harris Grant Associates (studio design consultant), Buro Happold (structure and services)
Ref Architecture Today (Nov 1990)

The Olivier Theatre, Bedales School, Petersfield (1996) p164
FCBa Peter Clegg, Linton Ross, Martin Benson, Anne Claxton
Client Bedales School
Consultants Max Fordham (m&e), Structures One (structural engineer), Carpenter Oak & Woodland (contractor)
Awards RIBA Award (1997), Carpenters' Award (1997), Civic Trust Award (1998), Royal Fine Art Commission/BSkyB Building of the Year: the Popli Khalat-Bari Award (1998)
Ref Architects' Journal (15 Feb 1996), Perspectives (Feb-March 1998), AIT (May 1998), The New Wood Architecture (Calmann & King 1998)

Wiltshire Music Centre, Bradford-on-Avon (1997) p168
FCBa Peter Clegg, Gill Smith, Linton Ross, Alan Wainer, Paul Redman
Client Wiltshire Music Centre Trust
Consultants Halcrow Gilbert Associates (m&e), Structures One (structural engineer), Stephens & Co (qs), Teasdale Environmental Design (landscape consultant), Wallis Western (contractor)
Ref Times (6 Jan 1998)

PLACE-MAKING

Morlands, Glastonbury (2002-) p176
FCBa Peter Clegg, Mike Keys, Bill Gething, Christophe Jouannin
Client South West of England Regional Development Agency
Consultants RPS Chapman Warren (planning consultant), Northcroft (project manager), King Sturge (commercial advisor)

Shipton on Cherwell Quarry (2005-) p178
FCBa Keith Bradley, Julian Gitsham, Penny Garrett
Client Bride Parks (Oxford)
Consultants Landmark (ecology), Arup (environmental engineer), Wardell Armstrong (land engineer), Grant Associates (landscape consultant), Intermodal (transport specialist), Pegasus Planning (planning consultant)
Ref Building (12 Sept 2003), Building Design (22 Oct 2004)

Emerson's Green, Bristol (2003-) p180
FCBa Peter Clegg, Toby Lewis, Penny Garrett, Iain Williams, Ken Grix
Client South West Regional Development Agency
Consultants GVA Grimley (project/planning consultant), Grant Associates (landscape consultant), White Young Green (traffic engineer), Clarke Willmott (legal consultant)

Exchange Greengate, Salford (2004-) p182
FCBa Keith Bradley, Julian Gitsham, Penny Garrett, Alex Whitbread, Jason Cornish, Lynton Pepper
Client Ask Property Development
Consultants Whitbybird (environmental, structural engineer), Davis Langdon & Everest (qs), Grant Associates (landscape consultant), Aitken Leclercq (urbanist)

Houndwood Housing, Street (2004 -) p184
FCBa Peter Clegg, Mike Keys, Bill Gething, Carl Gulland, Toby Lewis, Sara Haghshenass, Matt Williams, Penny Garrett, Ken Grix
Client C&J Clark Properties
Consultants ESD (environmental consultant), Arup (civil and environmental engineer), Gleeds (qs), Grant Associates (landscape consultant), Hamilton-Baillie Associates (shared-space consultant)

Photographers

Stuart Blackwood 152 (t)

Wayne Boucher/Cambridge 2000 50 (t)

Peter Cook/View 27 (t), 35 (tl, tr), 35 (bl), 36 (t, bl, bm), 37, 43 (br), 44 (t), 45, 60 (t, b), 61-62, 63 (t, bl, bm), 86-87, 89 (l), 154-155, 157 (bl, bm), 161 (tr), 224

Harry Cory Wright 163 (b), 167, 168 (bl, tr, br)

George Demetri 58

Simon Doling 13, 22-26, 29, 31, 34, 35 (lm), 36 (br), 70-73, 116-117, 126-127, 135, 138, 140-141, 165, 170, 171 (tl, tr, bm, br), 188-189, 197 (t, m, b), 210 (row 1 pic 3, row 4 pic 2), 232 (t)

Jo Fairfax 153 (tl)

Feilden Clegg Bradley Architects 43 (t), 44 (b), 68 (b), 144 (l), 171 (bl), 197 (r), 210 (row 1 pics 1, 4, row 3 pic 3), 232 (b)

Paul Eccleston/Arthouse 43 (bl)

Dennis Gilbert/View Front cover, 32-33, 56, 57, 59, 74 (tl), 74 (tr), 76, 77 (tl), 77 (tr), 94-99, 110-111, 119-125, 128 top, 129-133, 139 (br), 145, 146 (l, br), 148-149, 159, 163 (t), 166, 168 (tl), 169, 177, 210 (row 1 pic 2, row 2 pic 1, 2, row 3 pic 1, row 4 pic 1, row 5 pics 1, 2, row 6 pic 4), 223 (tl, bl, br)

Amos Goldreich 41, 60 (pic 3), 83-85, 88, 160, 161 (tl, bl)

David Grandorge 150, 151 (tl, bl), 153 (bl, r), 221 (b)

HBG Construction 64-65

Martine Hamilton-Knight 50 (2, 3), 52-53, 146 (mr), 151 (r), 152 (b), 221 (t)

Adams Kara Taylor 128 (br)

Yan Ki Lee/Architecture Foundation 40 (r)

Jose Lasheras 89 (r)

Will Pryce 63 (br)

Regional Development Agency 179

Mandy Reynolds /Fotoforum 39, 40 (l), 50 (pic 4, b), 51 (t, m), 54-55, 74 (b), 75, 77 (b), 92 (b), 93 (b), 100-107, 210 (row 2 pic 3, row 3 pic 2, row 6 pics 1, 3, 5)

Tim Soar 108-109

Andrew Southall 51 (b), 210 (row 6 pic 2)

Jonty Wilde/Yorkshire Sculpture Park 136-137, 157 (tl, tr, br), 158

Woodlands Enterprise Centre 223 (tr, m)